Peter C. Longden.

27:9:54.

6. Wayside Drive,
Poynton,
Cheshire.

SCHOOL CERTIFICATE
CHEMISTRY

BY MESSRS. HOLDERNESS AND LAMBERT

SCHOOL CERTIFICATE CHEMISTRY

BY

A. HOLDERNESS, M.Sc., F.R.I.C.

SENIOR CHEMISTRY MASTER AT
ARCHBISHOP HOLGATE'S GRAMMAR SCHOOL, YORK
CHIEF SECTIONAL EXAMINER IN 'ADVANCED' CHEMISTRY TO THE
JOINT MATRICULATION BOARD

AND

JOHN LAMBERT, M.Sc.

FORMERLY SENIOR CHEMISTRY MASTER AT
KING EDWARD'S SCHOOL, BIRMINGHAM

FOURTH EDITION

1954

WILLIAM HEINEMANN LTD
MELBOURNE :: LONDON :: TORONTO

First published July 1936
Reprinted, with corrections, February 1937
Reprinted August 1937
Reprinted July 1938
Reprinted August 1938
Reprinted August 1939
Reprinted June 1940
Reprinted December 1941
Reprinted August 1943
Reprinted May 1944
Reprinted January 1945
Reprinted January 1946
Reprinted June 1946
Reprinted September 1946
Reprinted March 1947
Reprinted June 1947
Second Edition February 1948
Reprinted January 1949
Reprinted September 1950
Third Edition May 1951
Reprinted October 1951
Reprinted May 1952
Reprinted March 1953
Fourth Edition January 1954

PUBLISHED BY
WILLIAM HEINEMANN LTD.
99 GREAT RUSSELL STREET, LONDON, W.C.1
PRINTED IN GREAT BRITAIN BY THE PUBLISHERS AT
THE WINDMILL PRESS, KINGSWOOD, SURREY

CONTENTS

CONTENTS

PREFACE

UNDER existing conditions, a teacher of Chemistry preparing pupils for a School Certificate examination is faced with one major problem. The problem is how he can ensure that the material available for his pupils' revision is adequate, without having to burden himself with an unreasonable amount of that examination of note-books and supervision of corrections which alone can make the pupils' own work a sound basis for revision. The root of the problem is to be found in the fact that much of the pupil's scientific progress must be the result of his own effort, applied to writing careful accounts of his own or demonstrated experiments, while, at the same time, his experience and immaturity make these accounts far from perfect. The authors believe that they have contributed to the solution of this problem by giving very full descriptions of all the experimental work in this book. The descriptions are presented, not as substitutes for the pupil's own note-book, but as a source on which he may draw to make good the defects of his own educationally valuable but always imperfect work, when the need for revision arises. In short, the authors present this feature of their book as supplementary to the pupil's own descriptive effort and do not expect his notes to make good the descriptive deficiencies of the book.

A difficulty which always arises in a course of elementary Chemistry is to find some way of preventing the work on metals and their compounds from appearing to be isolated scraps of information. The pupil is not yet ready for the fundamental classification of the Periodic Table nor is the number of elements treated great enough to make the table intelligible. As an alternative, the authors use a classification which their own teaching has shown to be most suitable at this stage, namely the Electrochemical Series. In this book, the properties and mode of extraction of a metal, and the properties of its compounds, are related throughout to the position of the metal in the Electrochemical Series, and the authors believe the series to be the most suitable nucleus round which the facts about metals may be grouped, both as a first exercise in classification and as a considerable aid to the memory. Arising out of this, another departure in this book from the usual School Certificate treatment of metallic compounds is to group

vii

them by the acid radical, not, as is customary, by the basic radical. The authors believe that the gradations of properties shown by, say, nitrates and carbonates, are more interesting and can be made the basis of more instructive teaching than those of, say, copper or zinc compounds taken as a whole. The adoption of this arrangement means that a reference to a metallic compound should be sought in the chapter corresponding to its electronegative radical, and in the order of the Electrochemical Series inside the chapter.

It will be found that the space allotted to the Atomic and Molecular Theories is much greater in proportion to the rest of the book than is usual. The authors believe that the importance and difficulty of these sections justify this step, and that there has been considerable gain in clarity by utilising the space to amplify, for example, the Atomic Theory, which seems so clear to the teacher who knows all about it and so obscure to the pupil meeting it for the first time. The authors fear it is too much to hope that such a pupil will acquire a good grasp of the theory from his own reading of their pages, but this is the goal at which they have aimed. Proofs of the formulæ of common gases are collected into a separate chapter of the book. This seemed to the authors desirable, for, in their experience, these proofs are usually taken together, because they depend on the difficult ideas of the Molecular Theory, which must come late in the course. A complete chapter may also be conveniently ignored in the case of weaker pupils for whom it is too difficult. Improved methods are given for the performing of experimental work under school conditions.

The book is intended for the use of pupils in the last two years of a School Certificate course. For this reason, those parts of the course which are usually taken early (air and water particularly) are presented, not as they would be taught to younger pupils, but in a form suitable for a later reading when the main facts are already reasonably familiar.

We have pleasure in acknowledging our indebtedness to the Copper Development Association for permission to use figures compiled by them; to Messrs. John Murray for permission to use two experiments from the *Science Masters' Book*; to Dr. F. Sherwood Taylor for obtaining the photographs of Hanley and Barcelona which he is utilising in his *World of Science*; and to those members of our publishers whose valuable assistance has enabled the book to appear as nearly as possible in accordance with the authors' wishes.

The thanks of the authors are also freely given to their colleagues, E. F. Wright, G. R. Galleymore and S. T. Trett, for their continuous interest and counsel, and to the eight School Certificate Examination Boards for permission to use their questions.

University of Bristol.   (B.)
University of Cambridge, Local.   (C.)
Central Welsh Boards.   (C.W.B.)
University of Durham.   (D.)
University of London.   (L.)
Joint Matriculation Board.   (N.U.J.B.)
Oxford Local.   (O.)
Oxford and Cambridge.   (O. and C.)

A. H.
J. L.

June, 1936.

PREFACE TO THIRD EDITION

The Third Edition includes a new Chapter on aluminium and its compounds. The section on hydrogen has been expanded to include the large scale manufacture and uses of the gas and the hydrogenation of coal. Minor additions have been made relating to fertilisers, smokeless fuel, exothermic and endothermic reactions, cement, the carbon-reduction method of extraction of lead, etc.

A. H.
J. L.

February, 1951.

PREFACE TO FOURTH EDITION

The Fourth Edition incorporates as an Appendix (on page 413) an up-to-date but simple account of Atomic Structure, electrovalency, covalency and isotopy. This was formerly published separately under the title *A Simple Approach to Atomic Theory*.

This Appendix takes the place of pages 12–20 of *School Certificate Chemistry* in the case of students requiring the more modern treatment. As most Examining Boards still adhere to the older treatment, this is allowed to stand as in previous editions.

No alteration in page numbering has been necessitated, except at the end of the book (page 413 onwards).

A. H.
J. L.

November, 1953.

A*

CHEMICAL NOMENCLATURE

THE word "nomenclature" means "system or scheme of naming". The following simple treatment of chemical nomenclature will enable you to state the composition of most chemical substances directly from their names.

ELEMENTS

The commonest elements have been known for a long time and there is generally no system about their naming. Recently isolated *metals*, however, have been given names ending in *-ium* or *-um*, e.g., radium, platinum, osmium, aluminium, while recently named *non-metals* have been given names ending in *-on*, e.g., argon, xenon.

COMPOUNDS

Binary Compounds

The name-ending -ide is given to compounds containing only two elements[1] and the nature of the elements is indicated in the two words of the name, *e.g.*, copper oxide, CuO; hydrogen sulphide, H_2S.

The number of atoms of one of the elements contained in a molecule of the compound is sometimes indicated by a prefix to the second part of the name, *e.g.*, carbon *di*sulphide, CS_2; phosphorus *tri*chloride, PCl_3; carbon *tetra*chloride, CCl_4; phosphorus *penta*xide, P_2O_5.

Acids and Salts

A great many acids contain hydrogen, oxygen and a third element, *e.g.*, H_2SO_4, HNO_3, H_3PO_4. The commonest and most stable of such acids is usually highly oxidised and to it is given a name which ends in *-ic* and is derived from the element it contains in addition to hydrogen and oxygen, *e.g.*, sulphuric acid, H_2SO_4, and nitric acid, HNO_3. An acid containing the same elements but *less oxygen* has the name-ending changed to *-ous*, while one with *less oxygen still* takes the prefix *hypo-* with the *-ous* ending. An acid with a *higher proportion of oxygen* than the *-ic* acid takes the prefix *per-* with the *-ic* ending.

---

[1] Hydroxides are exceptions to this rule but in these compounds the three elements present are indicated in the name. Another exception is an acid salt of hydrogen sulphide, *e.g.*, sodium hydrogen sulphide, NaHS, but here again the name is self-explanatory. In salts like ammonium chloride, NH_4Cl, the NH_4 group has been treated as if it were an element.

The corresponding salts have names in -*ate*, -*ite*, *hypo* - - -*ite* and *per* - - -*ate*. Thus:

Acids.	*Salts.*
*per*chlor*ic* acid, $HClO_4$.	potassium *per*chlor*ate*, $KClO_4$.
chlor*ic* acid, $HClO_3$.	potassium chlor*ate*, $KClO_3$.
chlor*ous* acid, $HClO_2$.	potassium chlor*ite*, $KClO_2$.
*hypo*chlor*ous* acid, $HClO$.	potassium *hypo*chlor*ite*, $KClO$.

Notice also the following common pairs of acids and salts:—

Acids.	*Salts.*
sulphur*ic* acid, H_2SO_4.	sulph*ates*, *e.g.*, Na_2SO_4.
sulphur*ous* acid, H_2SO_3.	sulph*ites*, *e.g.*, Na_2SO_3.
nitr*ic* acid, HNO_3.	nitr*ates*, *e.g.*, KNO_3.
nitr*ous* acid, HNO_2.	nitr*ites*, *e.g.*, KNO_2.

A useful rule to remember is that a salt with the name-ending -ate or -ite usually contains three elements, one of which is oxygen, *e.g.*, lead sulphate, $PbSO_4$, copper nitrate, $Cu(NO_3)_2$, sodium hypochlorite, $NaClO$. [Note the two compounds, ferrous sulph**ide**, FeS (two elements), and ferrous sulph**ate**, $FeSO_4$ (three elements including oxygen). These two are frequently confused by beginners.]

PLATE I

The De Havilland "Comet", the first jet-engined passenger airliner, illustrates an important use of light alloys. The principal structure is of light alloy aluminium with a fair proportion of high tensile steel. The engines utilise considerable quantities of nickle steel alloy.

(By courtesy of the De Havilland Aircraft Co., Ltd)

SCHOOL CERTIFICATE CHEMISTRY

CHAPTER I

PHYSICAL AND CHEMICAL CHANGE
ELEMENTS, COMPOUNDS, MIXTURES

PHYSICAL AND CHEMICAL CHANGE

THE science of Chemistry sets before itself, as its primary objects, first, the determination of the nature and properties of the non-living matter which surrounds us in that portion of the crust of the earth to which we have access, and secondly, the preparation of new substances, scientifically interesting or generally useful, from the materials which Nature has provided. In trying to determine the nature of substances, chemists have been greatly interested in the changes which these undergo when subject to conditions which they normally do not encounter—high temperature, high pressure, extreme cold, contact with other materials under varying conditions, and so on. It is largely from the changes which materials undergo when subject to these conditions that chemists, particularly in the last 150 years or so, have drawn conclusions about their nature.

But changes are multifarious. Some of them do not interest the scientist, as such, at all. The change wrought when the hand of an artist transfers paint from palette to canvas and, spreading it in a particular way, creates a work of art, is a matter of æsthetics, not of science. Any one change may be viewed from many different angles. When iron rusts, a chemist is concerned with the different properties which the iron and rust possess. How does each react with acids, alkalis and other reagents? He also tries to give an explanation of what occurred to the iron when it rusted. The physicist will want to know whether the density, the conductivity and the specific heat of the rust are the same as that of iron, from which it has been made. An economist thinks of the huge cost which accompanies the change, for millions of pounds are spent yearly in an endeavour to prevent iron from rusting. It may be

1

that what the chemist and the physicist find out about the rusting of iron will help the economist (or, more directly, the manufacturer of iron articles). It is mainly as a result of chemical research that rustless and stainless steels have appeared, while during that research, the physicist has been careful to ensure that the elasticity and tensile strength of the steel have not been impaired by the process which made them rustless. Clearly, we must attempt to define, if only roughly, the kind of changes in which the chemist is interested and to which the name "chemical" can properly be applied. With the object of attaining some kind of definition of "chemical changes", we will now examine a few changes in the hope that, from them, some conclusions may emerge.

1. Hold one end of a piece of magnesium ribbon in tongs and put the other end in a bunsen flame. Note the intense brilliance of the flame of the burning magnesium and the nature of the residue—a white ash—which remains.

Repeat the experiment with platinum by holding a loose coil of platinum wire in a bunsen flame. Note the white-hot glow of the metal, but contrast its unchanged appearance, after cooling, with the white ash left by the magnesium.

2. Take a small piece of sodium in tongs from the oil under which it is kept, and, never touching it with your fingers, cut it into pieces about the size of a **very small** pea. Drop these pieces in turn on to the surface of a little distilled water in a small beaker. Note how the sodium melts into a ball, darts about the surface of the water, produces a hissing sound and finally disappears with a small flash and explosion. Heat the resulting clear liquid on an iron dish until no more steam is given off. On cooling, a white solid is left. If added to water, this solid dissolves but does not show the same vigorous action as sodium. It is a new substance, caustic soda.

To distilled water in a beaker, add some common salt and stir the mixture. The common salt undergoes an obvious change; it gradually disappears, forming a solution and being no longer visible as a white solid. Put the liquid into a porcelain dish and heat gently until all the water has evaporated off. The common salt reappears in its original white solid form.

3. Heat some roll sulphur on a deflagrating spoon. Note how the sulphur melts and later begins to burn with a blue flame. It gradually decreases in amount and finally the spoon will be left empty. The sulphur has not

Powder some roll sulphur in a mortar, then heat it gently in a test-tube, shaking all the time. Notice how the sulphur melts to an amber-coloured liquid (other changes will occur if it is more strongly heated) and that this simply been annihilated. Its disappearance is due to its conversion into a new gaseous substance which is invisible, but whose presence in the air can be detected merely by its irritating smell or, if you prefer some less commonplace evidence, by burning the sulphur in a gas-jar and adding to the jar some blue litmus solution. The gas, sulphur dioxide, will turn it red.

liquid, on cooling, returns to its original condition as a yellow solid.

A little consideration will quickly show that the six changes we have considered above are not all the same in nature. They fall, actually, into two classes, which are distinguished by the following peculiarities.

1. All the changes in the right-hand column were **easily reversible;** the molten sulphur returned to the solid form when cooled; the platinum wire ceased to glow and regained its original appearance when removed from the flame; the common salt was recovered by evaporating off the water. Contrast these results with those of the changes in the left-hand column. The white ash from magnesium was totally unlike the original magnesium, and it would be a difficult matter to obtain magnesium from it; on evaporation of water in Experiment 2 we recovered not sodium, but caustic soda, from which sodium cannot easily be obtained; the sulphur became part of a gas from which it would be difficult to recover sulphur. These changes are not reversible. The easily reversible type of change is called "physical change"; the more permanent type "chemical change".

2. In none of the physical changes recorded in the right-hand column was a new kind of matter formed; we began with platinum, common salt and sulphur and, after the change, finished with just those materials. **In all the chemical changes recorded in the left-hand column, some new kind of matter was formed;** magnesium was converted to the white powdery ash, magnesium oxide, sodium to caustic soda and solid sulphur to the gas, sulphur dioxide—a new kind of matter each time. This is characteristic of chemical change.

3. The physical changes in the right-hand column were not accompanied by any marked external effects. The solution of common salt in water and the melting of sulphur were not violent changes. The action of sodium with water, however, produced enough heat to melt the sodium and was violent enough to be slightly explosive at the end; the burning of magnesium produced intense heat and light, and the burning of sulphur similar, but less

intense, effects. The chemical changes were the more violent, and were accompanied by heat changes. This is commonly the case.

4. We carried out no weighings during our experiments, but it could actually have been shown that, in all three physical changes which we recorded on the right, **no change of weight occurred ;** the sulphur, platinum and common salt weighed just as much before the changes as after them. In the three chemical changes, however, it would have been found that the white ash weighed more than the magnesium, the caustic soda more than the sodium and the gaseous sulphur dioxide more than the sulphur. (These gains in weight are made at the expense of other materials which lose in weight correspondingly; the gains in the case of magnesium and sulphur were made at the expense of the air and, in the case of sodium, at the expense of the water.)

We thus distinguish two kinds of changes—chemical changes and physical changes.

Now consider the following suggestions about a few common changes and decide by comparison with those discussed above whether the changes are physical or chemical. The correct classification appears on p. 5.

1. (*a*) Melting of ice, (*b*) conversion of water to steam.

Are the changes easily reversed? Are there any noticeably violent external effects?

2. Burning of coal.

Does the coal appear to weigh the same as the products after burning it? (Appearances here are deceptive, see p. 28.) Can we easily obtain coal again from its products of combustion? Are there any noticeable external effects while coal is burning?

3. Rusting of iron.

Can iron be easily recovered from the rust?

4. Magnetising iron.

Can the iron be readily de-magnetised? Are there any marked changes during magnetisation?

5. A coal-gas explosion.

Is this change violent? Is there considerable heat change?

6. Heating of the filament of an electric light globe by the current.

Is the filament readily cooled again? Does it appear changed when cooled?

7. The melting of candle-wax.

Is the liquid wax easily solidified again? Does it then appear the same as the original wax? Are there any marked heating effects as the melting occurs?

We may now summarise the characteristics of chemical and physical change in the table below.

Physical Change	Chemical Change
1. Is generally easily reversible	1. Is generally not easily reversible
2. Produces no new kind of matter	2. Always produces a new kind of matter
3. Is not accompanied by great heat change (except latent heat effects accompanying changes of state)	3. Is usually accompanied by considerable heat change
4. Produces no change of weight	4. Produces individual substances whose weights are different from those of the original individual substances. Thus, if two substances, A and B, react chemically and are changed into substances C and D, the weight of C will be different from the weight of A or B, and the weight of D will be different from the weight of A or B.
Examples	*Examples*
1. All cases of the melting of a solid to a liquid (or the reverse)	1. The burning of any substance in air
2. All cases of vaporisation of a liquid (or the reverse)	2. The rusting of iron
3. Magnetisation of iron	3. The slaking of lime
4. The heating of a metal wire by electricity	4. Explosion of coal-gas or hydrogen with air

ELEMENTS, MIXTURES AND COMPOUNDS

ELEMENTS AND COMPOUNDS. We will begin our study of elements and compounds by considering two fairly simple chemical changes.

1. Put a little red oxide of mercury (mercuric oxide) into a dry test-tube. Heat it, rotating the test-tube so that it does not become mis-shapen. A silvery mirror gradually appears on the upper part of the test-tube (where it is cool), and later silvery globules of mercury will be seen. When the mirror begins to appear, insert a glowing splint of wood into the test-tube. It is rekindled. This is because the invisible gas, oxygen, is coming off from the heated oxide.

It is clear that, under the action of heat, mercuric oxide has yielded two products—mercury and oxygen.

2. Repeat the above experiment, using lead nitrate. Brown fumes are given off in this case (they are called nitrogen peroxide), and, by the test given above, it can be shown that oxygen is also liberated. Finally a yellow solid will remain in the test-tube. This solid is litharge.

These experiments show that both mercuric oxide and lead nitrate must be fairly complex substances. This is obvious from the fact that mercuric oxide yielded, under the action of heat, two substances, mercury and oxygen, while lead nitrate yielded three— litharge, nitrogen peroxide and oxygen. The question now arises whether these products can themselves be split up further into still simpler substances. The answer to this question is that in two cases they can; from litharge we can, by suitable chemical means, obtain lead and oxygen, and from nitrogen peroxide, nitrogen and oxygen. This means that litharge and nitrogen peroxide are themselves complex substances. How much further can this process of splitting up into simpler products be carried? Can we obtain from the lead, nitrogen, oxygen and mercury, into which we have resolved our original lead nitrate and mercuric oxide, any substances which are simpler still? The answer now is that we cannot. By no chemical process whatever is it possible to obtain from lead, mercury, oxygen or nitrogen any substance simpler than themselves. Clearly, these four simple substances are different from the more complex mercuric oxide and lead nitrate. The number of substances which like lead, oxygen, mercury and nitrogen, are incapable of being split up into simpler substances is small. There is very good reason to believe that only ninety-two such substances may exist, and, of the ninety-two, all but two are actually known on the earth. To them the name "elements" has been given. We may now define this term.

Definition. **An element is a substance which cannot by any known chemical process be split up into two or more simpler substances.**

A list of the elements is given on p. 429. We may here mention a few of the commoner ones. All the metals—lead, zinc, iron, copper, tin, platinum, gold, silver and the rest—are elements; so also are the oxygen and nitrogen of the air, together with carbon, sulphur, phosphorus, iodine and others to the number of ninety. Remember the characteristic they all possess—they cannot by any known chemical process be made to yield substances simpler than themselves.

From this band of ninety elements, all other substances on the earth are made. The number of chemical substances known is more than a million and a half. All of these, except the elements themselves, are made up of two or more elements combined together. They are called "compounds". It is astounding to reflect that every compound on the earth, from the simplest, which, like water, contain only two elements, to those complex materials of which our own bodily tissues are composed, are made from less than one hundred simple, elementary materials. The elements are indeed a small select band—90 in 1,500,000.

There follows a short list of common compounds and the elements which compose them.

Compound	Elements contained
Water . . .	Oxygen; hydrogen.
Sugar . . .	Oxygen; hydrogen; carbon.
Common salt . .	Sodium; chlorine.
Saltpetre . . .	Potassium; nitrogen; oxygen.
Marble . . .	Calcium; oxygen; carbon.
Blue vitriol . .	Copper; sulphur; oxygen; hydrogen.
Oil of vitriol . .	Hydrogen; sulphur; oxygen.
Sand . . .	Silicon; oxygen.
Clay , . .	Aluminium; silicon; oxygen; hydrogen.

(Note how commonly oxygen occurs; it is the most widely distributed of all the elements.)

We may now define a compound.

Definition. **A compound is a substance which contains two or more elements chemically combined together.**

We have found it necessary to use the expression "chemically combined". The meaning of it is connected with the idea of chemical change which was discussed earlier. We must now try to obtain a clearer idea of the meaning of the expression and, to do this, we shall contrast the properties of mixtures and compounds in the work of the next section.

MIXTURES AND COMPOUNDS. Weigh out 28 gm. of iron filings and 16 gm. of sulphur (any multiples or fractions of these weights will do equally well). Grind the two thoroughly in a mortar and put about half of the mixture into a dry test-tube. Heat the test-tube, at the bottom, with a small flame. The mixture will glow. When it does so, remove the flame, and hold the test-tube over a mortar as a precaution against breakage. The glow will then spread slowly through the mixture without further heating. Allow the test-tube to cool, then break it away from the mass of material left. A dark grey, almost black, solid will be found.

In the following experiments, we shall compare the properties of the original mixture of iron and sulphur with those of the black solid left after heating it.

Experiment	*Mixture before heating*	*Solid left after heating*
1. Action with water.	Place enough of the mixture in a test-tube to fill about 1 inch of its depth. Half-fill the test-tube with water, shake it well, then allow the test-tube to stand. The denser iron will settle more rapidly than the lighter sulphur and form a layer below it. The experiment separates the iron from the sulphur	Carry out the same test. The solid settles as a single layer with no sign of separation of the iron from the sulphur.
2. Action of a magnet	Rub one end of a bar magnet well into the mixture, raise it and tap gently. The iron filings will have been attracted by the magnet and will adhere to it. The sulphur will not. They are separated	Repeat with the other end of the magnet. A very little iron (left unattacked by the sulphur) may be attracted by the magnet but it will be very much less than before. The bulk of the iron is not attracted from the black solid and is not separated from the sulphur
3. Action with carbon disulphide	Half-fill a test-tube with carbon disulphide, add some of the mixture and shake for a few minutes. Filter the mixture through a dry filter-paper and funnel on to a dry clock-glass. Allow the filtrate to evaporate to dryness (in a fume-chamber) at the ordinary temperature. On the clock-glass, a yellow deposit of solid sulphur will be left. The carbon disulphide has dissolved out the sulphur from the mixture and so separated it from the iron	Repeat the experiment described opposite. A very slight deposit of sulphur (left unattacked by the iron) may remain, but the great bulk of the sulphur has not been separated from the iron

Experiment	Mixture before heating	Solid left after heating
4. Action of dilute hydrochloric acid	Add dilute hydrochloric acid to some of the mixture in a test-tube. Warm gently. There is rapid effervescence. Apply a lighted taper to the test-tube. The resulting slight explosion shows that the gas is hydrogen. The iron has reacted with the acid to produce this gas. The sulphur remains unchanged	Repeat the experiment described opposite. Effervescence occurs again. Apply the following two tests to the gas:— 1. Smell very cautiously. The rather disgusting smell is similar to that of rotten eggs. 2. Apply a lighted taper to the test-tube. The gas burns with a blue flame but without explosion. It is HYDROGEN SULPHIDE.

REASON FOR THE ABOVE DIFFERENCES OF PROPERTIES

It is clear that the solid left after heating the mixture of iron and sulphur differs greatly in properties from the original mixture itself.

1. Before the heating, the iron could be separated from the sulphur by PHYSICAL methods. For example, by shaking with water, we took advantage of the physical property of density to separate the denser iron from the lighter sulphur; we also separated the iron from the sulphur by using its physical magnetic properties and by physical solution of the sulphur in carbon disulphide. In none of these experiments was any chemical action involved, but these physical methods could not separate the sulphur from the iron after the mixture had been heated. Physical methods of separation were then useless.

2. Again, in the mixture before heating, the two elements clearly exercised their own independent properties. The iron was attracted by the magnet just as it would have been if the sulphur had not been present; the sulphur dissolved in carbon disulphide without interference from the iron. Similarly, during the action of dilute hydrochloric acid on the mixture, the iron reacted with the acid exactly as if no sulphur were present, while the sulphur itself remained unchanged. After the heating, however, the black solid left showed properties of its own. The sulphur present in it was no longer dissolved out by carbon disulphide nor was the iron attracted by a magnet, while the separate densities of the two elements were no longer available for use in their separation. The action of dilute hydrochloric acid gave an entirely different reaction, with evolution of hydrogen sulphide instead of hydrogen. So we see that during the heating the separate properties of the iron and

sulphur were lost and the new properties of the black solid, ferrous sulphide, appeared.

The reason for this difference is that before the heating the two elements were simply mixed together, while during the heating they underwent chemical combination, forming the compound, FERROUS SULPHIDE. As a result of this change, the elements were united by a chemical link or bond instead of being merely close together in space. The nature of this bond has been the object of much speculation, and it is now known to be electrical. When the two elements were united by this chemical bond their separate properties disappeared and were replaced by different properties, those of the compound ferrous sulphide. This is always a consequence of chemical combination. The compound produced has properties of its own which are quite different from those of the elements from which the compound was formed. Compare, for example, the properties of a gaseous mixture of hydrogen and oxygen with those of their compound, liquid water, or the separate properties of sodium and the highly poisonous chlorine gas with those of their commonplace and useful compound, common salt.

3. Another characteristic difference between physical mixing and chemical combination is apparent from this experiment. During the mixing of the iron and sulphur in the mortar, no change was observed except a kind of averaging of the colours of the two elements so that the mixture had a colour between the grey of iron and the yellow of sulphur. During the chemical combination, however, enough heat was given out to raise the whole mass to a bright red glow, once the action had been started by the external application of heat. Chemical combination is often accompanied by heat changes of this kind, but physical mixing is not. All the vast amount of heat generated domestically and for industrial purposes by the burning of coal is the result of the heat change associated with the chemical combination of carbon with oxygen. Coal-gas, again, will mix quietly enough with the air, but if an accidental spark sets up chemical combination of the constituents of the coal-gas with the oxygen of the air, a violent explosion will occur, because the great amount of heat given out as the combination proceeds raises the whole mass of gases to a very high temperature, with consequent very rapid expansion.

4. A further and most important difference between mixtures and chemical compounds is that the composition of a compound by weight is fixed and unalterable, while that of a mixture may vary within wide limits. For example, pure ferrous sulphide always contains the iron and sulphur in the proportion of 56 gm. of iron to 32 gm. of sulphur, and no variation from this proportion is ever

found. Mixtures of iron and sulphur may, however, have any desired composition. Similarly, oxygen and hydrogen may be mixed in any desired proportion, but all samples of their compound, water, contain the two in the invariable proportion of 1 gm. of hydrogen to 8 gm. of oxygen.

These differences between compounds and mixtures are summarised below.

Mixtures	Compounds
(a) The constituents can be separated from one another by physical methods	The constituent elements cannot be separated by physical methods; chemical reactions are necessary.
(b) Mixtures may vary widely in composition	Compounds are absolutely fixed in their compositions by weight.
(c) Mixing is not usually accompanied by external effects such as explosion, evolution of heat or volume change (for gases)	Chemical combination is usually accompanied by one or more of these effects.
(d) The properties of a mixture are the sum of the properties of the constituents of the mixture.	The properties of a compound are peculiar to itself and are usually quite different from those of its constituent elements.

QUESTIONS

1. What are considered to be the main distinctions between a chemical compound and a mixture? Explain why the liquid obtained by mixing sodium chloride with water is not regarded as a chemical compound. (O. and C.)
2. When a piece of sodium is placed in water it diminishes in size gradually, and finally disappears. In what way is the disappearance of the sodium different from the ordinary process of solution in water? Give experiments in support of your views. How could metallic sodium be recovered from the liquid? (N.U.J.B.)
3. What is the essential difference between a chemical and a physical change?
   Indicate clearly the chemical and physical changes involved in the following processes, giving full reasons in each case: (a) the addition of metallic sodium to water; (b) the solution of sodium chloride in water; (c) the heating of magnesium in air; (d) the heating of ammonium chloride; (e) the addition of water to concentrated sulphuric acid. (L.)
4. Describe the experiments you would carry out in seeking to determine whether a given white powder is a pure substance or a mixture. If the substance is a pure chemical compound, how would you propose to ascertain whether it is (i) a salt, (ii) a basic oxide, or (iii) a peroxide? (N.U.J.B.)
5. Illustrate THREE differences between metallic and non-metallic elements by reference to the properties of iron and sulphur. Describe THREE tests by means of which you would prove that the compound, iron sulphide, formed by heating a mixture of iron filings and sulphur, differs from the original mixture. (N.U.J.B.)

CHAPTER II

THE ATOMIC THEORY [1]

We have seen in the last chapter that there are about 90 kinds of simple matter called **elements,** and that all other kinds of matter have been formed by the chemical combination of two or more of these elements. Thinkers have speculated for centuries in an endeavour to elucidate further the structure of matter, and, more particularly, to shed light on the structure of the elements. The ancient Greek thinker, Democritus (about 400 B.C.), began the speculations, the Roman Lucretius (about 350 years later) took up the question, and, following these two ancient philosophers, there has appeared a succession of thinkers, European and Arabian, whose speculations culminated at the beginning of the nineteenth century in the ideas of an Englishman, John Dalton, of Manchester. His suggestions have won universal acceptance for themselves and lasting scientific fame for their author.

Dalton. Dalton's life-time abounded in famous names and exciting happenings—the French Revolution, Austerlitz, Trafalgar, Nelson, Napoleon, Wellington, Waterloo—but the thoughts of this Quaker, slowly maturing as he pursued an obscure and uneventful existence, have proved more potent in their influence on human modes of living in the succeeding century than all the wars and alarums of his day. His Atomic Theory is the foundation of modern chemistry.

Dalton's love of precision and truth is illustrated by the following story concerning him. Dalton had given a course of lectures, and at the end a student came to him with the request for a certificate of attendance. The great chemist looked up his records and found that the student had missed one lecture during the course. Dalton refused to sign the attendance certificate, but, after considering a few minutes, he said, "If thou wilt come to-morrow I will go over the lecture thou hast missed." Having quietened his conscience in this manner over the missed lecture, Dalton presumably signed the certificate.

Ideas about Atoms.

You know well enough that if a cook wishes to separate a vegetable, say garden peas, from the water in which it has been

[1] See Appendix on page 413.

cooked, she strains it through a kind of domestic sieve, called a colander. The process is effective because the holes of the colander are too small to allow the peas to pass through them. In scientific work, the same problem of separating particles of suspended solid from a liquid often presents itself. You will have seen, for example, from the work of the last chapter, that if sulphur is finely ground and stirred with water, it does not dissolve and can be removed by filtering the mixture. This process of filtering is effective in separating the sulphur from the water because the filter-paper is porous and acts as a very fine sieve with very minute holes, which are too small to allow the sulphur particles to pass. If, however, we dissolve sulphur in carbon disulphide and filter the solution, no sulphur is retained by the filter-paper, and, on evaporating the filtered solution, sulphur is recovered. This can only mean that, when in solution, the sulphur was in such a finely divided state that it was capable of passing through the very tiny holes or pores of the paper.

This idea that elements are capable of being split up into very tiny particles was first evolved by Greek and Roman thinkers from another angle. They said that if we were to take a piece of, say, gold and cut it up into small pieces, and cut those pieces into smaller pieces, and those pieces into smaller pieces, and so on, a time would ultimately come when the dividing process would have to stop. The tiny particles of gold which we had then obtained would be incapable of being divided any further; they would be the smallest possible particles of gold which could ever be obtained. The Greeks gave them the name "atoms". As a temporary, though incomplete, definition of an atom we may say that it is the smallest, indivisible particle of an element. If the Greeks had been Englishmen they might have called these particles "indivisibles", for the word "atom" meant to a Greek what "indivisible" means to an Englishman. We still call them "atoms" today.

Hypothesis and Theory. The idea that elements are made up of atoms is called the **atomic theory.** This word "theory" does not often mean very much to a beginner in Chemistry, so let us be quite clear about it. A scientific theory is a scientific idea which was thought of by somebody, suggested by him in a scientific book or journal, and accepted by other scientists after due consideration. "So-and-so's THEORY" means "So-and-so's accepted idea". The process of getting an idea accepted may be a long one; there will be arguments, objections, inprovements of the idea, but, if it finally wins acceptance by scientists generally, it will be called a theory. When the idea is first put forward, and is still in the "argument-and-objection" stage, it is called a **hypothesis**; later, if generally accepted, a theory.

On May 12th, 1827, Mr. Pickwick read to his club a paper including "Some Observations on the Theory of Tittlebats"—or so Dickens tells us. But Dickens was wrong. Mr. Pickwick's ideas about tittlebats have so signally failed to secure general acceptance that to-day we do not even know what they were. The "Tittlebatian Theory" was really a "Tittlebatian Hypothesis", and, still a hypothesis, it died.

DALTON'S ATOMIC THEORY

The Atomic Theory, we have seen, goes back to the Greeks, yet we always speak to-day about *Dalton's* Atomic Theory. There is good reason for this. The reason is that, while the Greeks put forward the idea that atoms exist, they did no more. They left the idea vague and untested. Dalton changed this vague imagining into a set of concrete suggestions about atoms which could be tested by experiment. This change from vagueness to precision and experimental test justifies his claim to the theory. Below are given the ideas which together make up the Atomic Theory of Dalton.

THE ATOMIC THEORY (1810) states:—

1. Matter is made up of small, indivisible particles called atoms.
2. Atoms are indestructible and they cannot be created.
3. The atoms of a particular element are all exactly alike in every way and are different from the atoms of all other elements.
4. Chemical combination takes place between small whole numbers of atoms.

These ideas are so important that we shall discuss all except the first more fully.

Atoms are Indestructible and cannot be Created. The important aspect of this idea is that, by chemical action, it is possible to alter only the state of combination of a number of atoms, not to reduce their number or add to it. If we start a chemical reaction with, say, a thousand million atoms of hydrogen, then we shall finish that reaction with exactly a thousand million, neither more nor less. They may have altered their state of combination—they may have become, for example, free hydrogen gas instead of being combined with oxygen in water—but the same number will be there.

The Atoms of a Particular Element are all Exactly Alike in Every Way and are Different from the Atoms of all other Elements. The most important point is that this statement includes in it the idea that all atoms of the same element are exactly alike in *weight*, but are different in weight from the atoms of any other element. The theory says that if we collected together, say, one thousand atoms of sulphur from all corners of the earth, every one of those atoms of sulphur would be exactly the same as every other. The same would be true of any number of atoms of copper. But the weight of each sulphur atom would be different from the weight of each copper atom.

Be sure you understand the universality of this idea. Consider, say, oxygen. Oxygen occurs in hundreds of thousands of compounds—water, sugar, litharge, blue vitriol, alcohol, oil of vitriol, starch, and so on. If we were to collect one oxygen atom from each of these hundreds of thousands of compounds, every one of those oxygen atoms would, says the Atomic Theory, be absolutely and completely alike.

It is clear that we cannot test the theory in this way because the atoms are so small that we could not examine them or weigh them even if we could separate them.

Idea on Size of Atoms. It is difficult to have any conception of the size of atoms. The following diagram may help you to understand how small an atom really is.

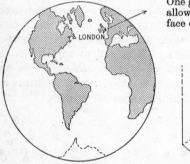

One gram of hydrogen liberated here and allowed to diffuse uniformly over the surface of the earth.

This column of air (1 square cm. cross section), anywhere on the surface of the earth, would contain over 100,000 of those hydrogen atoms. (It is assumed they are allowed to diffuse freely.)

FIG. 1.
Idea on size of atoms.

In other words, there are over 100,000 times more atoms in 1 gm. of hydrogen, than square cms. on the whole of the surface of the earth.

Chemical Combination takes place between Small Whole Numbers of Atoms. It follows from the supposition that atoms are indivisible that they must combine in whole numbers. Dalton made the additional assertion that these whole numbers are small. By this he meant that atoms commonly combine in such numbers as 3 atoms of one element with 1 atom of another, or 2 atoms of one element with 5 atoms of another, or 1 atom of one element with 1 atom of another. Cases such as 67 atoms of one element combining with 125 atoms of another, or 322 atoms of one element with

27 atoms of another, are unknown. The numbers of atoms combining together are always small,[1] though, of course, in any one laboratory experiment there will be millions of exactly similar combinations taking place.

We must now emphasise the fact that what has been stated above is a set of ideas. In science, ideas are treated with scant respect unless they can be backed up by experimental results. None of the statements made above can be tested by experiment or observation. We cannot line up a thousand oxygen atoms and inspect them to see if they are all alike, or count the number of hydrogen atoms which combine with one atom of oxygen to see if the number is small. We must deduce, from the Atomic Theory, some results which ought to follow from it, and which can be put to experimental test.

To Find an Experimental Test of the Atomic Theory's Assertion that Atoms are Indestructible and cannot be Created. We have seen above that this means that however many atoms are present at the beginning of a chemical action, the number remains unchanged at the end of it. For example, if we take a piece of iron and a piece of sulphur in the right proportions and combine them together, there are exactly as many atoms of iron and of sulphur in the ferrous sulphide formed, as there were in the original iron and sulphur. The only difference is that the atoms of the elements are now combined together, while formerly they were free.

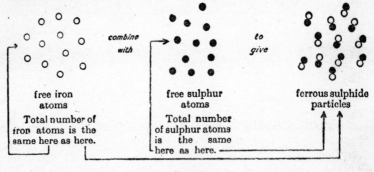

Fig. 2.

---

[1] This is not strictly true. Reactions in which carbon is involved may be exceptions. But, in these cases, special factors are at work into which it is not possible to enter here. The important general situation is that stated in the text.

Therefore, if this part of the Atomic Theory is true, the sum of the weights of the iron and sulphur *before* the combination ought to be exactly equal to the weight of the ferrous sulphide *after* it, or, in general, the total weight of the reacting substances should equal the total weight of the products formed. This can be tested by experiment. Experiments show that the deduction is realised in fact, and the general statement of the fact is called the **Law of Conservation**[1] **of Matter.** Experiments suitable for illustrating it are given on p. 27, where the law is formally stated.

To Find an Experimental Test of the Atomic Theory's Assertion that all Atoms of the Same Element are Exactly Alike but Different from Atoms of other Elements. It is hardly necessary to test whether atoms of different elements are different from one another. It seems obvious from the different properties of the elements that they are.

To test whether atoms of the same element are alike, we shall rely on gravimetric experiments again. The Atomic Theory says that all atoms of, say, copper, from whatever source, are all exactly alike in weight, and all atoms of, say, oxygen are all exactly alike also. Therefore, assuming that the same numbers of atoms of copper and oxygen always combine together, giving a compound called copper oxide, all samples of copper oxide we can obtain ought to have exactly the same proportions of copper and oxygen.

Let us take the case of copper atoms from three different sources combining with oxygen atoms from three different sources to give three samples of copper oxide as represented below.

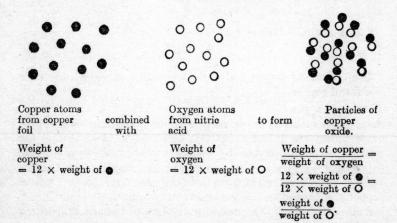

| Copper atoms from copper foil | combined with | Oxygen atoms from nitric acid | to form | Particles of copper oxide. |

Weight of copper = 12 × weight of ●

Weight of oxygen = 12 × weight of O

$$\frac{\text{Weight of copper}}{\text{weight of oxygen}} = \frac{12 \times \text{weight of ●}}{12 \times \text{weight of O}} = \frac{\text{weight of ●}}{\text{weight of O}}.$$

---

[1] Conservation has almost the same meaning as " preservation."

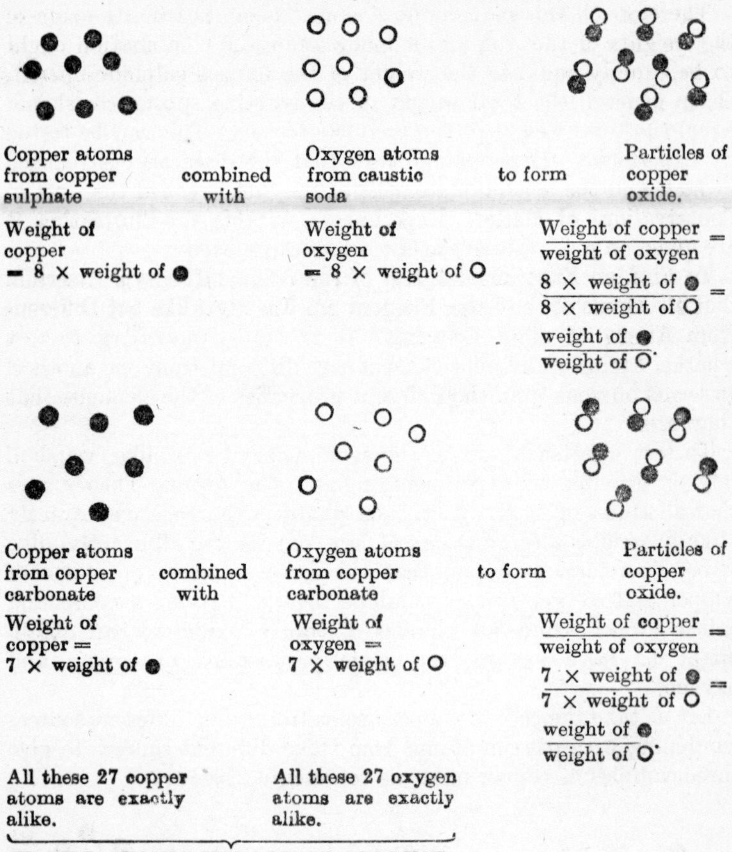

Copper atoms from copper sulphate	combined with	Oxygen atoms from caustic soda	to form	Particles of copper oxide.

Weight of copper
$= 8 \times$ weight of ●

Weight of oxygen
$= 8 \times$ weight of ○

Weight of copper / weight of oxygen $=$

$$\frac{8 \times \text{weight of} \ \bullet}{8 \times \text{weight of} \ \bigcirc} =$$

$$\frac{\text{weight of} \ \bullet}{\text{weight of} \ \bigcirc}.$$

Copper atoms from copper carbonate	combined with	Oxygen atoms from copper carbonate	to form	Particles of copper oxide.

Weight of copper =
$7 \times$ weight of ●

Weight of oxygen =
$7 \times$ weight of ○

Weight of copper / weight of oxygen $=$

$$\frac{7 \times \text{weight of} \ \bullet}{7 \times \text{weight of} \ \bigcirc} =$$

$$\frac{\text{weight of} \ \bullet}{\text{weight of} \ \bigcirc}.$$

All these 27 copper atoms are exactly alike.

All these 27 oxygen atoms are exactly alike.

IF THE ATOMIC THEORY IS CORRECT.

FIG. 3.

If all atoms of copper and oxygen are alike in weight, the ratio $\dfrac{\text{Weight of copper}}{\text{Weight of oxygen}}$ in all the samples of copper oxide must be the same. To test this by experiment, we must make samples of copper oxide by several different methods and analyse them to find the ratio of copper to oxygen by weight in each sample. A suitable experiment for this is given on p. 28. The results show that all samples of copper oxide have actually the same proportions of copper and oxygen and so the expectation from the Atomic Theory is realised. This fact is expressed in the **Law of Definite Proportions** (or Constant Composition). The argument applies equally well to any other compound.

To Find an Experimental Test of the Atomic Theory's Assertion that Atoms combine in Small Whole Numbers. If this statement is true, it means that if two elements combine together they must do so to form compounds similar to those shown below.

Let atoms of element A be ●.
Let atoms of element B be ○.

Compounds of A and B may be formed by such combinations as

1	2	3	4
One atom of A with one atom of B.	Two atoms of A with one atom of B.	Three atoms of A with two atoms of B.	One atom of A with two atoms of B.

FIG. 4.

We must find some way in which a test can be experimentally applied to this deduction.

We will begin by considering a *fixed* weight of B in each case and, since the Theory asserts that all atoms of B have exactly the same weight, we will take *one atom* of B as our fixed amount. Then the weights of element A which combine with *one atom* of B will be:—

In compound 1. In compound 2. In compound 3. In compound 4.

$1 \times$ weight of ● $\quad 2 \times$ weight of ● $\quad \dfrac{3}{2} \times$ weight of ● $\quad \dfrac{1}{2} \times$ weight of ●

If all the atoms of A are alike in weight, these weights of A are in the ratio of $1 : 2 : \dfrac{3}{2} : \dfrac{1}{2}$, or, (multiplying by 2) $2 : 4 : 3 : 1$. This is a simple whole number ratio.

We have reached the conclusion, therefore, that if the Atomic Theory is true, the **different** weights of A which combine with a **fixed** weight of B ought to be in a simple whole number ratio.

To test this conclusion experimentally, we must find a pair of elements which combine to form two or more different compounds, analyse those compounds to find the *varying* weights of one of the elements which combine with a *fixed* weight of the other and find whether these varying weights are in a simple whole number ratio to each other. This is done on p. 31 and the experimental result is shown to support the Atomic Theory. The **Law of Multiple Proportions** expresses these facts and is there stated.

Another law, the Law of Reciprocal Proportions, can also be shown to follow from the portions of the Atomic Theory we are considering. This is dealt with on p. 32.

We have now obtained, from the Atomic Theory, certain conclusions which can be made the subject of experimental test. It is the magnificent achievement of Dalton to have been the first to state the Atomic Theory, deduce from it these conclusions suitable for experimental check, and show that the experimental results support the Theory. It is a piece of work which stamps Dalton as a scientific genius of a very high order.

SYMBOLS

Having reached the conclusion that elements are made up of atoms, scientists needed some means of denoting *atoms*. Dalton invented a system, which is now purely of historical interest and is dealt with briefly on p. 24. The modern simple system of representing atoms was suggested by Berzelius, and consists generally of using the initial letter of the name of the element to stand for one atom of it, *e.g.*, one atom of hydrogen is denoted by H, one atom of oxygen by O, one atom of nitrogen by N. This rule cannot be universally applied because 90 elements have to share 26 letters. The difficulty has been readily overcome by using, for some of the elements, a symbol consisting of the initial letter, as a printed capital, together with one small letter from its name; for example, one atom of each of the elements carbon, chlorine, cerium, calcium and cæsium is denoted by the symbol C, Cl, Ce, Ca and Cs. In the case of the metals, the Latin names have sometimes been used as the source of the symbol, for example,

Metal	Latin Name	Symbol
copper	cuprum	Cu
iron	ferrum	Fe
lead	plumbum	Pb
silver	argentum	Ag
gold	aurum	Au
mercury	hydrargyrum	Hg
sodium	(natrium)	Na
potassium	(kalium)	K

These last two metals were unknown to the Romans, but a kind of pseudo-Latin name has been bestowed upon each, and from this its symbol is taken. A list of symbols of common elements is given on p. 429.

Definition. **The symbol of an element consists of one or more letters which denote one atom of the element.**

It is very important to keep it clearly in mind that the symbol of an element does stand for a perfectly definite amount of it, and that amount is one atom.

Molecules. We have seen that the smallest possible particle of an *element* is called an atom. It is obvious that the smallest possible particle of a *compound* must contain at least *two* atoms because a compound must contain at least *two* elements and cannot contain less than one atom of each. To the smallest possible particle of a compound is given the name "molecule".

The word molecule has, however, a wider meaning than this. We have seen that the smallest possible particle of an element is called one atom of it, but it does not follow, necessarily, that single atoms are the only particles normally existing in a mass of an element. Actually most elements usually exist as a mass of more complex particles, consisting of a number of atoms associated together and moving as a single particle. To this more complex particle is given the name "molecule". The distinction between the *atom* and the *molecule* of an element is that the *atom* is the smallest particle of it which can ever be obtained, and is the unit which is concerned in chemical reactions, while the *molecule* is the smallest particle of the element which is normally capable of a separate existence.

> Try to get this distinction quite clear; the atom is the smallest particle which can participate in chemical reactions while the molecule is the smallest particle which can normally exist when the element is not concerned in chemical reaction.

Definitions. **The atom is the smallest, indivisible particle of an element which can take part in chemical change.**

The molecule of an element or compound is the smallest particle of it which can normally exist separately.

Actually, most of the elementary gases consist of molecules each containing two atoms. The molecules of hydrogen, oxygen, nitrogen and chlorine are all of this type; a proof of this statement cannot be given until we have dealt with the Molecular Theory more fully, but it will be found, applied to hydrogen, on p. 76. This state of combination of the atoms is indicated by writing the molecules of these gases as H_2, O_2, N_2 and Cl_2, meaning a single unit consisting of two atoms of each of the gases. (2H or 2Cl would mean two separate atoms of each of these gases, a condition in which they do not normally exist.) The number of atoms in a molecule of an element is called its atomicity.

Definition. **The atomicity of an element is the number of atoms in one molecule of it.**

A molecule containing *one* atom is said to be **monatomic,** *e.g.,* He.

A molecule containing *two* atoms is said to be **diatomic,** *e.g.,* H_2, O_2, N_2, Cl_2.

A molecule containing *three* atoms is said to be **triatomic,** *e.g.,* O_3, ozone.

A molecule containing more than three atoms is said to be **polyatomic,** *e.g.,* P_4, S_8.

Molecules of hydrogen, diatomic, H_2.   Molecules of ozone, triatomic O_3.   Molecules of phosphorus (in certain solvents), polyatomic, P_4.

FIG. 5.

FORMULÆ AND EQUATIONS

From Berzelius' system of symbols is derived a simple method of denoting molecules of a compound or element.

Anticipating a little, we have already seen that a molecule of an element is denoted by writing the symbol of the element and, to the right and below it, a number expressing the number of atoms in the molecule; for example,

H_2 denotes one molecule of hydrogen containing two atoms.

P_4 denotes one molecule of phosphorus containing four atoms.

S_8 denotes one molecule of sulphur containing eight atoms.

The same device is adopted in representing the molecules of compounds, though here, of course, at least two symbols must appear because at least two elements must be present. Again, the small figure, to the right of a symbol and below it, expresses the number of atoms of the element present, the figure 1 being omitted. A few examples will make the idea clear.

CuO denotes one molecule of copper oxide containing one atom of copper and one atom of oxygen.

H_2O denotes one molecule of water containing two atoms of hydrogen and one atom of oxygen.

H_2SO_4 denotes one molecule of sulphuric acid containing two atoms of hydrogen, one atom of sulphur and four atoms of oxygen.

$CaCO_3$ denotes one molecule of chalk (calcium carbonate) containing one atom of calcium, one atom of carbon and three atoms of oxygen.

The close proximity of the symbols denotes that the elements are in chemical combination. The collection of symbols and numbers which together denote *one molecule* of a compound is called its formula. Thus, CuO, H_2O, H_2SO_4, and $CaCO_3$ are respectively the formulæ of copper oxide, water, sulphuric acid and calcium carbonate.

When a group of symbols is common to a class of compounds, it is frequently written as a bracketed group in their formulæ, together with a number to indicate the number of groups present. For example, all metallic nitrates are derived from *nitric acid*, HNO_3, and they all contain the nitrate group or radical, NO_3, in their formulæ. When formulæ of nitrates are written, this group is preserved intact, and, if two or more are needed, the number is indicated by enclosing the NO_3 group in a bracket and writing the number needed below and to the right. This arrangement is convenient because it emphasises the relation of the nitrates to nitric acid. For example, $Ca(NO_3)_2$ means the same as CaN_2O_6, because the 2 multiplies everything inside the bracket, but $Ca(NO_3)_2$ indicates the relation of calcium nitrate to nitric acid, HNO_3, more clearly than does CaN_2O_6. Similarly the formula of aluminium nitrate is written $Al(NO_3)_3$ rather than AlN_3O_9.

The sulphate radical, SO_4, which is common to sulphuric acid, H_2SO_4, and to all sulphates, is similarly treated. Thus the formula of aluminium sulphate, written as $Al_2(SO_4)_3$, indicates the derivation of this compound from sulphuric acid, H_2SO_4, more clearly than if written as $Al_2S_3O_{12}$. The hydroxyl group, OH, is also preserved in formulæ to emphasise the relation of hydroxides to water, $H.OH$, which is regarded as hydrogen hydroxide. Thus the formula of ferric hydroxide is written $Fe(OH)_3$, not FeO_3H_3.

If it is necessary to indicate a number of molecules of a compound, this is done by writing the appropriate number before the formula of the compound; for example,

$2H_2SO_4$ means two molecules of sulphuric acid.

$8HNO_3$ means eight molecules of nitric acid.

$4HCl$ means four molecules of hydrochloric acid.

$10H_2O$ means ten molecules of water.

It is important to notice carefully that the figure in front of the formula multiplies the *whole* of it. $2H_2SO_4$, for example, denotes two molecules of sulphuric acid each containing two atoms of hydrogen, one atom of sulphur and four atoms of oxygen, or four atoms of hydrogen, two atoms of sulphur and eight atoms of oxygen in all.

It is a common mistake of beginners to think that the figure multiplies only the symbol which immediately follows it, for example, that in $2H_2SO_4$ the 2 multiplies only the H_2 and not the SO_4. This is quite wrong. The 2 multiplies the *whole* of the formula H_2SO_4.

Notice that the formula of a compound denotes the perfectly definite amount of one molecule of it.

Dalton's System of Symbols. Dalton invented a number of symbols for the atoms of elements, a few of which are:—

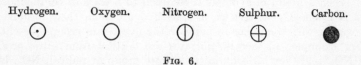

Hydrogen.   Oxygen.   Nitrogen.   Sulphur.   Carbon.

FIG. 6.

He then indicated the formulæ of compounds by combining the necessary numbers of these symbols, writing each one separately. Using modern knowledge of these compounds, his formulæ would be:—

Water.   Methane.   Sulphuric acid.   Ammonia.

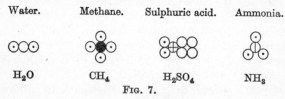

H_2O CH_4 H_2SO_4 NH_3

FIG. 7.

This very laborious system is quite unsuited to the representation of complex molecules. Think, for example, of the task of representing on this system the formula of cane sugar, $C_{12}H_{22}O_{11}$. It would entail the drawing of 12 separate symbols for carbon, 22 for hydrogen and 11 for oxygen, and the result would be an unwieldy and confusing jumble of 45 separate signs. The system was soon abandoned for that of Berzelius.

EQUATIONS

It is now possible for us to represent chemical reactions by means of statements involving only formulæ and symbols.

For example, if we wish to represent the fact that one molecule of copper oxide reacts with one molecule of sulphuric acid, producing one molecule of copper sulphate and one molecule of water, we can do so in the form:—

$$CuO + H_2SO_4 \rightarrow CuSO_4 + H_2O$$

This kind of statement is called "a chemical equation".

The $+$ sign on the left of the equation means "reacts with", but on the right it means simply "and", while the arrow means "producing".

Take another simple chemical equation.

$$Zn + H_2SO_4 \rightarrow ZnSO_4 + H_2$$

This means: "one atom of zinc reacts with one molecule of sulphuric acid producing one molecule of zinc sulphate and one molecule of hydrogen."

Again, the formula of potassium chlorate being $KClO_3$, and of potassium chloride KCl, the equation

$$2KClO_3 \rightarrow 2KCl + 3O_2$$

means: "two molecules of potassium chlorate decompose producing two molecules of potassium chloride and three molecules of oxygen."

It is important to notice that there must be the same number of each kind of atom on the right of a chemical equation as on the left. Otherwise the equation would imply that atoms had been created or destroyed, which is impossible. This process of equalisation is called "balancing" (see p. 68).

Notice further that chemical equations do not tell us under what conditions a reaction takes place. The equations given above do not tell us, for example, that heat is necessary to decompose potassium chlorate into potassium chloride and oxygen, or that the sulphuric acid must be dilute if it is to react with zinc to produce hydrogen.

The reactions of magnesium and iron with dilute sulphuric acid respectively can be represented by the equations

$$Mg + H_2SO_4 \rightarrow MgSO_4 + H_2$$
$$Fe + H_2SO_4 \rightarrow FeSO_4 + H_2$$

The equations correspond to, and represent, the observed fact that when these two metals are brought into contact with dilute sulphuric acid, hydrogen is liberated and the metals are converted into their sulphates. It is also possible to write an equation in which the symbol of copper, Cu, is substituted for Mg or Fe above. But such an equation would be a chemical falsehood, because copper is without action on dilute sulphuric acid.

QUESTIONS

1. State the meaning of the following formulæ: KNO_3 (nitre), $CuSO_4.5H_2O$ (blue vitriol), $PbCl_2$, $Na_2CO_3.10H_2O$ (washing soda), e.g., the formula H_2O (water) means that one molecule of water contains two atoms of hydrogen and one atom of oxygen.

2. How many atoms of the various elements are indicated by the following formulæ:—

$$2H_2O, \ 5HCl, \ 7HNO_3, \ 20PbSO_4, \ 11Cu(NO_3)_2 \ ?$$

3. Explain why the terms "atom" and "molecule" can both be correctly applied to particles of an element, but only one of them to particles of a compound.

4. What do you understand by the term atomicity? What is the atomicity usually assigned to the elements helium, chlorine, ozone, phosphorus?

5. Why is the formula for lead nitrate written $Pb(NO_3)_2$? (It could also be written PbN_2O_6.) Give three similar examples.

6. Using the Atomic Theory as your illustration, show the importance of the balance in determining the truth of a proposed theory.

7. State briefly Dalton's Atomic Theory. Explain why the theory is named after him in spite of the fact that he was not the first to bring forward the idea that matter consists of atoms.

8. State the Law of Multiple Proportions and show how it is explained by the Atomic Theory.

An element X forms two oxides containing 77·47 and 69·62 per cent of X respectively. If the first oxide has the formula XO, what is the formula of the second oxide? (C.)

CHAPTER III

EXPERIMENTAL ILLUSTRATION OF THE LAWS OF COMBINATION BY WEIGHT

THE LAW OF CONSERVATION OF MASS

The Law of Conservation of Mass (or Indestructibility of Matter) states that **matter is neither created nor destroyed in the course of chemical action.**

Let us illustrate this by an experiment.

Into a conical flask put some silver nitrate solution and lower into it carefully by means of a thread a small test-tube full of hydrochloric acid. Insert the stopper (Fig. 8). Place the flask on the pan of the balance and weigh it.

Note that you have just weighed (besides those portions of the apparatus which are unchanged throughout) some *water* and *silver nitrate* and *hydrogen chloride.*

Allow the two liquids to mix by tilting the flask a little, and you will observe a white precipitate of silver chloride whilst nitric acid will be formed in solution.

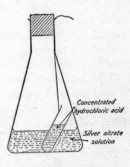

Concentrated hydrochloric acid

Silver nitrate solution

$$AgNO_3 + HCl \rightarrow AgCl + HNO_3$$

FIG. 8.

Experiment to illustrate the Law of Conservation of Mass.

Replace the flask on the pan of the balance and weigh again. You will find the weight is exactly the same as before.

This time you were weighing (besides those portions of the apparatus which are unchanged throughout) some *water* and *silver chloride* and *hydrogen nitrate* (or nitric acid).

Hence, although substances may undergo chemical changes, the *total* weight of the products of the reaction is exactly equal to the *total* weight of the reacting substances.

Other substances suitable for the above experiment are given in the following equations, which illustrate the chemical changes:—

$$BaCl_2 + H_2SO_4 \rightarrow BaSO_4 + 2HCl$$

barium   hydrogen   barium   hydrogen
chloride   sulphate   sulphate   chloride
            (sulphuric   (hydrochloric
            acid)   acid)

$$Pb(NO_3)_2 + 2NaCl \rightarrow PbCl_2 + 2NaNO_3$$

lead   sodium   lead   sodium
nitrate   chloride   chloride   nitrate

$$CuSO_4 + Zn \rightarrow Cu + ZnSO_4$$

copper   zinc   copper   zinc
sulphate   sulphate

There are many other examples.

These experiments are concerned with solutions. This is merely a matter of experimental convenience. It is difficult to weigh gases, and solids are unsuitable because they do not generally undergo rapid and complete reactions. The same experimental results are obtained, however, when solids and gases are involved.

Apparent Destruction of Coal. The above experiment may not seem conclusive to you because in it there seems little possibility of loss. If you consider the burning of coal, where only a small ash is left, it seems much more likely that the matter of the coal has been destroyed. The only real difference is that some of the reactants and products are invisible gases. Actually there is no loss of matter at all. If we could weigh all the oxygen which burns the coal, and all the ash, soot, water-vapour and carbon dioxide into which the coal is changed by the burning, we should again find that the total weight of the materials before the reaction was the same as the total weight of the total products after it (Fig. 9).

Invisible   Visible   Invisible   Invisible   Small amount
oxygen.   coal.   water-   carbon   of soot, ash
                        vapour.   dioxide.   and other
                                                  products.

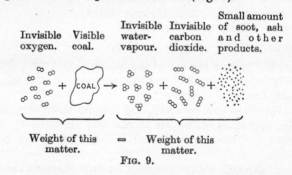

Weight of this   =   Weight of this
matter.   matter.

FIG. 9.

LAW OF DEFINITE PROPORTIONS (OR CONSTANT COMPOSITION)

The law of definite proportions states: **All pure samples of the same chemical compound contain the same elements combined in the same proportions by weight.**

The illustration of this law entails the performance of several experiments.

Principle of the Experiment. Black copper oxide (*i.e.*, cupric oxide) is prepared by several different methods and the samples are analysed by reduction in a stream of hydrogen, or coal-gas, and shown to contain copper and oxygen in the same proportions.

Preparation of the Samples of Copper Oxide

Sample A. Starting from Copper. Place a little clean, pure copper foil in a large crucible in a fume-chamber and carefully add concentrated nitric acid a little at a time. Brown fumes of nitrogen peroxide (poisonous) are seen and green copper nitrate solution is formed.

$$3Cu + 8HNO_3 \rightarrow 3Cu(NO_3)_2 + 4H_2O + 2NO$$

Evaporate the solution to dryness, then heat the green solid copper nitrate until no more brown fumes of nitrogen peroxide are evolved. The black solid left is the first sample of black copper oxide. Store it in a desiccator to keep it dry.

$$2Cu(NO_3)_2 \rightarrow 2CuO + 4NO_2 + O_2$$

Sample B. Starting from Copper Sulphate. Put some copper sulphate solution into a beaker and add excess of caustic soda solution. A blue gelatinous precipitate of copper hydroxide appears. Heat the beaker and its contents on a tripod and gauze by means of a bunsen burner. The precipitate changes to black copper oxide.

$$CuSO_4 + 2NaOH \rightarrow Cu(OH)_2 + Na_2SO_4$$
copper   caustic   copper   sodium
sulphate   soda   hydroxide   sulphate

$$Cu(OH)_2 \rightarrow CuO + H_2O$$

Filter off the black solid, wash it several times with hot distilled water, and allow it to dry in a hot oven or on a porous plate.

Transfer the oxide to a crucible and heat it with a burner to drive off the last traces of water. Store the copper oxide in a desiccator. The dry solid left is the second sample of black copper oxide.

Sample C. Starting from Copper Carbonate. Place a little copper carbonate in a dry crucible and warm it gently. It decomposes, turning from green to black, and carbon dioxide is given off. (Test— a drop of lime-water on the end of a glass rod is turned milky. The milkiness is caused by a precipitate of chalk.) Black copper oxide is left. After heating it for some time, put the black copper oxide into a desiccator to keep it dry.

$$CuCO_3 \rightarrow CuO + CO_2$$

B*

Analysis of the Samples of Copper Oxide by converting them to Copper by heating in coal-gas

Weigh three clean dry porcelain boats. Put into the boats 1–1½ grams of the three samples of copper oxide. Weigh all the boats again. Label them and put them in a hard glass test-tube

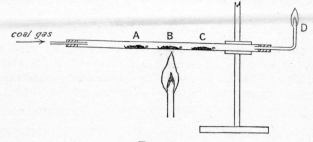

FIG. 10.

Reduction of three samples of black copper oxide by coal-gas.

and connect up the apparatus as shown in Fig. 10. The tube must slope so that the end C is the lower.

Turn on the coal-gas and light it at the jet D. Then heat each boat in turn. All the samples of copper oxide will glow and leave reddish-brown copper. The water formed by the combination of the oxygen of the copper oxide with the hydrogen of the coal-gas condenses at C, where the tube is cooler. The end C is lower than the end A to prevent this water from running back on to the hot part of the tube, which might be broken. When the action is complete, allow the tube to cool, keeping the coal-gas stream passing so that air cannot enter and oxidise the copper again. When the boats are cool, weigh all the three boats again. Work out the results as shown below.

$$CuO + H_2 \rightarrow Cu + H_2O$$
$$\text{from}$$
$$\text{coal-gas}$$

Specimen Results.

	Sample A.	Sample B.	Sample C.
Weight of porcelain boat . . .	3·01 gm.	2·50 gm.	2·70 gm.
Weight of porcelain boat and copper oxide	4·26 ,,	3·65 ,,	4·14 ,,
Weight of porcelain boat and copper	4·02 ,,	3·42 ,,	3·85 ,,
Weight of copper	1·01 ,,	0·92 ,,	1·15 ,,
Weight of copper oxide . . .	1·25 ,,	1·15 ,,	1·44 ,,
Percentage of copper in copper oxide	$\frac{1·01 \times 100}{1·25}$% = 80·8%	$\frac{0·92 \times 100}{1·15}$% = 80·0%	$\frac{1·15 \times 100}{1·44}$% = 79·8%

Within the limits of experimental error, the percentages of copper (and hence of oxygen) in all three samples of copper oxide are the same. It is found that, however samples of a given compound are prepared, they always contain the same elements in the same proportions by weight.

A similar experiment could be performed by obtaining litharge, PbO, in the ways indicated by the following equations, and then analysing the various samples in the same manner as described for copper oxide.

$$2PbO_2 \xrightarrow{\text{heat}} 2PbO + O_2$$
lead
peroxide

$$2Pb(NO_3)_2 \xrightarrow{\text{heat}} 2PbO + 4NO_2 + O_2$$
lead nitrate

$$PbCO_3 \xrightarrow{\text{heat}} PbO + CO_2$$
lead
carbonate

$$2Pb_3O_4 \xrightarrow{\text{heat}} 6PbO + O_2$$
red lead

LAW OF MULTIPLE PROPORTIONS

The law of multiple proportions states : **If two elements A and B combine together to form more than one compound, then the several weights of A, which separately combine with a fixed weight of B, are in a simple ratio.**

Principle of Experiment. Copper and oxygen form two oxides, cupric oxide (black copper oxide, CuO) and cuprous oxide (red copper oxide, Cu_2O). Pure samples of these two are reduced in a current of hydrogen and the amounts of copper which combine separately with, say, 100 grams of oxygen in the two compounds are calculated from the weighings.

Weigh two clean dry porcelain boats and weigh them again containing samples of pure, dry, red copper oxide and black copper oxide respectively. Reduce the oxides to copper in a stream of dry hydrogen, or coal-gas, as described in the last experiment. The following is a list of weighings and a specimen analysis.

	Red copper oxide.	Black copper oxide.
Weight of boat . . .	6·90 gm.	7·30 gm.
Weight of boat and oxide .	9·75 „	9·20 „
Weight of boat and copper .	9·43 „	8·82 „
∴ Weight of copper .	2·53 „	1·52 „
Weight of oxygen .	0·32 „	0·38 „
	∴ 0·38 gm. oxygen is combined with 2·53 gm. copper.	∴ 0·32 gm. oxygen is combined with 1·52 gm. copper.
	100 gm. oxygen are combined with	100 gm. oxygen are combined with
	$\dfrac{2\cdot53 \times 100}{0\cdot32}$ gm. copper	$\dfrac{1\cdot52 \times 100}{0\cdot38}$ gm. copper
	= 790 gm.	= 400 gm.

This ratio is 2 : 1 within limits of experimental error.

Hence the amounts of copper which have separately combined (*i.e.*, to form the two different oxides) with a **fixed** weight, 100 gm., of oxygen are in the ratio 2 : 1. The law could have been illustrated just as easily by fixing the weight of copper.

In a similar manner the three oxides of lead, litharge, lead dioxide, and red lead, could be used to illustrate the Law of Multiple Proportions by an experiment like the one just described.

Analysis of mercurous and mercuric chlorides as an illustration of the Law of Multiple Proportions.

The accuracy of the experiment described above depends on the purity of cuprous oxide, a material extremely difficult to obtain in a pure state. Mercurous and mercuric chlorides can both be obtained in a high degree of purity (Analar quality is used), and the following experiment may be performed as a class illustration of the law. Weigh a boiling-tube, add two or three grams of mercurous chloride, and weigh again. Add a teaspoonful of sodium hypophosphite (see p. 365), half fill with water, immerse in a beaker of water, and warm. Repeat using mercuric chloride, taking care to distinguish between the two boiling-tubes. After about 20 minutes, globules of mercury are seen in each tube. Wash the mercury by decantation several times with water (pouring the water into a beaker so that if mercury is lost, it may be retrieved), then with methylated spirit, and finally with ether. (*Care! Extinguish all flames in the vicinity.*) Replace the tubes in the warm water for a minute to remove traces of ether, dry the outside, and weigh. Calculate the separate weights of chlorine associated with, say, one gram of mercury in each of the two chlorides. These weights will be in the ratio 1 : 2.

$$NaH_2PO_2 + 2HgCl_2 + 2H_2O \rightarrow NaH_2PO_4 + 4HCl + 2Hg$$

sodium
hypophosphite
(*powerful reducing
agent*)

acid sodium
phosphate

Law of Reciprocal Proportions. This is a fourth law which can be deduced from the Atomic Theory. It is expressed in the statement —

If an element A combines with several other elements, B, C, D, the weights of B, C, D, which combine with a fixed weight of A are the weights of B, C and D which combine with each other, or simple multiples of those weights.

This rather complex statement will be made clearer by an example. Take a fixed weight of oxygen, say 8 gm. The weights of other elements which combine with 8 gm. of oxygen are zinc, 32·5 gm., sulphur, 8 gm., hydrogen, 1 gm. Then the Law of Reciprocal Proportions says that if zinc, sulphur or hydrogen combine with each other, they will so do in the proportions of 32·5 : 8 : 1, or some simple multiples of these proportions.

Actually, 32·5 gm. of zinc combine with 8 gm. of sulphur; 1 gm. of hydrogen combines with 16 gm. sulphur (2 × 8 gm.) and 1 gm. of hydrogen is displaced by 32·5 gm. of zinc, as the Law requires.

Like the Law of Multiple Proportions, this Law can be derived from Dalton's assumption that combination takes place between small whole numbers of atoms, all the atoms of a particular element being identical.

QUESTIONS

1. 1 gm. of one oxide of X contained 0·5 gm. of X, and 4 gm. of another oxide of X contained 1·6 gm. of X. Show these weights to be in accordance with the Law of Multiple Proportions.
2. Three oxides of nitrogen contain 53·3%, 69·6% and 36·4% of oxygen respectively. Show that the Law of Multiple Proportions is upheld.
3. Show that the following results obtained by the reductions of the two oxides of a metal are in agreement with the Law of Multiple Proportions.

	1st Compound.	2nd Compound.
Weight of boat . . .	5·30 gm.	4·45 gm.
Weight of boat + oxide .	13·85 „	13·05 „
Weight of boat + metal .	12·12 „	12·08 „

4. 1·90 gm. of one oxide of copper gave 1·52 gm. of copper on reduction. 2·85 gm. of another oxide gave 2·53 gm. of copper on reduction. Show these results to be in accordance with the Law of Multiple Proportions.

5. Two oxides of a metal contained respectively 7·41% and 3·85% of oxygen. Show these facts agree with the Law of Multiple Proportions.

6. The sulphides of a certain element contained 33·7% and 20·4% of sulphur. Do these figures agree with the Law of Multiple Proportions?

7. State the Law of Multiple Proportions. Describe how you would attempt to verify this law experimentally, if you were given specimens of litharge (PbO) and lead peroxide (PbO_2). Name one other pair of substances which you could use to verify this law. (N.U.J.B.)

8. A metal forms two oxides. 1·000 gm. of each oxide contains 0·239 and 0·385 gm. of oxygen respectively. Determine the equivalent of the metal in each oxide and show that these figures are in agreement with the Law of Multiple Proportions. (C.)

9. State the Law of Constant Composition (that is, Definite Proportions). You are required to verify this law by using the black oxide of copper, and for the purpose you are supplied with specimens of copper nitrate and copper carbonate. State clearly (a) how you would prepare specimens of copper oxide, (b) how you would use them to verify the law. (N.U.J.B.)

10. State the Law of Definite Proportions. Describe fully the experiments you would carry out in the laboratory in order to prove the truth of the law in the case of ONE chemical compound. (D.)

11. State the Law of Multiple Proportions. Show briefly how it is respectively by the Atomic Theory. Three oxides of a metal contain respectively 7·20, 9·39 and 13·44 per cent of oxygen. Show by calculation that these figures are in accordance with the law. (N.U.J.B.)

12. Two oxides of iron have the following percentage compositions by weight:—

	(i)	(ii)
Iron . . .	77·78	70·00
Oxygen . .	22·22	30·00

Calculate the equivalent of iron in each of these oxides.

State the law of chemical combination illustrated by the figures, and show how they illustrate this law. (O.)

13. State the Law of Multiple Proportions and describe an experimental verification of it. A metal forms three oxides which contain 76·47, 68·42 and 52 per cent of metal respectively. Show that these compounds are in agreement with the law. (B.)

14. State the Law of Multiple Proportions, illustrating your answer by reference to 4 examples. Specimens of two hydrocarbons were burnt in an excess of oxygen. 0·016 gm. of the one gave 23·9 c.c. of carbon dioxide, and 0·052 gm. of the other gave 95·8 c.c. of carbon dioxide, both volumes being measured at 15° C. and 750 mm. pressure. Show that these figures are in agreement with the above law. (C = 12.) (L.)

CHAPTER IV

EQUIVALENT WEIGHT, VALENCY AND ATOMIC WEIGHT

Introduction of the Chemical Balance. As soon as the existence of atoms was recognised, it was obviously desirable to try to obtain as much information as possible about the atoms of different elements, and, more particularly, to show how their weights compared with one another. This was necessary to enable quantitative experiments of various kinds to be made, to test doubtful points about the Atomic Theory, and also to enable chemists to make calculations of the quantities of materials involved in their experiments. Indeed, until the work of chemists could be made the subject of accurate weighings, and calculations could be tested by experiment, little progress could be expected. This was recognised more particularly by Black, a Scottish scientist working in Glasgow, and his name will always be honoured among chemists for his persistent and pioneer use of the chemical balance for checking his ideas. He taught scientists the importance of obtaining definite quantitative results instead of the vague qualitative statements with which they had been satisfied. The question for chemists became not only "What happens?" but also "What weight of each material is involved when it happens?"

Chaos of 1820-1850. We must not hide from ourselves the fact that the project of finding out how the weights of different atoms compared with each other proved extremely difficult to carry out. For about forty years after the Atomic Theory was suggested by Dalton, Chemistry was in a state of chaos. It is difficult for us now to read with understanding any book on Chemistry written between about 1820 and 1850, because chemists were simply groping about trying to solve the problem of comparing the weights of atoms, and they were making little progress. Let us try to understand where the difficulty lay and to follow the stages by which full knowledge was finally achieved.

In the first place, we must understand that chemists were not attempting to obtain the weights of *individual* atoms. It was clearly recognised that atoms were very small indeed and that there was no hope whatever at that time of obtaining the actual weight of a single atom of any element. The question was, rather: "How do the weights of the atoms of different elements compare with one another? Is, for example, a sodium atom heavier than an atom of oxygen, and, if so, how many times? Is a silver atom heavier than an atom of gold, and, if so, how many times?" Actually, we can to-day find the real weight in grams of a single atom of any element; we have accomplished what the chemists of 1836 regarded as a vain aspiration, but the process has taken 100 years, and when you read that the weight of a hydrogen atom is 0·000,000,000,000,000,000,000,0014 gm., you will not be surprised that science has consumed a great deal of time, and the patient efforts of many, to reach a stage at which such a minute quantity can be reasonably accurately measured.

Meaning of the term Atomic Weight. Returning to the simpler problem of comparing the weights of atoms, it became necessary first to fix some standard of weight with which all the atoms could be compared. We measure potatoes in stones, chocolates in lbs., and masses of steel in tons. In what weight-units can we express the weights of atoms? It was not possible to use the common scientific weight-unit and compare the weights of atoms in grams, and, in any case, as we saw previously, the numbers obtained would have been far too small for convenient use. To compare weights of atoms by using grams would, in fact, have been far less sensible than trying to express the weight of grains of sand in tons. Chemists recognised this and decided to compare the weights of all other atoms with the weight of a hydrogen atom.

The hydrogen atom was chosen because it is the lightest of all the atoms and would give numbers greater than unity for the comparative weights of all the other heavier atoms. This is more convenient than working in fractions or decimals, which the choice of any other atom as standard would necessitate.

Definition. **The Atomic Weight of an element is the number of times one atom of the element is heavier than one atom of hydrogen.**

You must understand clearly what this most important characteristic of an atom is. If you look in a "Table of Atomic Weights", you will see some statement such as $O = 16$ or $Na = 23$ or $P = 31$. This is the chemist's shorthand way of saying "The Atomic Weight of oxygen is 16, of sodium 23, and of phosphorus 31"; or, more fully, "Every atom of oxygen is 16 times as heavy as any atom of hydrogen"; or "Every atom of sodium is 23 times as heavy as any atom of hydrogen"; or "Every atom of phosphorus is 31 times as heavy as any atom of hydrogen." All this is conveyed by $O = 16$, $Na = 23$, $P = 31$. You do not yet know how these figures have been obtained; take them for granted for the moment. It will be obvious that if the weights of all atoms are compared with the weight of a hydrogen atom in this way, the weights of all atoms are also compared with each other. When we say, for example, that the Atomic Weight of oxygen is 16 and that of sodium is 23, we also state that the sodium atom is heavier than the oxygen atom in the proportion of 23 to 16.

The fact that we have chosen the weight of a hydrogen atom as our unit of atomic weight leads to the statement that the Atomic Weight of hydrogen is 1 (H = 1).

It is most important to get this idea of comparing the weights of all other atoms with that of a hydrogen atom firmly fixed in your mind. Consider it for a moment from another angle. A fairly complicated set of chemical experiments and theoretical arguments has established the conclusion that the Atomic Weight of sulphur is 32 (S = 32). In the long run, this simply means that if we could separate out from a piece of sulphur one single atom of it, place it on a sufficiently delicate see-saw and then, to the other side of the

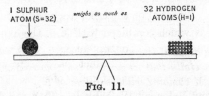

I SULPHUR ATOM (S=32) weighs as much as 32 HYDROGEN ATOMS (H=1)

Fig. 11.

see-saw, add, one at a time, some hydrogen atoms, the see-saw would just balance when exactly 32 hydrogen atoms had been added (Fig. 11).

In actual practice, we cannot separate out the one single atom of sulphur and the single atoms of hydrogen we should need, but, if we could, all the chemical experiments which have been required to find the result S = 32 would be unnecessary.

Molecular Weight. The weights of molecules of elements or compounds are also compared with the weight of a hydrogen atom.

Definition. **The molecular weight of an element or compound is the number of times one molecule of it is heavier than ONE ATOM of hydrogen.**

Some methods of determining molecular weights are given in Chapter IX.

Theory of the Method of Determining Atomic Weights. Since we cannot be provided with these separate atoms, we must now try to find other ways of arriving at Atomic Weights. We must first recall two of the statements about atoms which Dalton made in his Atomic Theory; the first, that all atoms of the same element are exactly alike in every way, and the second, that chemical combination takes place between small numbers of atoms of different elements. It is the first of these two statements which enables us to overcome the difficulty of not being able to isolate single atoms. Suppose we consider two elements M and N, and we know (by evidence not yet dealt with) that, when they combine, one atom of M combines with one atom of N. Then, since every atom of M acts just like every other, it must also be true that 50 million atoms of M combine with 50 million atoms of N, neither more nor less. So, although we cannot weigh one atom of M, we can weigh millions and millions of them, and we can also weigh the compound of M and N produced when the millions and millions of atoms of M combine with a precisely equal number of atoms of N. Then the weight of these millions and millions of atoms of N is the difference in weight between the compound, MN, and the element, M. So

$$\frac{\text{Wt. of a very large no. of atoms of M}}{\text{Wt. of an exactly equal no. of atoms of N}} = \frac{\text{Wt. of 1 atom of M}}{\text{Wt. of 1 atom of N}}$$

$$= \frac{\text{Wt. of M on the laboratory balance}}{\text{Wt. of N which combined with M in the experiment}}$$

and we have compared the weights of single atoms of M and N.

(*Note very carefully that we have, as yet, no evidence to prove how many atoms of M combine with one atom of N.*)

Equivalent and Valency. We have seen that the Atomic Weight of an element is the number which expresses how many times one atom of the element is heavier than one atom of hydrogen. From this it is clear that the Atomic Weight of an element must be connected in a very important way with the weights of hydrogen and the element which combine together.

To clear up this point, consider an element, M, which combines with hydrogen. Suppose that, by a laboratory experiment, we find that 1 gm. of hydrogen combines with 35·5 gm. of M. Clearly, the atomic weight of M must be connected in some way with this 35·5.

If *one* atom of M combines with *one* atom of hydrogen to give a compound which must have the formula, MH, then, from this formula, the Atomic Weight of M in grams must combine with 1 gm. of hydrogen ($H = 1$); but, by experiment, 1 gm. of hydrogen combines with 35·5 gm. of M; therefore the Atomic Weight of M must be 35·5.

If *two* atoms of hydrogen combine with *one* atom of M to give a compound which must have the formula MH_2, then the Atomic Weight in grams of M must be great enough to combine with 2 gm. of hydrogen ($H_2 = 2$); but, by the experiment, 35·5 gm. of M combine with 1 gm. of hydrogen, and the Atomic Weight of M must therefore be $2 \times 35·5$, or 71.

Similarly, if *three* atoms of hydrogen can combine with *one* atom of M to give a compound, MH_3, the atomic weight of M must be 3×35.5, or 106.5. From this follows the following important conclusion, that one way of determining the atomic weight of an element will be to find:—

(i) the number of grams of the element which combine with one gram of hydrogen;

(ii) the number of atoms of hydrogen which combine with one atom of the element.

Then the atomic weight of the element is the product of the two.

The first of the two requirements is called the *Equivalent Weight* of the element.

Definition. **The Equivalent Weight of an element is the number of grams[1] of it which will combine with or displace ONE GRAM[1] of HYDROGEN.**

It is fairly easy to determine the equivalent weights of most elements in the laboratory. Chapter VII will be devoted to describing a few of the methods which are available.

The second of the two requirements stated above is called the *Valency* of the element.

Definition. **The Valency of an element is the number of hydrogen atoms which will combine with or displace ONE ATOM of the element.**

Using these new terms, we can now state the following very important conclusion. Learn it thoroughly, together with the definitions of all the three terms used.

Atomic Weight = Equivalent Weight × Valency

We have now advanced a considerable distance along the road to our goal of finding atomic weights. We have split the problem into the fairly simple task of finding out by a laboratory experiment how many grams of a given element combine with 1 gm. of hydrogen (its equivalent) and the separate task of finding how many atoms of hydrogen will combine with one atom of the element (its valency). It was in this second requirement that the chemists of a century ago found their difficulty. They could not determine the valencies of elements, because no methods for the purpose were yet known, and it was just because these methods were not available that chemistry was in a chaotic state. In fact, it is probably true to say that chemists did not clearly realise the meaning of valency and the need for knowing it until it was specifically defined by Frankland in 1853, half a century after Dalton's Atomic Theory was suggested.

Without clearly formulating the idea of valency, Dalton did, of necessity, make certain assumptions in which the idea of valency was

---

[1] "Part(s) by weight" can be substituted for the word gram(s) to make this definition complete.

involved, and in this way connected the combining or "equivalent" weights of elements with their atomic weights. The assumption that Dalton made was that, if only one compound of two elements A and B existed, it would be the simplest possible compound of the two and would be formed by the combination of one atom of A with one atom of B to give the compound AB. This was giving Nature credit for making chemical combination as simple as possible, and, we need hardly say, the credit was often undeserved and the assumption wrong. One very important case in which Dalton was wrong was that of water. In Dalton's time, water was the only compound known which contained hydrogen and oxygen alone, and Dalton assumed that a molecule of water was formed in the simplest possible way, *i.e.*, by the combination of one atom of hydrogen with one atom of oxygen to give one molecule of water HO. This is the same as saying that the valency of oxygen is 1, for here one atom of oxygen combines with one atom of hydrogen. This is wrong; the valency of oxygen is really 2 and the formula of water H_2O. The fact that an incorrect formula for so simple a compound as water was proposed, and accepted by the scientific world, shows the confusion in which scientists were floundering. We need not elaborate the point further. All that is important about it is to recognise that Dalton's assumptions were nothing but guesses. Out of these guesses, however—for we must remember that they were the guesses of genius— came progress. It happened that, in a certain number of cases, Dalton's guesses about valency were correct or he made errors which cancelled each other. This was so in the case of some of the commoner metals. This meant that, within the limits of the experimental errors of the time, correctly related atomic weights were assigned to these metals. From this fact arose the first definite step of advance towards methods of determining valency, and it came indirectly from work undertaken with quite a different object in view.

Valency from Dulong and Petit's Law. The end of the eighteenth century had seen great activity in what we now call Physics and, in particular, Lavoisier and Laplace had determined the specific heats[1] of a number of metals with considerable accuracy. In 1819, Dulong and Petit, two French scientists, pointed out that, using the accepted atomic weights for many metals and multiplying them by the specific heats, an approximately constant figure was obtained for each metal. The average value of this constant is 6·4. In some cases, the accepted atomic weight of a metal, when multiplied by its specific heat, gave a result considerably removed from 6·4. Where this was so, Dulong and Petit suggested that probably the accepted atomic weight was wrong, that the metal probably obeyed their rule and that the Atomic Weight should be altered accordingly. Subsequent work has shown that they were right. This rule is generally known as

Dulong and Petit's Law. For solid elements, more particularly metals,

Atomic Weight × Specific Heat = 6.4 approximately

[1] The specific heat of a substance is the number of calories of heat required to raise 1 gm. of it from 0° C. to 1° C.

This product, Atomic Weight × Specific Heat, is known as the "Atomic Heat" of the element.

This law was the first step in the effort to determine valencies. Note its limited application—to solid elements only. It is also important to note that the law is only an approximation. The value, 6·4, for the "constant" is obtained by averaging the figures for the different elements. They vary from about 5·7 to 6·7. Thus the chances are that when applied to a given solid element the law will give an approximate, but not accurate, value for its atomic weight.

Application of Dulong and Petit's Law. Suppose that zinc is a newly discovered metal and its atomic weight is to be determined. Experiment will show:

(1) that if we wish to obtain 1 gm. of hydrogen from dilute sulphuric acid by dissolving zinc in it, we shall have to use 32·5 gm. of zinc, *i.e.*, the equivalent of zinc is 32·5;

(2) that the specific heat of zinc is 0·096.

The atomic weight of zinc is, therefore, 32·5 × 1, or 32·5 × 2, or 32·5 × 3, and so on, according to whether the valency of zinc is 1 or 2 or 3, etc.

Applying Dulong and Petit's Law:

$$\text{Atomic Weight} \times \text{Specific Heat} = 6\cdot4 \text{ (approx.)}$$

$$\therefore \text{Atomic Weight of zinc} = \frac{6\cdot4}{\text{Specific Heat}}$$

$$= \frac{6\cdot4}{0\cdot096} = 67$$

But this figure is only approximate because it is derived by using the 6·4 from Dulong and Petit's Law which is itself only approximate.

We can, however, now use the equation

$$\text{Atomic Weight} = \text{Valency} \times \text{Equivalent Weight}$$

to obtain the valency of zinc, for, using the figures so far obtained,

$$67 = \text{Valency} \times 32\cdot5$$

$$\therefore \text{valency of zinc} = \frac{67}{32\cdot5} \text{ (again approximately)}$$

Recall the definition of valency—the number of hydrogen atoms needed to combine with or displace one atom of the element. Since it is a "number of hydrogen atoms", valency must be **a whole number** because we cannot divide atoms. An atom may combine with 1 or 2 or 3 hydrogen atoms, but not with 1·3 or 2·6 or 3·2.

As above, valency of zinc $= \dfrac{67}{32\cdot5}$.

This value is very close to 2 and we therefore assume that the valency of zinc is actually 2. (Be sure you understand why the value of valency obtained in this way may appear not to be a whole number. It is because Dulong and Petit's Law is only very approximately true, and its errors are reflected in the atomic weight values derived from it and hence in the valency.)

Applying this value for the valency, we now obtain the **accurate** value of the atomic weight of zinc, for:

$$\text{Atomic weight of zinc} = \text{Equivalent Weight} \times \text{Valency}$$
$$= 32 \cdot 5 \qquad \times 2$$
$$= 65 \cdot 0$$

This argument is rather difficult to follow unless you grasp two facts (i) that Dulong and Petit's Law is first used to give an *approximate* atomic weight, which is discarded as soon as it has done its work of providing the valency of the element from the fraction $\dfrac{\text{Atomic Weight}}{\text{Equivalent Weight}}$, (ii) that the valency can then be used to give a second value of atomic weight, which is **accurate**, by multiplying the valency by the equivalent.

Let us apply the idea to another example.

"The equivalent of a certain metal is 29·75. Its Specific Heat is 0·056. Find the valency and accurate Atomic Weight of the metal."

1. *Find the equivalent of the metal.*

This is given—29·75.

2. *Find, by Dulong and Petit's Law, the approximate Atomic Weight.*

$$\text{Atomic Weight} \times \text{Specific Heat} = 6 \cdot 4$$
$$\therefore \text{Atomic Weight} = \frac{6 \cdot 4}{0 \cdot 056} = 114 \text{ (approx.)}$$

3. *Find the valency from (1) and (2).*

$$\text{Atomic Weight} = \text{Valency} \times \text{Equivalent Weight}$$
$$\therefore \quad 114 = \text{Valency} \times 29 \cdot 75$$
$$\text{Valency} = \frac{114}{29 \cdot 75} = 4 \quad \begin{pmatrix} \because \text{ the valency must be} \\ \text{a whole number} \end{pmatrix}$$

4. *Find the accurate atomic weight from (1) and (3).*

$$\text{Atomic Weight} = \text{Equivalent Weight} \times \text{Valency}$$
$$= 29 \cdot 75 \qquad \times 4$$
$$= 119 \cdot 00$$

Other methods of determining Atomic Weights are also available. We shall deal with them in subsequent chapters. The one involving Dulong and Petit's Law, which we have just been considering, was historically the earliest reliable method.

CHAPTER V

VALENCY AND FORMULÆ

THE valency of an element has been defined, in the last chapter, as the number of hydrogen atoms needed to combine with or displace one atom of the element. We shall proceed in this chapter to consider the subject of valency more fully and to study its relation to the chemical formulæ of compounds.

Numerical Value of Valency. It is most important to remember that *the valency of an element must be a whole number*. This follows at once from the definition of it as "the number of hydrogen atoms needed to combine with or displace one atom of the element", for "the number of hydrogen atoms" cannot be anything but a whole number, parts or fractions of an atom being impossible, as the atom is indivisible.

Keep this fact clearly in mind and avoid the absurdity of returning the valency of an element in a calculation as 2·5 or 3·7. Such a result simply means that you have made some mistake in the calculation.

Variable Valency. We have proceeded so far on the assumption that a given element exerts only one valency. For the commoner elements, this is generally true, *e.g.*, sodium and potassium exert univalency (or a valency of 1), zinc and calcium are bivalent (or possess a valency of 2), and these elements exercise no other valencies. Certain elements, however, exert two (and sometimes more) different valencies according to the conditions under which they are reacting. Phosphorus, for example, exerts valencies of three and five (*i.e.*, it is tervalent or quinquevalent). When exercising its valency of 3, it forms with chlorine the fuming liquid, phosphorus trichloride, PCl_3; when exercising the valency of 5, it forms the yellow solid, phosphorus pentachloride, PCl_5. Similarly, iron exercises in ferr*ous* compounds a valency of 2 and forms, for example, ferr*ous* chloride, $FeCl_2$, while in ferr*ic* compounds it exercises a valency of 3 and forms, for example, ferr*ic* chloride, $FeCl_3$. The reason for this exercise of variable valency has also been found to lie in the internal structure of the atom of the element concerned.

We saw in the last chapter that equivalent, atomic weight and valency are connected by the equation:—

$$\text{Atomic Weight} = \text{Equivalent} \times \text{Valency}$$

You must bear in mind that the atomic weight of an element is absolutely fixed and cannot vary. When the element exerts two different valencies, its atomic weight remains fixed, but it has two different equivalents. In the case of iron, the atomic weight has the fixed and invariable value of 56; when the element exerts its valency of 2 in ferrous compounds, the equivalent of iron is $\frac{56}{2}$ or 28, while the equivalent of ferric iron, of which the valency is 3, is $\frac{56}{3}$ or 18·7. Similarly, phosphorus, atomic weight 31, has an equivalent of $\frac{31}{3}$ or 10·3 when 3-valent and an equivalent of $\frac{31}{5}$ or 6·2 when 5-valent.

FORMULÆ

We shall consider now the connection between the valency of an element and the formulæ of its compounds, confining ourselves first to binary compounds, that is, compounds containing only two elements.

Hydrogen Compounds. It is very easy to write down the formulæ of many binary compounds by simply considering the definition of valency—the number of hydrogen atoms needed to combine with or displace an atom of the element. For example, the valency of the elements chlorine, bromine and iodine is 1. From this it follows that one atom of each of these elements must combine with one atom of hydrogen and the formulæ of hydrogen chloride, bromide and iodide must be HCl, HBr and HI respectively. Similarly, the valency of oxygen and sulphur being 2, one atom of each of these elements combines with *two* atoms of hydrogen, and the formulæ of hydrogen oxide (water) and hydrogen sulphide are H_2O and H_2S. Again, elements such as phosphorus and nitrogen, exercising a valency of 3, form hydrogen compounds, PH_3 (phosphine) and NH_3 (ammonia), while carbon and silicon, of valency 4, form hydrogen compounds CH_4 (methane) and SiH_4 (silicon hydride).

Chlorides. The formulæ of other binary compounds can be similarly derived from consideration of the corresponding hydrogen compounds. Take, for example, chlorides. Chlorine and hydrogen both possess a valency of 1, so the formula of hydrogen chloride is HCl. All other elements of valency 1 will form their chlorides by supplying one atom of the element to replace the one atom of hydrogen in HCl. Thus, sodium, potassium and silver form chlorides whose formulæ are NaCl, KCl and AgCl respectively. In each case, one atom of the univalent metal has taken the place of the single atom of hydrogen in HCl.

Elements of valency 2 (bivalent) have twice the combining power of a hydrogen atom and so one atom of a bivalent element, such as zinc, will combine with two atoms of chlorine to form a chloride of the type, $ZnCl_2$. Such elements are calcium, lead, ferrous iron, magnesium and copper, which form chlorides possessing the formulæ $CaCl_2$, $PbCl_2$, $FeCl_2$, $MgCl_2$, and $CuCl_2$ respectively. Similarly, elements of valency 3, for example, ferric iron and aluminium, form chlorides having the formulæ $FeCl_3$ and $AlCl_3$, carbon of valency 4 forms the chloride CCl_4, and phosphorus of valency 5 forms the chloride PCl_5.

Metallic Hydroxides and Nitrates. Metallic hydroxides are derived from the compound $H.OH$ (water, regarded as hydrogen hydroxide) and nitrates from HNO_3, nitric acid. Comparing these formulæ with hydrochloric acid, HCl, from which chlorides are derived, we see that the OH and NO_3 groups have the same combining power as a chlorine atom, that is, all three are univalent. From this it follows that the **formulæ of metallic hydroxides and nitrates must be similar to those of chlorides, substituting OH or NO_3 for Cl;** thus:—

Metal.	Valency.	Chloride.	Hydroxide.	Nitrate.
Sodium . .	1	NaCl	NaOH	$NaNO_3$
Calcium . .	2	$CaCl_2$	$Ca(OH)_2$	$Ca(NO_3)_2$
Ferric Iron .	3	$FeCl_3$	$Fe(OH)_3$	$Fe(NO_3)_3$

Oxides. The valency of oxygen is 2 and the formula of water is therefore H_2O, one oxygen atom being able to combine with two hydrogen atoms.

One atom of univalent elements such as silver, sodium or potassium can each replace one atom of hydrogen, so the formulæ of the oxides of these elements are Ag_2O, Na_2O and K_2O, two atoms of each of the elements being needed to replace the two atoms of hydrogen in H_2O.

One atom of bivalent elements such as calcium, zinc, magnesium, lead and copper has twice the combining power of a hydrogen atom, therefore only one atom of each of these elements is needed to replace the two hydrogen atoms of water, H_2O. The formulæ of the oxides of these elements are, therefore, CaO, ZnO, MgO, PbO and CuO.

A tervalent element, such as ferric iron or aluminium, exerts as much combining power as three hydrogen atoms. We have seen that one oxygen atom combines with two hydrogen atoms, so that one atom of a tervalent element has the same combining power as one and a half oxygen atoms. Since half an oxygen atom cannot exist, the simplest formula for the oxide of a tervalent element must contain three oxygen atoms and they must be combined with two atoms of the tervalent element; that is, the formulæ of ferric oxide and aluminium oxide are Fe_2O_3 and Al_2O_3 respectively.

Metallic Sulphates and Carbonates. Sulphuric acid, from which sulphates are derived, has the formula H_2SO_4, and carbonic acid, from which carbonates are derived, has the formula H_2CO_3. Comparing these formulæ with that of water, H_2O, it is clear that the sulphate (SO_4) group and carbonate (CO_3) group have, as a whole, the same combining power as an oxygen atom, that is, they are bivalent. The sulphates and carbonates of metals will, therefore, have formulæ similar to those of their oxides, substituting SO_4 and CO_3 respectively for O. Thus:—

Element.	Valency.	(H_2O) Oxide.	(H_2SO_4) Sulphate.	(H_2CO_3) Carbonate.
Sodium .	1	Na_2O	Na_2SO_4	Na_2CO_3
Calcium .	2	CaO	$CaSO_4$	$CaCO_3$
Ferric iron .	3	Fe_2O_3	$Fe_2(SO_4)_3$	Carbonate unknown.

Valencies of Metals. This rather difficult subject of valency is considerably simplified if you remember that **the valency of most of the common metals is 2,** the exceptions being sodium, potassium, ammonium and silver of valency 1, and aluminium and ferric iron of valency 3.

Typical formulæ of the common metallic compounds are given in the table on p. 47.

The Ammonium Radical. The ammonium radical requires special consideration. This radical is the group NH_4—.

It can have no separate existence, but acts as if it were a metal of valency 1 and forms salts similar to those of other monovalent metals such as sodium.

The formulæ of these salts are analogous to those of sodium salts, the only difference being the exchange of the monovalent NH_4— group for a sodium atom. Compare the formulæ:—

sodium chloride	$NaCl$	ammonium chloride	NH_4Cl
sodium hydroxide	$NaOH$	ammonium hydroxide	NH_4OH
sodium nitrate	$NaNO_3$	ammonium nitrate	NH_4NO_3
sodium sulphate	Na_2SO_4	ammonium sulphate	$(NH_4)_2SO_4$
sodium carbonate	Na_2CO_3	ammonium carbonate	$(NH_4)_2CO_3$

Notice that, in each case, the NH_4 group takes the place of the sodium atom.

Compound.	Formula of corresponding hydrogen compound.	Metals of $V = 1$, e.g., Na.	Metals of $V = 2$, e.g., Ca.	Metals of $V = 3$, e.g., Al.
Oxide	H_2O	Na_2O	CaO	Al_2O_3
Hydroxide	$H.OH$	$NaOH$	$Ca(OH)_2$	$Al(OH)_3$
Chloride	HCl	$NaCl$	$CaCl_2$	$AlCl_3$
Nitrate	HNO_3	$NaNO_3$	$Ca(NO_3)_2$	$Al(NO_3)_3$
Sulphate	H_2SO_4	Na_2SO_4	$CaSO_4$	$Al_2(SO_4)_3$
Carbonate	H_2CO_3	Na_2CO_3	$CaCO_3$	
Other elements of same valency.	—	K, Ag, NH_4	Zn, Mg, Pb, Fe(*ous*) Cu, Sn(*ous*)	Fe(*ic*)

QUESTIONS ON THIS CHAPTER WILL BE FOUND ON PAGE 62.

CHAPTER VI

THE BEHAVIOUR OF GASES UNDER TEMPERATURE AND PRESSURE CHANGE

The Nature of Gas Pressure. Any gas consists of a collection of molecules of a particular kind which are in a state of rapid motion. The fact that the molecules are in motion is evident from the fact that if a small quantity of an odorous gas, such as hydrogen sulphide, is liberated at any point in a laboratory the smell of the gas soon pervades the whole room.

If the gas is confined in a closed vessel, some of the moving molecules strike the sides of the vessel and each impact exerts a small force upon the side. The number of molecules of gas inside such a vessel will normally be very large and, on the average, the same number of molecules will strike a given area on the sides of the vessel each second, so producing a steady pressure.

Relation between Pressure and Volume. Now suppose that one of the sides of a cylindrical vessel is a smooth piston and that there

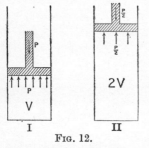

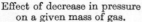

FIG. 12.

Effect of decrease in pressure on a given mass of gas.

is a pressure, P, exerted on the piston just great enough to resist the pressure of the gas, of which the volume is V. (Fig. 12, I). The piston will remain still.

Now suppose that the pressure on the piston is suddenly reduced to $\frac{1}{2}$P, without temperature change. The gas pressure is the greater and the piston will move up. As it does so the gas will fill the greater volume now available. The molecules will be more loosely packed in this larger space and so fewer will strike the sides of the vessel in a given time; that is, the pressure of the gas falls as the piston slides upwards. A stage will be reached when the gas occupies so large a volume that its pressure has also been reduced to $\frac{1}{2}$P and the piston will then stop. (Fig. 12, II.) This will happen when the volume of the gas has doubled; that is, a halving of the pressure causes the volume of the gas to be doubled. Similarly, it would be found that if the pressure on the piston was reduced to $\frac{1}{4}$P, it would come to a stop when the volume of the gas had increased to four times its original value.

Expressing the result generally, the pressure of a gas decreases in the same proportion as its volume increases.

From this, it is clear that if we multiply the varying volumes of a given mass of gas by the corresponding pressures, any decrease in the value of one of them will be exactly counterbalanced by the increase in the value of the other, and the result will always be the same.

Expressed mathematically, this may be stated in the form:—

$$P_1 V_1 = P_2 V_2 \text{ (Temperature constant)}$$

Where P_1 and P_2 are two pressures and V_1 and V_2 the corresponding volumes of a given mass of gas.

This result is known by the name of its discoverer as Boyle's Law.

Boyle's Law. **The volume of a given mass of gas is inversely proportional[1] to its pressure, if the temperature remains constant.**

TEMPERATURE CHANGE

It is common knowledge that a rise of temperature causes objects to expand and a fall of temperature causes contraction. The rule applies to gases, liquids and solids, but the effect is much more marked in the case of gases than in the case of the other two. Charles found that, if pressure is constant, the volume of a gas increases or decreases by $\frac{1}{273}$ rd of its volume at 0° C. for every °C. rise or fall of temperature; that is, if we take 273 c.c. of any gas at 0° C. its volume will rise or fall by 1 c.c. for every °C. rise or fall of temperature. Thus at -1° C., the volume will be 272 c.c.; at -2° C., 271 c.c.; at -3° C., 270 c.c., and so on. This leads to the absurdity that if the temperature falls to -273° C., the volume of the gas will be 0 c.c.—the gas will have vanished! In actual practice, no substance can remain gaseous at such low temperatures; all become solids and the law of Charles does not then apply, but this temperature, at which the volume of a gas would theoretically be reduced to zero, gives us the lowest possible temperature that can ever be reached. It is called *Absolute Zero* and temperatures measured from this as the starting point are called *Absolute Temperatures*. Since Absolute Zero (0° A.) is the same as -273° C., it is clear that the Absolute Scale starts measuring temperature from a point 273° C. lower than the starting point of the Centigrade Scale and **to convert Centigrade Temperatures to Absolute Temperatures, we must add 273°.** Thus:—

[1] "Inversely proportional" is the mathematical expression of the fact that as the pressure *increases* the volume *decreases* in the same proportion.

$-273°$ C. is the same as $0°$ A. $(-273 + 273)$
$0°$ C. is the same as $273°$ A. $(0 + 273)$
$15°$ C. is the same as $288°$ A. $(15 + 273)$
$40°$ C. is the same as $313°$ A. $(40 + 273)$
$100°$ C. is the same as $373°$ A. $(100 + 273)$.

Restating the Law of Charles, using Absolute Temperatures, we find that 273 c.c. of gas at $273°$ A. $(0°$ C.), will become 274 c.c. at $274°$ A. $(1°$ C.), 275 c.c. at $275°$ A. $(2°$ C.), 276 c.c. at $276°$ A. $(3°$ C.), and so on; or, for falling temperatures, the volume will become 272 c.c, at $272°$ A. $(-1°$ C.), 271 c.c. at $271°$ A. $(-2°$ C.) and so on. This gives us the rule (known as Charles' Law) that the volume of a given mass of gas increases in the same proportion as its absolute temperature, if pressure is constant.

Charles' Law. **The volume of a given mass of gas is directly proportional**[1] **to its absolute temperature, if pressure is constant.**

From this it follows that if we divide the varying volumes of a given mass of gas by the corresponding absolute temperatures, any increase in the volume will be exactly cancelled by the increase in the temperature, and the result will always be the same. This can be expressed in the form

$$\frac{V_1}{T_1 \,°A} = \frac{V_2}{T_2 \,°A} \quad \text{(Pressure constant)}$$

where V_1 and V_2 are the volumes of the gas at absolute temperatures $T_1 \,°A$ and $T_2 \,°A$ respectively.

Combining this with the equation expressing Boyle's Law (p. 49) we obtain the equation:—

$$\frac{P_1 V_1}{T_1 \,°A} = \frac{P_2 V_2}{T_2 \,°A}$$

and, by the use of this equation, we can find the volume (V_2) that a gas will occupy at any desired temperature and pressure $(T_2° $ A. and $P_2)$ from its volume (V_1) at a given temperature and pressure $(T_1° $ A. and $P_1)$.

Example. A gas occupies 211 c.c. at $18°$ C. and 740 mm. pressure. What volume will it occupy at $-20°$ C. and 770 mm. pressure?

Convert the temperatures to the Absolute Scale.

$$18° \text{ C.} = (18 + 273)° \text{ A.} = 291° \text{ A.}$$
$$-20° \text{ C.} = (-20 + 273)° \text{ A.} = 253° \text{ A.}$$

Then
$$\frac{P_1 V_1}{T_1 \,°A} = \frac{P_2 V_2}{T_2 \,°A}$$

[1] "Directly proportional" is the mathematical expression of the fact that the volume *increases* in the same proportion as the absolute temperature *increases*.

Substituting $\dfrac{740 \times 211}{291} = \dfrac{770 \times V_2}{253}$

$\therefore\ 740 \times 211 \times 253 = 770 \times 291 \times V_2$

$\therefore\ V_2 = \dfrac{740 \times 211 \times 253}{770 \times 291}$ c.c.

At this stage, inspect your fraction to see if it agrees with what common sense would lead you to expect.

Thus (a) the 211 of the numerator is the original volume of the gas in c.c. The pressure is changing from 740 to 770 mm.; that is, an *increase* of pressure. This should *decrease* the volume. The fraction $\dfrac{740}{770}$ is actually doing so and is therefore correct.

(b) The temperature is *falling* from 291° A. to 253° A.; that is, the volume of the gas should be *decreasing*. The fraction $\dfrac{253}{291}$ *decreases* the volume as required and is, therefore, correct.

Using logarithms, $V_2 = 176$ c.c.

Normal Temperature and Pressure. Since the volumes of gases change in such a marked manner with changes of temperature and pressure, it is necessary to choose a suitable value of each as standards to which gas volumes can be referred. The standards chosen are 0° C. and 760 mm. pressure and these are known as Normal Temperature and Pressure, usually contracted to N.T.P.

N.T.P. means Normal Temperature and Pressure or 0° C. (273° A.) and 760 mm. pressure. Sometimes, the expression Standard Temperature and Pressure (S.T.P.) is used instead of N.T.P.

Example. A gas occupies 146 c.c. at 18° C. and 738 mm. pressure. Find its volume at N.T.P.

$$18° \text{ C.} = 291° \text{ A.}$$
$$\text{N.T.} = 0° \text{ C.} = 273° \text{ A.}$$

$$\frac{P_1 V_1}{T_1\ °A} = \frac{P_2 V_2}{T_2\ °A}$$

$$\text{N.P.}$$
$$\downarrow$$

$$\therefore\ \frac{738 \times 146}{291} = \frac{760 \times V_2}{273}$$
$$\uparrow$$
$$\text{N.T.}$$

$\therefore\ V_2 = \dfrac{738 \times 146 \times 273}{760 \times 291}$ c.c.   (Inspect this fraction as described above).

$= 133$ c.c.

QUESTIONS

Calculate the volumes which will be occupied at the given final temperatures and pressures by the gases whose initial volumes, temperatures and pressures are given.

	Initial Volume.	Initial T. & P.	Final T. & P.
(a)	273 c.c.	0° C. and 760 mm.	14° C. and 861 mm.
(b)	1,638 c.c.	0° C. and 819 mm.	15° C. and 864 mm.
(c)	1,000 c.c.	−23° C. and 750 mm.	23° C. and 800 mm.
(d)	500 c.c.	17° C. and 870 mm.	−48° C. and 750 mm.
(e)	1,000 c.c.	182° C. and 722 mm.	N.T.P.
(f)	760 c.c.	27° C. and 700 mm.	N.T.P.

The examples below need the use of logarithms.

	Initial Volume.	Initial T. & P.	Final T. & P.
(g)	700 c.c.	17° C. and 740 mm.	N.T.P.
(h)	133 c.c.	14° C. and 745 mm.	17° C. and 750 mm.
(i)	55 c.c.	14° C. and 744 mm.	N.T.P.
(j)	574 c.c.	N.T.P.	15° C. and 735 mm.
(k)	70 c.c.	N.T.P.	18° C. and 745 mm,
(l)	121 c.c.	150° C. and 780 mm.	120° C. and 742 mm.
(m)	534 c.c.	N.T.P.	−15° C. and 740 mm.

CHAPTER VII

EXPERIMENTAL METHODS OF DETERMINING EQUIVALENTS

Relation between Atomic Weight, Equivalent and Valency. We have seen in the last chapter that one method of determining atomic weights of elements is to find:—

(1) the equivalent of the element;
(2) the valency of the element.

Then, atomic weight = equivalent weight × valency.

In the present chapter equivalents are considered more fully and the methods available for their determination are described in detail.

The equivalent of an element has already been defined (p. 39) as the number of grams of the element which will combine with or displace 1 gm. of hydrogen.

Equivalent by Combination with Hydrogen. From this definition it will be obvious that one experimental method of finding the equivalent of an element would be to cause the element to combine with a known weight of hydrogen, to weigh the compound formed and so find the weight of the element (say x gm.) which has combined with the known weight of hydrogen (say y gm.). Then, by definition, the equivalent weight of the element is x/y. This method is of very limited application, partly because few elements combine with hydrogen easily enough to allow the method to be applied, and partly because of the great difficulty of obtaining accurate weighing of the very light gas, hydrogen. Morley has, however, applied the method to find very accurately the equivalent of oxygen.

Equivalent by Displacement of Hydrogen. Another method of determining the equivalent of an element is available when the element displaces hydrogen from one of its compounds and liberates the hydrogen as the free gaseous element. Then it is possible to take a known weight of the element, allow it to displace hydrogen from a hydrogen compound, and measure the liberated hydrogen. This method is applied for finding the equivalent weights of metals which displace hydrogen from acids, *e.g.*, zinc, magnesium or iron.

$$Zn + H_2SO_4 \rightarrow ZnSO_4 + H_2$$
$$Fe + H_2SO_4 \rightarrow FeSO_4 + H_2$$

Equivalent by Combination with Oxygen. The two methods

already dealt with can be applied to only a very small proportion of the known elements. A great many elements will not combine with hydrogen, nor will they displace it from acids or other compounds. Other methods must be devised. It is known, by the first of the two methods already mentioned, that, when water is formed, 1 gm. of hydrogen combines with 8 gm. of oxygen (to produce 9 gm. of water), *i.e.*, the equivalent of oxygen is 8.

Now nearly all other elements will combine with oxygen and it is supposed that the number of grams of an element which combine with 8 gm. of oxygen would also combine with or displace 1 gm. of hydrogen.

Thus, copper will neither combine directly with hydrogen nor liberate it from an acid, but experiment shows that, in black copper oxide, 8 gm. of oxygen are always combined with 31·8 gm. of copper. Then, the reasoning is:—

8 gm. of oxygen combine with 1 gm. of hydrogen
Also   8 gm. of oxygen combine with 31·8 gm. of copper
Therefore 31·8 gm. of copper are equivalent to 1 gm. of hydrogen.

This method is of very wide application. It can be used either by starting with a known weight of the pure element and converting it into its oxide, which is then weighed, or by starting with a known weight of the pure oxide and converting it into the pure element by removal of oxygen (reduction) and then weighing the pure element. Examples of both methods are given later.

Equivalent by Displacement of one Element by Another. A third method of finding equivalents is available for elements which do not combine directly with hydrogen or liberate it from its compounds. As we have already noted, copper will do neither. Copper is, however, displaced from copper sulphate solution by zinc and it is found that 32·5 gm. of zinc always displace 31·8 gm. of copper. Also, when zinc is treated with dilute sulphuric acid, 32·5 gm. of zinc always displace 1 gm. of hydrogen. From these figures again, we assume that 31·8 gm. of copper would combine with, or displace, 1 gm. of hydrogen.

To summarise briefly, the chief methods available for determining equivalents of elements are:—

(1) Direct combination of the element with hydrogen (very limited application).
(2) Displacement of hydrogen by the element, *e.g.*, to find the equivalents of zinc, magnesium, iron.
(3) By combination of the element with oxygen.
   (*a*) By conversion of the element into its oxide.
   (*b*) By reduction of the oxide to the element.
This is of very wide application.

(4) By displacement of one element by another (of limited application).

Below is a detailed account of these methods.

TO DETERMINE THE EQUIVALENT BY DISPLACEMENT OF HYDROGEN

The hydrogen is displaced from an acid by means of magnesium (zinc, iron, tin). We set out to determine the weight of magnesium (in grams) which will displace 1 gm. of hydrogen from the acid.

Since hydrogen is a gas, and a very light gas also, **its weight is difficult to determine,** and therefore in this case we find the **VOLUME** of hydrogen and convert it into weight by a suitable calculation.

Experiment. The apparatus consists of a wide graduated tube, A, of about 300 c.c. capacity, drawn out at both ends to a tube of a narrow bore. This is connected to a levelling apparatus, B, at the

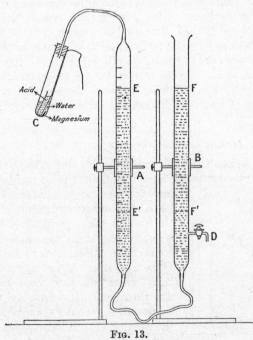

FIG. 13.
Equivalent by displacement of hydrogen.

bottom and to a boiling-tube complete with cork and tube at the top (Fig. 13).

A piece of magnesium ribbon about 35 cm. long (it should weigh about $\frac{1}{4}$ gm.) is very carefully cleaned and then weighed and dropped into water in the boiling-tube. A small test-tube (about 2 in. × $\frac{3}{8}$ in.) is filled with concentrated hydrochloric acid and lowered by means of a piece of thread into the boiling-tube. The stopper is firmly fitted. Water is poured into tube B until the level in tube A is very near the top of the scale and the apparatus C is attached, It is necessary to test whether the apparatus is gas-tight. To do this, raise the tube B till the level of water in it is several inches higher than in tube A. Leave it in this position for a few minutes. If the level in tube B is constant the apparatus is gas-tight; if the level in tube B falls, the apparatus leaks and it must be repaired. Now **make the water levels E and F in tubes A and B equal** so that the gas in C is at atmospheric pressure, and read off the level E on the scale of A. The boiling-tube is now shaken and the tap D opened, the rate of flow of water from D being adjusted so as to keep the levels in the tubes about equal (or slightly lower in B), in this way keeping the pressure in the graduated tube atmospheric or slightly less than atmospheric. When effervescence ceases, the apparatus must be allowed to cool. The level of water in tube B, (F') is then adjusted so as to be equal to the level of the water in tube A, (E'), making the pressure in the tube again atmospheric. The new level, E', is noted, as also are the temperature of the room and the barometric height. The difference between the readings E and E' is the volume of hydrogen liberated at laboratory temperature and pressure.

Alternative Apparatus. See Fig. 14.

Fill the siphon tube with water by blowing into the short tube attached to the aspirator; close the clip and place the delivery tube

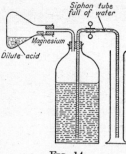

Siphon tube full of water

Magnesium

Dilute acid

Fig. 14.

into the measuring cylinder. Pour about 30 c.c. of dilute hydrochloric acid into the conical flask, carefully lodge a clean weighed piece of magnesium as shown, and connect the conical flask to the aspirator. Open the clip. If the apparatus is air tight, water will flow for a few seconds and then stop. (If a leak exists it must be remedied.) Shake the magnesium into the acid. Wait until the action has ceased and the apparatus has cooled. Adjust the cylinder so that the levels of water in the cylinder and the aspirator are the same, and measure the volume of water displaced.

Specimen Readings.

> Weight of magnesium = 0·26 gm.
> Volume of hydrogen = 252 c.c.
> Temperature of room = 10° C.
> Barometric height = 752 mm.
> (Corrected for vapour pressure of water.)

The equivalent is determined in 3 stages.

1. *Reduce the Volume of Hydrogen to N.T.P.* Using the usual symbols (see p. 50) we may write:—

$$\frac{P_1 V_1}{T_1 {}^\circ A} = \frac{P_2 V_2}{T_2 {}^\circ A}$$

i.e., $\dfrac{752 \times 252}{283} = \dfrac{760 \times V_2}{273}$ $\left\{\begin{array}{l}\text{For this particular kind of equi-}\\ \text{valent calculation, this right-hand}\\ \text{expression is always the same.}\end{array}\right.$

$$\frac{752}{760} \times 252 \times \frac{273}{283} \text{ c.c.} = V_2$$

$$= 240\cdot5 \text{ c.c.}$$

logs.	
2·8762	2·8808
2·4014 —	2·4518
2·4362	
	5·3326
7·7138	
5·3326	
2·3812	

2. *Find the Weight in Grams of this Volume of Hydrogen.*

1 litre of hydrogen at N.T.P. weighs 0·09 gm.

∴ 1 c.c. of hydrogen at N.T.P. weighs 0·00009 gm.

∴ 240·5 c.c. of hydrogen at N.T.P. weighs 0·00009 × 240·5 gm.
= 0·02165 gm.

3. *Find the Weight of the Metal which displaces 1 gm. of Hydrogen.* In any type of calculation involving ratio arrange to have the item required on the right-hand side:—

0·02165 gm. of hydrogen was displaced by 0·26 gm. magnesium

∴ 1 gm. hydrogen was displaced by $\dfrac{0\cdot26}{\cdot02165}$ gm. of magnesium

= 12 gm. magnesium

Therefore the equivalent of magnesium is 12.

DETERMINATION OF EQUIVALENT BY COMBINATION WITH OXYGEN

Many elements do not displace hydrogen from compounds nor do they combine with hydrogen, *e.g.*, copper. We have already seen, however, that we can find its equivalent by determining the weight of copper which will combine with 8 gm. of oxygen.

Method 1. Reduction Method (lead, copper). Black copper oxide has been made by the chemical union of copper and oxygen. By the removal of oxygen in a stream of hydrogen the weights of copper and oxygen which were in combination can be determined (Fig. 15).

(Coal-gas can be used instead of hydrogen for this experiment. Its use is not dangerous.)

The tube must slope downwards towards A, otherwise water condensed during the experiment might run back on to the heated part and crack the tube.

Weigh a porcelain boat and weigh again with some pure dry copper oxide in it. Place the boat inside a hard glass tube. Generate hydrogen as in Fig. 15 and pass it through a calcium chloride tube to dry it. **Allow the hydrogen to pass over the oxide until, when collected in a test-tube as shown, it burns quietly on exposure to a flame.** This shows that all the oxygen in the apparatus has been expelled. Then light the hydrogen at the jet and warm the copper oxide. Soon a glow spreads through the oxide (an indication that chemical change is taking place). A reddish brown powder, copper, is left, and drops of water collect at A.

Allow the copper to cool in a current of hydrogen so that air cannot enter and so convert the red metallic copper into the oxide

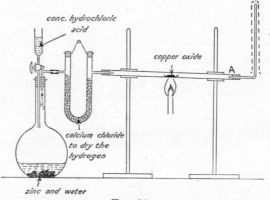

FIG. 15.

Reduction of copper oxide by heating in hydrogen.

again. Weigh the boat and copper when cool. (The boat and contents should, to ensure complete reaction, be heated to constant weight.)

Note that the copper oxide has been **reduced** by the hydrogen to red metallic copper, whereas the hydrogen has been **oxidised** to water. (See p. 130.)

$$CuO + H_2 \rightarrow Cu + H_2O$$
copper   hydrogen   copper   water
oxide

Specimen analysis.

$$\text{Weight of boat} = 4\cdot32 \text{ gm.} = a \text{ gm.}$$
$$\text{Weight of boat} + \text{oxide} = 5\cdot61 \text{ gm.} = b \text{ gm.}$$
$$\text{Weight of boat} + \text{copper} = 5\cdot35 \text{ gm.} = c \text{ gm.}$$
$$\therefore \quad \text{Weight of oxygen} = 0\cdot26 \text{ gm.} = (b-c) \text{ gm.}$$
$$\therefore \quad \text{Weight of copper} = 1\cdot03 \text{ gm.} = (c-a) \text{ gm.}$$

$\therefore$ 0·26 gm. of oxygen has combined with 1·03 gm. copper

$$(b-c) \quad \text{,,} \qquad \text{,,} \qquad \text{,,} \qquad \text{,,} \quad (c-a) \text{ gm. ,,}$$

$$1 \text{ gm.} \quad \text{,,} \qquad \text{,,} \qquad \text{,,} \qquad \text{,,} \quad \frac{1\cdot03}{0\cdot26} \text{ gm.} \quad \text{,,}$$

$$i.e., \quad \frac{c-a}{b-c} \text{ gm.} \quad \text{,,}$$

$\therefore$ 8 gm. of oxygen have combined with $\dfrac{1\cdot03 \times 8}{0\cdot26}$ gm. copper

$$i.e., \quad \frac{c-a}{b-c} \times 8 \text{ gm.} \quad \text{,,}$$

$$= 31\cdot7 \text{ gm. copper}$$

$\therefore$ Equivalent of copper is 31·7.

If coal-gas is used for this experiment, all details are the same except that the air can be swept out so quickly that there is no need to test for its removal.

For class use the following method is satisfactory:—

Blow a small hole in a test-tube and weigh the test-tube. Weigh again with some pure dry copper oxide in it. Push the rubber tube

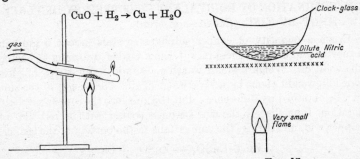

$$CuO + H_2 \rightarrow Cu + H_2O$$

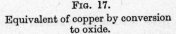

FIG. 16.

Equivalent of copper by reduction.

FIG. 17.

Equivalent of copper by conversion to oxide.

from the bunsen-burner into the test-tube, pass coal-gas through it and light it as shown in Fig. 16.

Conduct the experiment in a similar manner to that described in the previous experiment and work out the result.

Method 2. Oxidation Method. (Copper, lead, zinc, magnesium.) To determine the equivalent of copper, starting with metallic copper.

Weigh a small evaporating dish and clock-glass (3 inch diameter is suitable), and weigh again having added one or two small pieces of copper (not more than half a gram). Remove the clock-glass, add about 10 c.c. of bench dilute nitric acid (approx. 4N), replace the clock-glass, and heat *gently* on a tripod and gauze in a fume chamber (Fig. 17). There is a vigorous effervescence, brown fumes of nitrogen dioxide are seen, and the copper finally dissolves, giving a blue solution of copper nitrate.

$$3Cu + 8HNO_3 \rightarrow 3Cu(NO_3)_2 + 2NO + 4H_2O$$

Continue to heat the solution (increasing the size of the flame to maintain a steady but not too vigorous evolution of vapour) until the whole of the excess nitric acid has been driven off and the copper nitrate converted to black copper oxide.

$$2Cu(NO_3)_2 \rightarrow 2CuO + 4NO_2 + O_2$$

copper copper nitrogen oxygen
nitrate oxide oxide

Heat the dish very strongly for a few minutes to decompose any copper nitrate on the sides of the dish or on the clock-glass, allow to cool, and weigh the apparatus. Repeat the heating to constant weight. Calculate the equivalent in exactly the same way as in the previous experiment.

Note. The clock-glass minimises the loss of liquid by spurting, but does not materially reduce the rate of evaporation.

DETERMINATION OF EQUIVALENT OF COPPER BY DISPLACEMENT BY ZINC. (Magnesium, iron)

Crush a quantity of copper sulphate crystals (about 5 gm.) in a mortar and dissolve them in water in a beaker, warming to hasten the solution. Weigh a small watch-glass, add a few strips of pure zinc foil (weight about 1 gm.) and weigh again. The weight of the zinc can be obtained by difference. Put the zinc into the copper sulphate solution. Immediately the zinc becomes coated with a red film of copper and, on stirring, the copper falls to the bottom of the beaker.

$$Zn + CuSO_4 \rightarrow ZnSO_4 + Cu$$

zinc sulphate

After a while the whole of the zinc will have disappeared and there will be a layer of red metallic copper on the bottom of the beaker. (More copper sulphate crystals can be added if the colour indicates that the solution is weak.)

Filter off the copper and wash the small particles of copper adhering to the beaker into the filter-paper by means of a jet of water from a wash-bottle. Wash the copper several times with hot distilled water, and finally two or three times with methylated spirit (care being taken to extinguish any burners likely to set fire to the spirit). Allow the copper to dry and weigh it, together with the filter-paper, a clean filter-paper being placed on the right-hand pan of the balance and the weights on top of the filter-paper.

Specimen Weighings.

0·92 gm. of zinc displaced 0·89 gm. copper

$$1 \text{ ,, } \text{ ,, } \text{ ,, } \frac{0·89}{0·92} \text{ ,, } \text{ ,,}$$

$$32·5 \text{ ,, } \text{ ,, } \text{ ,, } \frac{0·89}{0·92} \times 32·5 \text{ gm. copper}$$

∴ Equivalent of copper is 31·5.

Use of the Equivalent. Here is a list of approximate equivalent weights determined practically by methods given above, or similar ones

1 gm. Hydrogen
- combines with 8 gm. Oxygen.
- combines with 16 gm. Sulphur.
- combines with 4⅔ gm. Nitrogen.
- is displaced by 32·5 gm. Zinc.
- is displaced by 12 gm. Magnesium.

From this list it is obvious that the equivalent of oxygen is 8, whilst that of magnesium is 12, of sulphur 16, and so on. All these weights of the different elements are equivalent to 1 gm. of hydrogen, so, if we can find the equivalent weight for any element, it is the weight of it which will combine with or displace the equivalent weight of any other element, provided that valencies do not change.

This can be shown diagrammatically by Fig. 18. By selecting any two at random, we obtain the ratio of their combining or displacing weights, *e.g.*,

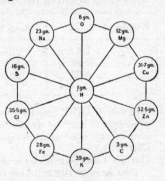

FIG. 18.

31·7 gm. copper combine with 35·5 gm. of chlorine.

28 tons of iron combine with 8 tons of oxygen.

32·5 oz. of zinc combine with 16 oz. of sulphur.

12 kilograms of magnesium displace 1 kilogram of hydrogen. Notice that any units of weight may be used. The equivalent is a number, possessing no units.

c*

QUESTIONS

1. Define the equivalent weight of an element.
2. Mention 3 ways in which the equivalent of an element may be determined.
3. By reduction in a stream of hydrogen, 3·36 gm. of a metal oxide were converted into 3·12 gm. of the metal. Calculate the equivalent weight of the metal.
4. What weight of copper oxide could be obtained from 6·3 gm. of copper? What weight of copper chloride could be obtained from the same weight of copper? (Equivalent of copper = 31·5.)
5. 340 c.c. of hydrogen measured at 16° C. and 750 mm. were liberated by dissolving 0·8 gm. of a metal in dilute acid. Calculate (a) the volume the gas would occupy at 0° C. and 760 mm., (b) the weight of the gas, (c) the equivalent of the metal. (1 litre of dry hydrogen at N.T.P. weighs 0·09 gm.)
6. 2 gm. of a certain metal were converted into its oxide, and the weight of the oxide was 3·78 gm. Find the equivalent weight of the metal. The specific heat of the metal is 0·24. What is (a) the valency, (b) the exact atomic weight of the metal?
7. What weight of litharge (lead oxide) could be obtained from 10·35 tons of lead? (Equivalent of lead = 103·5.)
8. Calculate the equivalent weight of a metal from the following data:—

Weight of boat	.	.	.	.	12·32 gm.
Weight of boat and oxide		.	.	14·71 ,,
Weight of boat and metal		.	.	14·39 ,,

9. 11·48 gm. of silver chloride were obtained from 8·64 gm. of silver. Calculate the equivalent weight of silver.
10. By a similar method to that suggested in Question 5, find the equivalent weight of the metals A, B, C from the following data:—

Weight of Metal.	Vol. of Hydrogen.	Temperature.	Pressure.
A . . 1·5 gm.	295·5 c.c.	17° C.	765 mm.
B . . 0·24 ,,	324·0 ,,	23° C.	770 ,,
C . . 0·35 ,,	353·5 ,,	15° C.	740 ,,

11. Mention THREE general methods by which the equivalent weights of elements may be determined. Describe in detail the determination of the equivalent weight of copper by one of these methods. (N.U.J.B.)
12. Outline 4 methods of determining the equivalent weights of metals.
    3·82 gms. of the sulphide of a bivalent metal were quantitatively transformed into 3·18 gm. of the oxide. Calculate the equivalent and atomic weight of the element. (L.)
13. By heating 1·248 gm. of a metal in a stream of oxygen, 1·392 gm. of the oxide were obtained. Calculate the equivalent weight of the metal.
    Calculate the atomic weight of the metal by two methods, firstly from the fact that its specific heat is 0·03, and secondly by using the fact that the vapour density of the hydride of the metal is 105·5. (N.U.J.B.)
14. What is meant by the equivalent weight of an element?
    Describe carefully one method by which you could determine

the equivalent weight of a metal which does *not* liberate hydrogen from an acid.

A metal has an equivalent weight of 12. Calculate the weight of the metal required to liberate from an acid 525 c.c. of hydrogen at 15° C. and 750 mm. pressure. (1 litre of hydrogen at N.T.P. weighs 0·09 gm.) (C.)

15. The oxide of a certain metal is completely decomposed by moderate heat. Describe and explain suitable apparatus for measuring the volume of gas evolved from a known weight of the oxide.

   If the volume of oxygen obtained from 0·86 gm. of the oxide is 47 c.c. at 12° C. and 750 mm. pressure, what is the equivalent weight of the metal? (L.)

16. What is meant by the term equivalent weight? A compound of magnesium with an element, E, contains 28·00% of E. A compound of oxygen with E contains 63·63% of E. Calculate the equivalent of E in each of these compounds. What explanation can you offer for the difference in the equivalent weights? The equivalent weight of magnesium is 12, and that of oxygen is 8. (D.)

17. 0·054 gm. of a metal, X, yields 0·267 gm. of the chloride. Calculate the equivalent weight of the metal. If the valency of the metal is three, calculate the atomic weight of the metal and give the formula of (a) the nitrate, (b) the oxide, (c) the sulphate of X. (C.)

18. When 0·18 gm. of a metal was dissolved in hydrochloric acid, 250 c.c. of hydrogen, measured at 15° C. and 720 mm. pressure, were evolved. Calculate the equivalent weight of the metal. What would be the percentage weight of chlorine in the chloride formed in this experiment? (The weight of a litre of hydrogen at N.T.P. is 0·09 gm.) (N.U.J.B.)

19. Define the terms (a) equivalent weight, (b) atomic weight.

   Why is there a simple relation between these weights? How would you find the equivalent weight of *either* copper *or* oxygen? (O. and C.)

20. Find the accurate atomic weights of the metals X, Y and Z from the following data:—
   (a) Equivalent of X = 103·5.   Specific heat of X = 0·031.
   (b) Equivalent of Y = 31·71.   Specific heat of Y = 0·095.
   (c) Equivalent of Z = 23·00.   Specific heat of Z = 0·27.

21. A metal has two equivalents, namely 27·89 and 18·69, and it has a specific heat of 0·11. Find the mean atomic weight as indicated by the above figures.

22. State Dulong and Petit s Law and explain how it is used in the determination of atomic weights.

   If the specific heats of two elements, X and Y. be 0·22 and 0·17, and their equivalents 9 and 20 respectively, what are the formulæ of their oxides and chlorides? (C.)

23. One gram of metallic wire when dissolved in dilute sulphuric acid yielded 422 c.c. of hydrogen measured dry at 17° C. and 760 mm. pressure. Calculate the gram equivalent weight of the metal.

   1·40 grams of the same wire on oxidation yielded 2·00 grams of the oxide. Calculate the gram equivalent weight of the metal.

   What explanation can you give of the difference in the two equivalents? Use the results to illustrate the law of multiple proportions. (C.W.B.)

CHAPTER VIII

CALCULATIONS INVOLVING WEIGHTS

WE have seen in Chapter II that every definite chemical reaction can be represented by means of an equation. In Chapter IV, the question of atomic weights was considered. In the present Chapter we shall combine the knowledge obtained in both and show how a quantitative meaning can be assigned to an equation in terms of the commonly used weight units—more particularly the scientific unit, the gram.

To Calculate the Molecular Weight of a Compound from its Molecular Formula. We have noted that the molecular formula of a compound indicates the kind of atoms present in the molecule and their number; thus the formula H_2SO_4, for sulphuric acid, indicates that one molecule of the acid contains 2 atoms of hydrogen, 1 atom of sulphur and 4 atoms of oxygen. The atomic weight of each of these elements is known and can be obtained from tables. The molecular weight of sulphuric acid can now be calculated by allowing the appropriate number of weight units for each element present and adding to obtain the total. ($H = 1$; $S = 32$; $O = 16$.)

Thus
$$H_2 \qquad S \qquad O_4$$
$$(2 \times 1) + 32 + (4 \times 16)$$
$$= 2 + 32 + 64$$
$$= 98 = \text{molecular weight of sulphuric acid.}$$

Taking another example: *Calculate the molecular weight of red lead,* Pb_3O_4. ($Pb = 207$; $O = 16$.)
$$Pb_3 \qquad O_4$$
$$(3 \times 207) + (4 \times 16)$$
$$= 621 + 64$$
$$= 685 = \text{molecular weight of red lead.}$$

If the formula of the compound contains bracketed acid radicals, it will be simpler and more accurate for you to remove the brackets first and then proceed as above. Thus: *Calculate the molecular weight of calcium nitrate,* $Ca(NO_3)_2$. ($Ca = 40$; $N = 14$; $O = 16$.)
$$Ca(NO_3)_2$$
$$\text{or } CaN_2O_6$$
$$40 + (2 \times 14) + (6 \times 16)$$
$$= 40 + 28 + 96$$
$$= 164 = \text{molecular weight of calcium nitrate.}$$

Later, with practice, you will be able to carry out the removal of the bracket mentally.

It is also possible to calculate the weight of each element present in a given weight of compound from its formula. This information is usually stated as the percentage composition of the compound.

To Calculate the Percentage by Weight of Each Element present in a Compound from its Formula. Example: *Calculate the percentage by weight of each element in calcium sulphate, $CaSO_4$.* ($Ca = 40; S = 32; O = 16$.)

First calculate the molecular weight of calcium sulphate.

$$CaSO_4$$
$$40 + 32 + (4 \times 16)$$
$$= 40 + 32 + 64$$
$$= 136.$$

40 of these 136 units of weight are calcium, that is, the fractional weight of calcium in calcium sulphate is 40/136. Then the percentage weight is $\frac{40}{136} \times 100$ or 29.4%.

Similarly the fractional weight of sulphur is $\frac{32}{126}$ and the percentage is $\frac{32}{136} \times 100$ or 23.5%.

The percentage weight of the third element, oxygen, need not be calculated as it is given by the expression $100 - (\%$ of calcium $+ \%$ of sulphur),

$$\text{or } 100 - (29.4 + 23.5)$$
$$= 47.1\%.$$

These calculations can be set out compactly as below: *Calculate the percentage composition of calcium hydroxide, $Ca(OH)_2$.* ($Ca = 40; O = 16; H = 1$.)

$$Ca(OH)_2$$
$$\text{or } CaO_2H_2$$
$$40 + (2 \times 16) + (2 \times 1)$$
$$= 40 + 32 + 2$$
$$= 74.$$

Calcium. Fractional weight $\frac{40}{74}$. Percentage weight $\frac{40}{74} \times 100$
$$= 54.1\%$$

Oxygen. Fractional weight $\frac{32}{74}$. Percentage weight $\frac{32}{74} \times 100$
$$= 43.2\%$$

Hydrogen. Percentage weight $= 100 - (54.1 + 43.2) = 2.7\%$

It is also possible to calculate the formula of a compound from its composition by weight.

To Calculate the Simplest Formula of a Compound from its Composition by Weight. This calculation is illustrated by the following worked example.

Calculate the formula of a compound which has the following percentage composition:—sodium 43·4%, carbon 11·3%, oxygen 45·3%. (Na = 23; C = 12; O = 16.)

The fact that the atomic weight of sodium is 23 means that every 23 parts by weight of sodium in the compound represent one atom of sodium.

Thus 43·4 parts by weight of sodium represent $\dfrac{43·4}{23}$ atoms of sodium. Similarly for the other elements present:

11·3 parts by weight of carbon represent $\dfrac{11·3}{12}$ atoms of carbon.

45·3 parts by weight of oxygen represent $\dfrac{45·3}{16}$ atoms of oxygen.

∴ Number of atoms represented is:—

sodium	carbon	oxygen
$\dfrac{43·4}{23}$	$\dfrac{11·3}{12}$	$\dfrac{45·3}{16}$

or   1·89   0·94   2·83

These cannot be the actual numbers of atoms present because fractions of atoms are impossible. We have to find the **whole numbers** which are in the ratio 1·89 : 0·94 : 2·83. To do this, divide all these figures by the lowest or, if this does not result in a whole number ratio, by the smallest difference. Then the number of atoms of each element is:—

sodium	carbon	oxygen
$\dfrac{1·89}{0·94}$	$\dfrac{0·94}{0·94}$	$\dfrac{2·83}{0·94}$

or   2   1   3

That is, the formula is Na_2CO_3.

The calculation is set out compactly in the following example:—

Calculate the formula of a compound which has the composition: magnesium 9·8%, sulphur 13%, oxygen 26%, water of crystallisation 51·2%.

(Mg = 24; S = 32; O = 16; H_2O = 18)

	Magnesium.	Sulphur.	Oxygen.	Water.
% by weight . . .	9·8	13	26	51·2
Ratio of atoms or molecules	$\dfrac{9·8}{24} = 0·408$	$\dfrac{13}{32} = 0·406$	$\dfrac{26}{16} = 1·63$	$\dfrac{51·2}{18} = 2·84$
Divide by smallest (or smallest difference) .	$\dfrac{0·408}{0·406}$	$\dfrac{0·406}{0·406}$	$\dfrac{1·63}{0·406}$	$\dfrac{2·84}{0·406}$
	1	1	4	7

$$\therefore \text{ the formula is } MgSO_4.7H_2O.$$

Empirical and Molecular Formulæ are discussed on p. 84.

CALCULATIONS FROM EQUATIONS

We have seen already that the equation:

$$\begin{array}{cccc}
CuO & + & H_2SO_4 & \to & CuSO_4 & + & H_2O \\
(63·5 + 16) & (2 + 32 + 64) & (63·5 + 32 + 64) & (2 + 16) \\
79·5 & 98 & 159·5 & 18
\end{array}$$

means: "One molecule of copper oxide reacts with one molecule of sulphuric acid producing one molecule of copper sulphate and one molecule of water."

The appropriate molecular weights having been inserted, as above, it also means that 79·5 parts by weight of copper oxide react with 98 parts by weight of sulphuric acid, producing 159·5 parts by weight of copper sulphate and 18 parts by weight of water. These "parts by weight" may be any desired weight-units—grams, tons, ounces, pounds, kilograms—provided that the same unit is used throughout.

Obviously, the figures given by the equation can be used to calculate any required information about the weights of the four substances concerned.

Example 1. *What weight of copper sulphate could be obtained by starting with 10 gm. of copper oxide?*

From the equation, 79·5 gm. copper oxide yield 159·5 gm. copper sulphate.

$$\therefore 10 \text{ gm. copper oxide yield } 159·5 \times \frac{10}{79·5} \text{ gm. copper sulphate}$$

$$= 20·1 \text{ gm. copper sulphate.}$$

Example 2. *What weight of pure sulphuric acid would be needed to react with 15 tons of copper oxide?*

From the equation, 79·5 tons of copper oxide need 98 tons of sulphuric acid.

$$\therefore 15 \text{ tons of copper oxide need } 98 \times \frac{15}{79·5} \text{ tons of sulphuric acid}$$

$$= 18·5 \text{ tons sulphuric acid.}$$

This means that equations have now been given a quantitative meaning in terms of ordinary weight-units, instead of simply in terms of atoms and molecules. This makes them extraordinarily useful for making calculations of the weights of materials needed for chemical reactions and the weights of products obtainable. Chemical manufacturers base all their calculations of weights of materials on equations.

We will now discuss the steps necessary in using an equation correctly for weight calculations of this type.

A BALANCED Equation is Necessary. It has already been explained (p. 25) that, by a balanced equation, we mean one which has the same number of each kind of atom on the right of the equation as on the left. An unbalanced equation implies that atoms have been created or destroyed; it is therefore wrong, and calculations based on it are certainly unreliable. The first and absolutely essential step, then, is to obtain a balanced equation.

Facility in producing balanced equations is only attainable with practice, but this absolutely inviolable rule must be remembered: **The formula of a compound is absolutely fixed and unalterable and an equation must be balanced by taking appropriate numbers of molecules of the substances concerned, not by attempting alteration of their formulæ.**

The following brief account will illustrate the process of balancing.

To obtain a balanced equation for the action of hydrogen sulphide, H_2S, on sulphur dioxide, SO_2, producing water, H_2O, and sulphur, S.

The skeleton, but unbalanced and incorrect, "equation" will be:—

$$H_2S + SO_2 \rightarrow H_2O + S \text{ (UNBALANCED)}$$

We cannot alter any of these formulæ or the symbols.

Now, both the oxygen atoms of the SO_2 molecule form water, therefore $2H_2O$ must be obtained. This gives:—

$$H_2S + SO_2 \rightarrow 2H_2O + S \text{ (UNBALANCED)}$$

The $2H_2O$ on the right now requires $2H_2$, which must be provided by taking $2H_2S$. This gives:—

$$2H_2S + SO_2 \rightarrow 2H_2O + S \text{ (UNBALANCED)}$$

We now have, on the left, $2S$ from the $2H_2S$ (remember the 2 multiplies *all* the H_2S) and S from the SO_2, therefore we must have $3S$ on the right and the balancing is complete.

$$2H_2S + SO_2 \rightarrow 2H_2O + 3S.$$

Some such balancing process is necessary for all equations, but many of them become so familiar with frequent use that they can be set down correctly at once.

Insertion of Molecular Weights into the Equation. Here, it is very desirable to remember that it is unnecessary to insert the molecular weights of any materials unless they are actually concerned in the calculation you are performing.

Consider, for example, this problem.

Calculate the weight of calcium nitrate which would be formed by treating 148 grams of slaked lime, $Ca(OH)_2$, with excess of dilute nitric acid. (Ca = 40; O = 16; H = 1.)

Here the balanced equation is:—

$$Ca(OH)_2 + 2HNO_3 \rightarrow Ca(NO_3)_2 + 2H_2O$$

slaked   nitric   calcium   water
lime   acid   nitrate

In the problem, the only two substances mentioned quantitatively are calcium nitrate, of which a weight is to be calculated, and slaked lime, of which the weight is given. (Nitric acid is only mentioned as "excess".) The only molecular weights we need insert are, therefore, those of calcium nitrate and slaked lime. $2HNO_3$ and $2H_2O$ may be ignored once the equation has been balanced, because the problem is not concerned with them.

So we get,

$$Ca(OH)_2 + 2HNO_3 \rightarrow Ca(NO_3)_2 + 2H_2O$$

40 + 32 + 2   40 + 28 + 96
74   164

From the equation, 74 gm. slaked lime yield 164 gm. calcium nitrate.

$\therefore$ 148 gm. slaked lime yield $164 \times \dfrac{148}{74}$ gm. calcium nitrate.

$= 328$ gm. calcium nitrate.

Another example illustrates this very important calculation process.

Calculate the weight of lead which would be obtained by heating 34·25 gm. of red lead in a stream of hydrogen and the weight of water formed at the same time. (Pb = 207; H = 1; O = 16.)

Writing the balanced equation and inserting the molecular weights of the materials concerned in the calculation, we have:—

$$Pb_3O_4 + 4H_2 \rightarrow 3Pb + 4H_2O$$

red lead
621 + 64   4(2 + 16)
685   621   72

This problem is really two smaller problems.

(i) To find the weight of lead obtainable from 34·25 gm. red lead.

(ii) To find the weight of water obtainable from 34·25 gm. red lead.

Treat them separately.

(i) From the equation, 685 gm. red lead yield 621 gm. lead.

$$\therefore 34.25 \text{ gm. red lead yield } 621 \times \frac{34.25}{685} \text{ gm. lead.}$$

$$= 31.05 \text{ gm. lead.}$$

(ii) From the equation 685 gm. red lead yield 72 gm. water.

$$\therefore 34.25 \text{ gm. red lead yield } 72 \times \frac{34.25}{685} \text{ gm. water.}$$

$$= 3.6 \text{ gm. water.}$$

QUESTIONS

All Atomic Weights required for these calculations can be found on p. 428.

1. How many tons of copper could be obtained by displacing copper from copper sulphate solution by 16·25 tons of zinc?
2. What weight of sodium oxide, Na_2O, could be made from 1·15 gm. sodium?
3. Find the empirical formulæ of the following compounds from their compositions by weight:—

   (a) Zn, 47·8%; Cl, 52·2%.
   (b) Na, 39·3%; Cl, 60·7%.
   (c) Cu, 39·5%; S, 20·3%; O, 40·2%.
   (d) Pb, 62·5%; N, 8·45%; O, 29·05%.

4. Calculate the percentage by weight of each element in the following compounds:—

   (a) Sodium bicarbonate, $NaHCO_3$.
   (b) Calcium chloride, $CaCl_2$.
   (c) Ammonium sulphate, $(NH_4)_2SO_4$.
   (d) Sodium thiosulphate, $Na_2S_2O_3$.

5. What weight of dilute nitric acid (containing 10% of the pure acid) will be required to dissolve 5 gm. of chalk?
6. How many grams of sulphuretted hydrogen would be necessary to precipitate 7·5 gm. of copper sulphide from a copper sulphate solution?
7. 76·5 gm. of sodium bicarbonate were heated strongly. What weight of carbon dioxide was obtained? If a dilute acid had been added, what weight of carbon dioxide would have been obtained in this case?
8. What weight of nitrogen peroxide could be obtained by heating 11·1 gm. of lead nitrate?
9. 50 gm. of ammonium chloride were heated with 40 gm. of slaked lime. What weight of ammonia gas would be evolved? Which of the reagents is in excess and by how much?
10. How many ounces of anhydrous zinc sulphate ($ZnSO_4$) would be formed on completion of the reaction between 2 oz. of zinc and dilute sulphuric acid containing 2 oz. of the pure acid (H_2SO_4)? (N.U.J.B.)

11. How many grams of hydrochloric acid, containing 20% by weight of hydrogen chloride, would be required to dissolve 13 gm. of zinc? (N.U.J.B.)

12. In a determination of the equivalent weight of carbon, 0·74 gm. of the element was burnt in a current of oxygen, the products of combustion were passed over heated copper oxide, and the resulting carbon dioxide was absorbed in potash bulbs. The increase in weight of the potash bulbs was 2·69 gm. Calculate to two places of decimals the equivalent weight of carbon.

What was the object of using copper oxide in this experiment? (C.)

13. A compound has the percentage composition N = 19·31%, Ca = 27·58%, Cl = 48·96%, and H = 4·13%. Calculate (a) the simplest formula for the compound, (b) the volume which the nitrogen, present in 14·5 gm. of the compound, would occupy at N.T.P.

Atomic weights: N = 14, Ca = 40, Cl = 35·5, H = 1. A molecular weight in grams of a gas occupies 22·4 litres at N.T.P. (D.)

14. Give a brief account of the chemical reactions involved in the extraction of iron from its ores. 0·1867 gm. of a sample of iron containing carbon as an impurity was dissolved in dilute sulphuric acid, filtered, and the filtrate heated with a slight excess of concentrated nitric acid. An excess of ammonium hydroxide solution was then added to the solution and the resulting precipitate was filtered off, washed, dried, and finally heated to redness until the weight was constant. The weight of the product was 0·2600 gm. Give the reactions involved in this process and calculate the percentage of iron in the original sample. (Fe = 56.) (L.)

15. Pure calcium carbonate contains 44 per cent by weight of carbon dioxide. Some dried chalk weighing 0·4 gm. was dissolved in dilute hydrochloric acid. The carbon dioxide given off had a volume of 85·5 c.c. measured at 750 mm. pressure and 12° C. Find:

(a) The volume of the carbon dioxide at N.T.P.

(b) The weight of the carbon dioxide.

(c) The percentage of pure calcium carbonate in the chalk.

(H = 1, = 12, O = 16. Weight of 1 litre hydrogen at (N.T.P. = 0·09 gm.) (N.U.J.B.)

CHAPTER IX

THE MOLECULAR THEORY AND THE INTERPRETATION OF AN EQUATION

The Gas Laws. We have already seen (Chapter VI) that the behaviour of gases, when subject to temperature and pressure change, can be expressed by two simple laws, those of Boyle and Charles.

Boyle's Law. **The volume of a given mass of gas is inversely proportional to its pressure, temperature remaining constant.**

With the usual symbols, this is expressed mathematically as:—

$$PV = K \text{ (T constant)}$$

Charles' Law. **The volume of a given mass of gas is directly proportional to its absolute temperature, pressure remaining constant.**

With the usual symbols, this is expressed mathematically as:—

$$\frac{V}{T} = K \text{ (P constant)}$$

Gay-Lussac's Law of Combining Volumes. A third Law, describing the behaviour of gases, when involved in chemical reactions, was stated by Gay-Lussac.

We can illustrate the Law of Gay-Lussac by quoting first some of the experimentally observed results of chemical reaction between gases, upon which the Law is based. Temperature and pressure are to be considered constant throughout each statement.

1. *Ammonia.*
    2 volumes of ammonia decompose to give 1 volume of nitrogen and 3 volumes of hydrogen.
2. *Steam.*
    2 volumes of hydrogen combine with 1 volume of oxygen, giving 2 volumes of steam.
3. *Hydrogen chloride.*
    1 volume of hydrogen combines with 1 volume of chlorine to give 2 volumes of hydrogen chloride.
4. *Nitric oxide.*
    2 volumes of nitric oxide decompose to give 1 volume of nitrogen and 1 volume of oxygen.

Examining these experimental results (the methods by which they have been obtained are given in Chapter X), we notice at once that all the volumes of the gases concerned are related to each other by simple whole number ratios.

Whenever gases are concerned in chemical action, simple whole-number relations between their volumes are always found. This is the fact which was first noted by Gay-Lussac and expressed in his Law of Gaseous Volumes, which is now stated.

Gay-Lussac's Law of Gaseous Volumes. **When gases react they do so in volumes which bear a simple ratio to one another, and to the volume of the product if gaseous, temperature and pressure remaining constant.**

SIMPLE BEHAVIOUR OF GASES: AN EXPLANATION REQUIRED

These three Laws of Boyle, Charles and Gay-Lussac express among them a highly interesting fact about gases—a curious similarity of behaviour. In chemical properties, and such physical properties as density and solubility in water, gases show marked variations. There are neutral gases such as nitrogen, oxygen and hydrogen, acid-producing gases such as sulphur dioxide, hydrogen chloride and nitrogen peroxide, alkali-producing gases such as ammonia; gases of very high solubility in water, such as hydrogen chloride (500 volumes of gas dissolve in 1 volume of water), gases of moderate solubility, such as hydrogen sulphide (3 volumes of gas dissolve in 1 volume of water) and gases of very low solubility, such as nitrogen (0·02 volumes dissolve in 1 volume of water); some gases are chemically very reactive, *e.g.*, chlorine, and some are entirely inert, *e.g.*, argon. **But, however great the variations in these properties may be, all the gases obey the Laws of Boyle, Charles, Gay-Lussac.** There must be some explanation of this similarity. Note that it does not matter whether the gas is an element, *e.g.*, hydrogen, or a compound, *e.g.*, hydrogen chloride; each obeys the laws equally well.

Avogadro's Hypothesis. The explanation was put forward in 1811 by Avogadro, an Italian scientist, in the form known as Avogadro's Hypothesis. We have seen in Chapter II that the smallest particle of an element or compound which can exist separately is called a molecule of it. Avogadro's explanation of the simple behaviour of gases, especially as expressed in Gay-Lussac's Law, was that equal volumes of all gases, under the same temperature and pressure conditions, contain the same number of molecules. When this suggestion was put forward it was purely a hypothesis, that is, an idea which had occurred to Avogadro, which appeared to him sensible, but which still required to be tested further before it could be fully accepted. The truth of it has since become **experimentally** demonstrable, and it is frequently known on that account as Avogadro's Law.

Avogadro's Hypothesis. **Equal volumes of all gases at the same temperature and pressure contain the same number of molecules.**

This hypothesis has been of the greatest value in the development of chemistry since about 1860. It is a rather curious fact that its importance was at first unnoticed, and the full recognition of its implications, a few of which we shall now examine, is due to the work, not of Avogadro himself, but of another Italian, Cannizzaro, some 47 years after the hypothesis had been first put forward, and after Avogadro himself was dead.

Why Avogadro's Hypothesis is Important. The importance of the hypothesis lies in this fairly simple fact, that, since it asserts that equal volumes of gases contain equal numbers of molecules, it enables us to change over directly from a statement about *volumes* of gases to the same statement about *molecules* of gases. Every time we make a statement about *one volume* of any gas, we are also making a statement about a certain number of *molecules* of it, and that number, by Avogadro's Hypothesis, is always the same, no matter what the gas may be. Consequently, we can change over at will, in any statement about gases, from volumes to molecules and *vice versa*.

This means that by applying the hypothesis to volume measurements of gases, we can probe right to the heart of a chemical reaction, to the actual molecules themselves. It is an enormous step to change directly from an experimental statement like:—

2 volumes of hydrogen combine with 1 volume of oxygen giving
    2 volumes of steam
                    (Temperature and pressure constant)
                                to
2 *molecules* of hydrogen combine with 1 *molecule* of oxygen giving
    2 *molecules* of steam.

The second of these two statements goes right to the essentials of the reaction, to the very molecules themselves. The hypothesis is important because it gives us this power to reveal the molecules themselves at work in chemical reactions. **Note, however, that it applies only to gases.**

Other examples illustrating this important change from volume measurements to statements about molecules are:—

Ammonia. By experiment, 2 volumes of ammonia decompose to give 1 volume of nitrogen and 3 volumes of hydrogen.

Applying the Hypothesis,
> 2 molecules of ammonia contain 1 molecule of nitrogen and 3 molecules of hydrogen.

Hydrogen Chloride. By experiment, 1 volume of hydrogen combines with 1 volume of chlorine to give 2 volumes of hydrogen chloride.

Applying the Hypothesis,
> 1 molecule of hydrogen combines with 1 molecule of chlorine to give 2 molecules of hydrogen chloride.

Nitric Oxide. By experiment, 2 volumes of nitric oxide decompose to give 1 volume of nitrogen and 1 volume of oxygen.

Applying the Hypothesis,
> 2 molecules of nitric oxide contain 1 molecule of nitrogen and 1 molecule of oxygen.

(Temperature and pressure assumed constant throughout.)

From these statements, it is only a further step to the deduction of the formulæ of the gaseous compounds concerned. This step is given in the later part of this chapter, and the formulæ of the common gases are considered in the next.

How Avogadro's Hypothesis Explains Gay-Lussac's Law. *Assume throughout the following paragraph that temperature and pressure are constant.*

When gases react chemically, the reaction must take place between individual molecules of the gases. As Dalton suggested in the similar case of combination between atoms, the reactions will take place between small whole numbers of molecules of the reactants to produce small whole numbers of molecules of the products.

We have seen in the last section that, employing Avogadro's Hypothesis, we can change over directly from statements about molecules to statements about volumes, provided that gases only are concerned. Making this change, the last sentence of the last paragraph becomes: the reactions will take place between small whole numbers of *volumes* of the reactants to produce small whole numbers of *volumes* of the products (all being gases). This is what Gay-Lussac's Law states. Hence, Avogadro's Hypothesis has enabled us to deduce the experimentally observed Law.

Avogadro's Hypothesis and the Molecular Weights of Gases. We have seen in Chapter IV, that molecular weights are expressed as the number of times one molecule of the substance is heavier than one *atom* of hydrogen. We have also seen, in this chapter, the very important relation which exists between the number of *volumes* of gases and the number of *molecules* of gases involved in chemical reaction. It is now necessary to find how the atom and the molecule of hydrogen are related to one another. This will lead us to a method of determining molecular weights.

The Nature of the Hydrogen Molecule. By experimental work which is fully described later (p. 89), it has been found that (at constant temperature and pressure):

1 volume of hydrogen combines with 1 volume of chlorine to give 2 volumes of hydrogen chloride.

Applying Avogadro's Hypothesis we can say at once:

1 molecule* of hydrogen combines with 1 molecule of chlorine to give 2 molecules of hydrogen chloride.

Now each of the two molecules of hydrogen chloride must contain some hydrogen. The least amount of hydrogen which can be contained in one molecule of hydrogen chloride is one atom, because the atom of hydrogen is indivisible. Consequently, the least amount of hydrogen there can be in two molecules of hydrogen chloride is 2 atoms of hydrogen. But these 2 atoms of hydrogen must have come from the 1 molecule of hydrogen marked *; therefore, a molecule of hydrogen must contain at least two atoms of hydrogen.

But hydrochloric acid forms with caustic soda one salt only, sodium chloride. Two series of salts have never been obtained from hydrochloric acid as they have from, for example, sulphuric acid. Thus with caustic soda, sulphuric acid can be made to form both normal sodium sulphate and acid sodium sulphate. Since the hydrogen of hydrochloric acid cannot be replaced in two stages, the explanation is that there is only one hydrogen atom in the molecule. But the two hydrogen atoms necessary for two molecules of hydrogen chloride have been obtained from one molecule of hydrogen. Hence the molecule of hydrogen contains two atoms.

Try to visualise what this means. It means that, in ordinary gaseous hydrogen, no separate atoms of hydrogen exist. All the particles consist of two hydrogen atoms, locked in a chemical embrace, and moving always as a single unit, the molecule. It is as if the hydrogen atoms are paired off to run a perpetual three-legged race. The molecule, consisting of two hydrogen atoms, never breaks up, except for the purpose of engaging in chemical reactions. This fact is expressed by writing the hydrogen molecule as H_2, which means a single molecule of hydrogen containing two atoms. ($2H$ would mean two separate hydrogen atoms.)

By a somewhat similar argument (see p. 99) it can be shown that the molecule of chlorine contains two atoms, and the reaction between hydrogen and chlorine may be diagrammatically expressed as:—

TEMPERATURE AND PRESSURE CONSTANT.

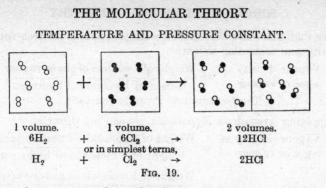

1 volume.	1 volume.	2 volumes.
$6H_2$	$+$ $6Cl_2$ $\rightarrow$	$12HCl$
	or in simplest terms,	
H_2	$+$ Cl_2 $\rightarrow$	$2HCl$

Fig. 19.

Note that equal numbers of molecules of hydrogen, chlorine and hydrogen chloride are contained in equal volumes.

It is known, from similar experimental evidence and argument, that nitrogen and oxygen (see p. 98) also have two atoms per molecule and their molecules are written N_2 and O_2. This is expressed by saying that the molecules of hydrogen, chlorine, nitrogen and oxygen are *diatomic* or that their *atomicity* is 2.

Atomicity.

The atomicity of an element is the number of atoms contained in one molecule of the element.

Relation between Vapour Density and Molecular Weight. The relative densities of solids and liquids are expressed with reference to water, but it would be most inconvenient to deal with gases in this way because of the great difference between the densities of water and gases.

Definition. **The vapour density of a gas or vapour is expressed as the number of times a certain volume of the gas or vapour is heavier than the same volume of hydrogen at the same temperature and pressure.** Expressed in another form, this becomes:—

$$\text{Vapour density of a gas or vapour} = \frac{\text{Weight of 1 volume of gas or vapour}}{\text{Weight of 1 volume of hydrogen}}$$

Temperature and Pressure constant.

Note that vapour density can be experimentally determined because it only involves weighing equal volumes of hydrogen and the vapour.

The molecular weight of a gas or vapour is expressed in the form:—

$$\text{Molecular weight of a gas or vapour} = \frac{\text{Weight of 1 molecule of the gas or vapour}}{\text{Weight of 1 atom of hydrogen}}$$

We shall now show that there is a simple relation between vapour density and molecular weight.

$$\text{Vapour density of a gas or vapour} = \frac{\text{Weight of 1 volume of gas or vapour}}{\text{Weight of 1 volume of hydrogen}}$$

Temperature and Pressure constant.

Applying Avogadro's Hypothesis, we can say directly:

$$\text{Vapour density of a gas or vapour} = \frac{\text{Weight of 1 molecule of gas or vapour}}{\text{Weight of 1 molecule of hydrogen}}$$

$$= \frac{\text{Weight of 1 molecule of gas or vapour}}{\text{Weight of 2 atoms of hydrogen}}$$

Multiplying both sides by 2:

$$2 \times (\text{Vapour density of a gas or vapour}) = \frac{\text{Weight of 1 molecule of gas or vapour}}{\text{Weight of 1 atom of hydrogen}}$$

$$= \text{Molecular Weight of the gas or vapour}$$

i.e., the molecular weight of a gas or vapour is twice its vapour density.

Molecular Weight from Vapour Density. Regnault's Method. We have already noted that to find the vapour density of a gas or vapour it is only necessary to obtain the weight of a certain volume of the gas or vapour and the weight of an equal volume of hydrogen both at the same temperature and pressure.

Unfortunately, direct weighing of hydrogen and other gases in this way is very difficult, partly because the actual weights of convenient volumes of the gases are small, and partly because changes of temperature, pressure and humidity in the atmosphere introduce errors during the course of the experiments.

In principle it is only necessary to evacuate a globe, weigh it and fill it with hydrogen and weigh it; then evacuate it again, fill with the gas and weigh again, temperature and pressure remaining constant. This is known as Regnault's Method. Then,

$$\text{Vapour density of the gas} = \frac{(\text{Weight of globe} + \text{gas}) - (\text{weight of globe})}{(\text{Weight of globe} + \text{hydrogen}) - (\text{weight of globe})}$$

and   Molecular weight of the gas = $2 \times$ vapour density.

A simpler method of finding molecular weight, which can be applied to the particular case of oxygen, is described in the next section.

Determination of Molecular Weight of Oxygen. This method is simplified by:—

1. Weighing the oxygen as a loss in weight of potassium chlorate.
2. Using the fact that 1 litre of hydrogen at N.T.P. weighs 0·09 gm., and measuring the volume of oxygen.

Weigh a hard glass test-tube containing potassium chlorate. Connect the tube to apparatus similar to that used in the determination of the equivalent of a metal by displacement of hydrogen (see p. 55). Test the apparatus, as there described, to see if it is gastight. Make the levels of water in the manometer equal to obtain atmospheric pressure and read the level in the graduated tube. Heat the hard glass tube and run water off at the tap. When a sufficiently large volume of oxygen has been given off, leave the apparatus to cool. Read the final level of the water in the graduated tube after the levels in both tubes have been equalised in order to restore the pressure to atmospheric. Weigh the hard glass tube again, read the barometer and take the laboratory temperature.

Readings.

Weight of hard glass tube and potassium chlorate	21·32 gm.
Weight of hard glass tube after heating	21·03 gm.

$$\therefore \ Weight \text{ of oxygen} \ = \ 0·29 \text{ gm.}$$

Volume of oxygen	=	217 c.c.
Temperature	=	15° C.
Pressure (corrected for vapour pressure of water) =		750 mm.

$$\text{Volume of gas at N.T.P.} = 217 \times \frac{273}{288} \times \frac{750}{760} \text{ c.c.}$$

$$= 203 \text{ c.c.}$$

$$\therefore 1,000 \text{ c.c. of oxygen weigh } \frac{0·29 \times 1000}{203} \text{ gm.}$$

$$= 1·43 \text{ gm.}$$

But 1 litre of hydrogen at N.T.P. weighs 0·09 gm.

$$\therefore \text{ Vapour density of oxygen} \ = \frac{1·43}{0·09}$$

$$= 15·9$$

$$\therefore \text{ Molecular weight of oxygen} = 15·9 \times 2$$

$$= 31·8$$

Gram-molecular Volume of Hydrogen. We have stated, in Chapter IV, that the weights of all other atoms are compared with the weight of a hydrogen atom, or that atomic weights are stated with reference to the standard H = 1. On this standard the atomic weight of oxygen is 15·88, or O = 15·88. It has been found desirable in practice to alter this atomic weight standard, and instead of taking H = 1 and O = 15·88, to alter the atomic weight of oxygen to 16, O = 16. This involves the raising of all other atomic weights in the ratio $\frac{16}{15·88}$ to keep the correct relation between them. We then get an atomic weight of $1 \times \frac{16}{15·88}$ or 1·008 for hydrogen, H = 1·008.

There are two reasons which make this change, small as it is, desirable. They are:—

(1) On the standard O = 15·88 and H = 1, many elements have atomic weights slightly less than whole numbers. The change to O = 16, H = 1·008 raises these atomic weights to whole numbers, which are rather convenient to use.

(2) The equivalents of many elements are found by combining them with oxygen. If the standard, O = 15·88 and H = 1 is used, any error in this 15·88 is transferred to the equivalent and atomic weights of all elements whose equivalents are found by combining them with oxygen. If the standard O = 16 and H = 1·008 is used, any error in the 1·008 affects hydrogen only.

For approximate calculations, the difference between the two standards is often ignored and O = 16 and H = 1 are used together. Strictly, however, modern atomic weights are all based on O = 16, not on H = 1.

It was shown on p. 76 that the hydrogen molecule is diatomic and is written as H_2.

Expressing this on the standard O = 16 and H = 1·008, we have:—

$$H_2$$
$$2 \times 1·008$$
$$\text{or } 2·016$$

If this is expressed in the scientific weight unit—grams—it becomes 2·016 gm., and this is called the gram-molecular weight of hydrogen or one gram-molecule of hydrogen.

Definition. The **Gram-Molecular Weight** (G.M.W.) of any substance is its molecular weight expressed in grams.

We now have

$$H_2$$
$$\text{G.M.W.} \quad 2·016 \text{ gm.}$$

By experiment, it has been found that 1 litre of hydrogen at N.T.P. weighs 0·09 gm. Therefore, 2·016 gm. of hydrogen occupy $\dfrac{2·016}{0·09}$ litres, or 22·4 litres at N.T.P.

This volume is called the gram-molecular volume of hydrogen.

We see, from this, that if we use grams as our weight-unit, the formula H_2 may denote either 2·016 gm. of hydrogen or 22·4 litres of it at N.T.P. We have connected the molecular formula of hydrogen with a volume, rather a convenient result because hydrogen, a gas, is usually measured as a volume.

Gram-Molecular Volumes of Other Gases. Consider the same volume, 22·4 litres at N.T.P., of some other gas, say oxygen. Since we are considering the *same* volume of both oxygen and hydrogen, we know, by Avogadro's Hypothesis, that we must be considering the same number of *molecules* of the two gases. But we started from one gram-molecule of hydrogen, H_2, therefore the 22·4 litres at N.T.P. must represent the same number of molecules of oxygen, *i.e.*, one gram-molecule of oxygen, O_2, or 32 gm. of oxygen.

The same argument will apply to any gas, which gives us this very important result:—

The gram-molecular weight of any gas occupies 22·4 litres at N.T.P. This volume is known as its gram-molecular volume (G.M.V.).

Definition. **The gram-molecular volume of any gas is the volume occupied at N.T.P. by its gram-molecular weight and is 22.4 litres at N.T.P.**

This is a most important and useful result because it means that if we write the molecular formula of any gas, and agree to work in grams as weight-units, all those molecular formulæ represent 22·4 litres of the gas at N.T.P. Thus:—

H_2	O_2	N_2	CO_2	H_2S	SO_2	Cl_2	
2·016	32	28	44	34	64	71	grams
22·4	22·4	22·4	22·4	22·4	22·4	22·4	litres at N.T.P.

Application of the Gram-Molecular Volume to Determination of Molecular Weight of a Gas. It follows from the above result, that, to find the molecular weight of a gas in grams, we have simply to find the weight of the gas in grams which occupies 22·4 litres at N.T.P. An example will illustrate the point.

Example. 350 c.c. of a certain gas at N.T.P. were found to weigh 1 gm. What is the molecular weight of the gas?

The weight of 22·4 litres (or 22,400 c.c.) of the gas at N.T.P.

$$= \frac{1 \times 22,400}{350} \text{ grams} = 64 \text{ grams}$$

∴ The molecular weight of the gas is 64

This method of calculation is alternative to the vapour density method given on p. 78.

Application of the Gram-Molecular Volume to Gas Calculations. The gram-molecular volume of gases enters very frequently into calculations. Two examples will illustrate its use.

Example 1. Calculate the volume of oxygen at 12° C. and 745 mm. which could be obtained by heating 5 gm. of potassium chlorate. (K = 39; Cl = 35·5; O = 16; G.M.V. of a gas at N.T.P. is 22·4 litres.)

Calculation. The first requirement is the equation.

$$2KClO_3 \rightarrow 2KCl + 3O_2$$

potassium   oxygen
chlorate

Note that, in the example, a **volume** of oxygen is asked for and a **weight** of potassium chlorate given. Consequently, in the equation, we insert the **weights** appropriate to potassium chlorate and the **volume** appropriate to oxygen. It is quite unnecessary to insert weights of oxygen because the problem set is not concerned at all with a weight of oxygen, only with a volume. Using grams as the weight units for potassium chlorate, O_2 (one gram-molecule of oxygen) represents 22·4 litres at N.T.P.; $3O_2$ represents, therefore, $3 \times 22\cdot4$ litres at N.T.P.

Inserting weights and volumes, we have:—

$$2KClO_3 \qquad \rightarrow \qquad 2KCl \quad + \quad 3O_2$$
2(39 + 35·5 + 48) gm. $3 \times 22\cdot4$ litres
245 gm.   at N.T.P.

From the equation:

245 gm. potassium chlorate liberate $3 \times 22\cdot4$ litres of oxygen at N.T.P.

5 gm. potassium chlorate liberate $3 \times 22\cdot4 \times \dfrac{5}{245}$ litres of oxygen at N.T.P.

$\qquad\qquad = 1\cdot37$ litres of oxygen at N.T.P.

Converting this volume to 12° C. and 745 mm. as the example requires:

$$\frac{P_1V_1}{T_1{}^\circ A} = \frac{P_2V_2}{T_2{}^\circ A}$$

$$\therefore \quad \frac{760 \times 1\cdot37}{273} = \frac{745 \times V_2}{285}$$

$$V_2 = \frac{760 \times 1\cdot37 \times 285}{273 \times 745} \text{ litres}$$

$$= 1\cdot458 \text{ litres.}$$

Example 2. Calculate the volume of hydrogen sulphide at 14° C; and 770 mm. which will react with 10 gm. of lead nitrate. (Pb = 207. N = 14; O = 16; G.M.V. of a gas is 22·4 litres at N.T.P.)

Calculation. Here again we require first the equation; the lead nitrate is given as a **weight,** so we insert the appropriate weights under its formula, while the hydrogen sulphide is required as a **volume,** so we insert its G.M.V. under its formula.

Thus: H_2S + $Pb(NO_3)_2 \rightarrow PbS + 2HNO_3$
          22·4 litres $(207 + 28 + 96$ gm.$)$
          at N.T.P.   331 gm.

From the equation:

331 gm. of lead nitrate react with 22·4 litres of hydrogen sulphide at N.T.P.

$\therefore$ 10 gm. of lead nitrate react with $22·4 \times \dfrac{10}{331}$ litres of hydrogen sulphide at N.T.P.

          = 0·677 litres of hydrogen sulphide at N.T.P.

Converting this volume to 14° C. and 770 mm.

$$\frac{P_1V_1}{T_1 °A} = \frac{P_2V_2}{T_2 °A}$$

$$i.e., \quad \frac{760 \times 0·677}{273} = \frac{770 \times V_2}{287}$$

$$\therefore V_2 = \frac{760 \times 0·677 \times 287}{770 \times 273} \text{ litres}$$

$$= 0·7025 \text{ litres.}$$

INTERPRETATION OF AN EQUATION

We are now in a position to present all the information conveyed by a chemical equation.

Consider the following equation which represents the action of marble (calcium carbonate) upon hydrochloric acid, producing calcium chloride, water and carbon dioxide.

$CaCO_3$ + $2HCl$ $\rightarrow$ $CaCl_2$ + H_2O + CO_2
$40+12+48$ $2(1+35·5)$ $40+(35·5\times2)$ $(2\times1)+16$ $12+(16\times2)$
  100   73   111   18   44 gm.
                                             or 22·4 litres at
                                                  N.T.P.

The equation expresses the following facts:—

1. *About the individual compounds*:

   (a) One molecule of calcium carbonate contains one atom of calcium, one atom of carbon, and three atoms of oxygen.

   One molecule of hydrochloric acid contains one atom of hydrogen and one atom of chlorine.

   One molecule of calcium chloride contains one atom of calcium and two atoms of chlorine.

   One molecule of water contains two atoms of hydrogen and one atom of oxygen.

   One molecule of carbon dioxide contains one atom of carbon and two atoms of oxygen.

(b) 100 parts by weight of calcium carbonate contain 40 parts by weight of calcium, 12 of carbon and 48 of oxygen.
Similarly for the other compounds, as expressed in the figures under their formulæ.

2. *About the reaction:*

(a) One molecule of calcium carbonate reacts with two molecules of hydrochloric acid producing one molecule of calcium chloride, one molecule of water, and one molecule of carbon dioxide.

(b) 100 parts by weight of calcium carbonate react with 73 parts by weight of hydrochloric acid, producing 111 parts by weight of calcium chloride, 18 parts by weight of water, and 44 parts by weight of carbon dioxide.

(c) If the weight-units used are grams, CO_2 represents one gram-molecule of carbon dioxide, which occupies 22·4 litres at N.T.P.

The equation does *not* state:—

1. The conditions of the reaction:
   for example, whether heat is required or not; whether the acid is dilute or concentrated.
2. Whether the reaction is rapid or slow.
3. Whether heat is evolved or absorbed during the course of the reaction.
4. Whether the various substances are solids, liquids or gases, and whether they are in solution, precipitated or evolved as gases.

Sometimes, to indicate precipitation of a substance, an arrow $\downarrow$ is used, and to indicate evolution of a gas, an arrow $\uparrow$.
Thus:

$$NaCl + H_2SO_4 \rightarrow NaHSO_4 + HCl \uparrow$$

indicates that hydrogen chloride is evolved as gas and

$$Ca(OH)_2 + CO_2 \rightarrow CaCO_3 \downarrow + H_2O$$

indicates that calcium carbonate is precipitated.

Empirical and Molecular Formulæ. A method was given on p. 66 for the calculation of a formula for a compound from its percentage composition by weight. It is quite possible for two different compounds to have the same percentage composition by weight either because the compounds have different arrangements of the same atoms inside the molecule, or because the molecular formula of one is a multiple of that of the other. Considering the second of these possibilities, it is clear that acetylene, C_2H_2, and benzene, C_6H_6, both having 92·3% of carbon, will both appear to have the same formula, when the calculation of p. 66 is applied. Thus:—

	Carbon.	Hydrogen.
Per cent by weight . . .	92·3	7·7
Number of atoms is represented by .	$\frac{92·3}{12} = 7·7$	$\frac{7·7}{1} = 7·7$
Dividing by smallest . . .	$\frac{7·7}{7·7} = 1$	$\frac{7·7}{7·7} = 1$

The formula appears to be CH for both. The reason is that this calculation always yields the *simplest* formula which expressed the composition of the substance by weight. Since the ratio of carbon atoms to hydrogen atoms is the same in CH, C_2H_2 and C_6H_6, the same composition by weight is expressed in all three. This simplest formula which expresses the composition of a compound by weight is called its **empirical formula.** Thus, the empirical formula of both benzene and acetylene is CH.

Clearly we must devise a method of finding the true or molecular formula of the compounds. This is simple enough. If the true formula is CH, the molecular weight is $(12 + 1)$ or 13; if C_2H_2, 26; if C_6H_6, 78, and so on. Thus, a determination of molecular weight will at once decide the true formula, and, in practice, this means determining the vapour density (p. 78) of the compound. The vapour density of acetylene is 13, and of benzene 39; that is, their molecular weights are 26 and 78 respectively. This gives a molecular formula C_2H_2 for acetylene and C_6H_6 for benzene.

Definitions. **The empirical formula of a compound is the simplest formula which expresses its composition by weight.**

The molecular formula of a compound is one which expresses the actual number of each kind of atom present in its molecule.

Another example will illustrate the point further.

A gaseous compound of carbon and hydrogen contains 80% carbon by weight. One litre of the compound at N.T.P. weighs 1·35 gm. Find its molecular formula. (C = 12; H = 1. G.M.V. of any gas is 22·4 litres at N.T.P.)

	Carbon.	Hydrogen.
Per cent by weight . . .	80	20
Number of atoms is represented by .	$\frac{80}{12} = 6·7$	$\frac{20}{1} = 20$
Divide by smallest . . .	$\frac{6·7}{6·7}$	$\frac{20}{6·7}$
	1	3

The empirical formula is CH_3

D

∴   The molecular formula is C_nH_{3n}, where n is a whole number

∴   the molecular weight is $(12n + 3n)$.

From the problem, 1 litre of the compound at N.T.P. weighs 1·35 gm.

∴   22·4 litres of the compound at N.T.P. weigh $\dfrac{1·35 \times 22·4}{1} = 30·2$ gm.

$$12n + 3n = 30·2$$
$$15n = 30·2$$
$$n = 2$$

∴   Molecular Formula is C_2H_6 (ethane).

Application of Avogadro's Hypothesis to Determination of Atomic Weights.

We have seen in Chapter IV the great difficulty encountered, in the first half of the nineteenth century, in the determination of atomic weights and how the difficulty was overcome in the case of metals by the application of Dulong and Petit's Law. A development from Avogadro's Hypothesis, which we are now to consider, supplied a method of determination of the atomic weight of non-metals of a certain type.

The most convenient case for us to consider is that of carbon. Suppose we take the symbol X to denote the atomic weight of carbon. In a molecule of a carbon compound, there cannot be less than one atom of carbon, and there may be two, three, four or any small whole number of carbon atoms. This means that, in the molecular weight of a carbon compound, there must be X, 2X, 3X or nX units of weight of carbon (n is a small whole number).

The molecular weight of any carbon compound can be found by determining first its vapour density (by the method on p. 78, provided that the compound is gaseous). The compound can then be analysed and the percentage of weight of carbon in it determined. The weight of carbon in the molecular weight is then given by the expression

$$\frac{\text{Percentage of carbon}}{100} \times \frac{\text{Molecular weight of compound}}{1}$$

If this is applied to several carbon compounds, the results must represent the weights of the number of carbon atoms in the molecules. In the table on p. 87, the figures are given for several compounds.

The figures in the last column correspond to the presence of one, two, three or more carbon atoms. The lowest weight is 12 and the others are multiples of 12. Now it is obvious that, if we have included in our list any compound containing only one carbon atom per molecule, that compound will be the first, methane, or the last, formaldehyde, because in these the weight of carbon is the least. If, therefore, the molecules of methane and formaldehyde do actually contain only one carbon atom, the atomic weight of carbon is 12. This process has been applied to a very large number of carbon compounds, and the weight of carbon in the molecular weight has always been found to be 12, or a multiple of 12, but never less. From this we conclude that the least weight of carbon there can ever be in the molecular weight of one of its compounds is 12, that this weight corresponds to the presence of one carbon atom and that the atomic weight of carbon is 12.

The method can be applied to determine the atomic weight of any element forming a large number of gaseous or easily volatile compounds.

Compound.	Vapour density by experiment.	Molecular weight ($= 2 \times$ V.D.).	% of carbon by weight (by experiment).	Weight of carbon in the molecular weight.
Methane . .	8	16	75·0	$75 \times \dfrac{16}{100} = 12$
Ethane . .	15	30	80·0	$80 \times \dfrac{30}{100} = 24$
Propane . .	22	44	81·8	$81·8 \times \dfrac{44}{100} = 36$
Ethylene . .	14	28	85·7	$85·7 \times \dfrac{28}{100} = 24$
Acetylene . .	13	26	92·3	$92·3 \times \dfrac{26}{100} = 24$
Formaldehyde .	15	30	40·0	$40 \times \dfrac{30}{100} = 12$

QUESTIONS

All necessary atomic weights may be found on p. 428.

1. What is the weight of 22·4 litres (gram-molecular volume) of the following gases at N.T.P. (a) ammonia, (b) sulphuretted hydrogen, (c) nitrogen, (d) chlorine, (e) nitrous oxide?
2. Calculate the molecular weights of the following gases from the statements:—
   (a) 0·8 gm. of oxygen occupied at N.T.P. a volume of 560 c.c.
   (b) 1,400 c.c. of sulphur dioxide measured at N.T.P. weighed 4 gm.
   (c) 1·12 litres of nitric oxide measured at N.T.P. weighed 1·5 gm.
3. What volume of carbon dioxide at N.T.P. could be obtained by dissolving 150 gm. of pure marble (calcium carbonate) in dilute nitric acid?
4. 1·16 gm. of magnesium was allowed to react with excess dilute sulphuric acid. What volume of hydrogen measured at N.T.P. was liberated?
5. An evacuated flask weighed 20·70 gm. Filled with dry hydrogen, it was found to weigh 20·94 gm. Filled with dry chlorine at the same temperature and pressure as the hydrogen, the flask weighed 29·22 gm. Using these data alone, find the molecular weight of chlorine.
6. 1 litre of ozone measured at 20° C. and 750 mm. was converted into oxygen by heating. If the resulting oxygen was measured at 30° C. and 750 mm., what volume would it occupy?
7. 100 c.c. of hydrogen were sparked with 30 c.c. of oxygen, both gases at 110° C. and 760 mm. What is the total volume of gas left after cooling to the original temperature and pressure? What percentage of this gas by volume is steam?
8. By heating a certain weight of lead peroxide with excess of concentrated hydrochloric acid, 743 c.c. of chlorine were obtained measured at 27° C. and 755 mm. Calculate the weight of lead

peroxide used and find the weight of lead chloride which was produced during the reaction.

9. Explain carefully the term "molecular weight". Give a short account of the experiments and reasoning which lead to the conclusion that the molecular weight of steam is 18. (O. and C., 1932.)

10. Define the terms "vapour density" and "molecular weight", and deduce from your definition the relation that exists between them, stating any assumptions that you make in the deduction. A metallic chloride has a vapour density of 130 and contains 54·6 per cent of chlorine by weight. How many atoms of chlorine does its molecule contain? (Cl = 35·5.) (C.)

11. What is the relation between molecular weight and vapour density, and how do you account for it?

At atmospheric pressure and 546° C., 50 c.c. of phosphorus vapour weigh 0·093 gm. What is the molecular weight of phosphorus? (1 litre of hydrogen at N.T.P. weighs 0·09 gm.) (O. and C.)

12. Explain how Avogadro's Law can be used to establish (a) molecular weights, (b) atomic weights. Illustrate your answer by reference to oxygen and carbon. (O. and C.)

13. A flask of about 500 c.c. capacity, fitted with a rubber stopper, weighed 90·512 gm. when filled with air. Hydrogen chloride from a generator was passed in for a few minutes, the stopper was replaced, and the flask and its contents now weighed 90·660 gm.

The flask was inverted in a trough of water, the stopper was removed under water, and eventually 456 c.c. of liquid entered when the levels had been adjusted. Given that the temperature of the gases was 13° C. and that the atmospheric pressure was 770 mm. of mercury, find:—

(a) The weight of a litre of hydrogen chloride at N.T.P.;

(b) The molecular weight of hydrogen chloride from the given data. (One litre of hydrogen at N.T.P. weighs 0·09 gm., one litre of air at N.T.P. weighs 1·293 gm.) (B.)

14. Explain the use of a chemical equation and the information which it conveys.

Give equations representing three chemical reactions and state the exact meaning of each equation. (O. and C.)

15. Describe in detail the qualitative *and* quantitative experiment you would carry out to show that the equation $CuO + H_2 = H_2O + Cu$ represents the action of hydrogen on red hot copper oxide. (O.)

16. Write the equation for the action of hydrochloric acid on zinc. Using this as an example, state the information given by the equation. Indicate what the equation does *not* tell us about the reaction. Write *equations only*, showing the reaction between: (a) iron and sulphur, (b) silver nitrate solution and sodium chloride solution, (c) sulphuric acid and potassium nitrate, (d) sulphuric acid and copper, (e) carbon dioxide and excess sodium hydroxide solution, (f) copper oxide and gaseous ammonia. (L.)

CHAPTER X

THE FORMULÆ OF SOME GASES

(Emphasis must be laid on mentioning the conditions of temperature and pressure whenever gas volumes are measured.)

IN this chapter, we shall give the experimental evidence, and the reasoning from it, by which the formulæ of a number of common gases have been established. It is most important that you should note carefully the way in which Avogadro's Hypothesis is continually employed in establishing these formulæ, both directly in converting volume measurements into evidence of the numbers of molecules involved and, indirectly, when vapour density measurements are employed. The importance of the Hypothesis in the following work cannot be over-estimated.

The Formula of Hydrogen Chloride. All volume measurements made during the following experiment are under the same conditions of temperature and pressure.

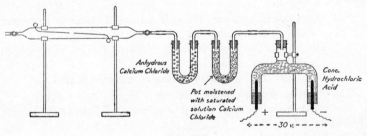

FIG. 20.

The apparatus usually supplied for this experiment (see Fig. 20) is far too large to be filled in a reasonable period of time, and is too liable to burst. A smaller model of about 50 c.c. capacity (obtainable from manufacturers quite easily) is very suitable and the experiment can be completely performed in 20 minutes.

Set up the apparatus of Fig. 20 in diffused daylight, and allow the mixed gases to pass for five to ten minutes. Close both taps. Attach wires from a coil, and arrange a plate of thick glass between the tube and the observers. Close the circuit and a flash is seen but no sound is heard. Note that the green colour of chlorine has now disappeared. Fill the tube leading to one tap with mercury, and, holding the liquid in place with the finger, invert under mercury in a mortar. Open the tap. No gas enters or leaves. Close the tap, replace the mercury in the tube by water, and open under the surface of water. The latter rises and almost fills the tube.

Note. The experiment of page 117 (Electrolysis of hydrochloric acid) *shows that the gases which fill the eudiometer tube consist of equal volumes of hydrogen and chlorine.*

This proves that the whole of the gas in the tube was hydrogen chloride because any excess of hydrogen or chlorine would not have dissolved with this rapidity. This experiment proves that, starting with half a tubeful of hydrogen and half a tubeful of chlorine (see p. 117), we obtain, by their combination, a tubeful of hydrogen chloride (temperature and pressure constant) or

> 1 volume of hydrogen combines with 1 volume of chlorine to give 2 volumes of hydrogen chloride (temperature and pressure constant).

Applying Avogadro's Hypothesis, we may substitute molecules for volumes, all the substances being gases.

∴ 1 molecule of hydrogen combines with 1 molecule of chlorine to give 2 molecules of hydrogen chloride.

But 1 molecule of hydrogen and 1 molecule of chlorine each contain 2 atoms.

> ∴ 2 molecules of hydrogen chloride contain 2 atoms of hydrogen and 2 atoms of chlorine
> ∴ 1 molecule of hydrogen chloride contains 1 atom of hydrogen and 1 atom of chlorine
> ∴ The formula of hydrogen chloride is HCl.

The equation for the above reaction is $H_2 + Cl_2 \rightarrow 2HCl$.

Note. Since the reactants and products are all gaseous the vapour density is not required.

The Formula of Ammonia Gas. The full argument depends upon two experiments (*a*) and (*b*).

(*a*) Ammonia gas can be formed by sparking nitrogen and hydrogen in suitable proportions. This proves that ammonia contains these two elements only. (This experiment is not described here.)

(*b*) Hofmann's method (described below) may be used to demonstrate the volume proportions of the nitrogen and hydrogen combined in ammonia. The method depends on the following facts:—

(i) That ammonia reacts with chlorine, liberating nitrogen and forming hydrogen chloride.

(ii) That the hydrogen and chlorine combine in *equal* volumes when hydrogen chloride is formed. (See last experiment.)

Take an apparatus similar to that of Fig. 21. It can easily be made by heating a burette (a damaged one will be quite satisfactory if the length from the tap to the open end is 15 inches or more) and drawing out the heated portion until it forms a constriction of which the diameter is about that of ordinary glass-tubing, and then making a file-scratch on the constriction and breaking AB separate from C. AB should be about 12 inches long and graduated into three equal portions. Attach AB to a chlorine generator[1] in a fume-chamber and fill it with chlorine. Add the rubber-tubing and clip, and the portion C, and clamp the whole apparatus in a vertical position. Put a little concentrated ammonia into C, **cautiously** release the clip and allow a little of the ammonia to enter AB. There will be a flash of light and white fumes of ammonium chloride will appear. Carefully allow more ammonia to enter AB until there is no further reaction and a few drops of liquid have collected at B. Then put dilute sulphuric acid into C, colour it with a little litmus solution and run it into AB to neutralise the excess ammonia, taking care that C does not become empty of liquid or air will be drawn into AB. When the solution in AB is red (*i.e.* when all the ammonia has been neutralised) remove C and place AB in a wide, deep vessel filled with water so that the tap B is well immersed. Open the tap. Water will enter. Push AB down into the vessel until the levels of water inside and outside are equal, so giving atmospheric pressure inside AB. It will then be found that the gas left occupies one-third of the volume of AB. The gas is nitrogen.

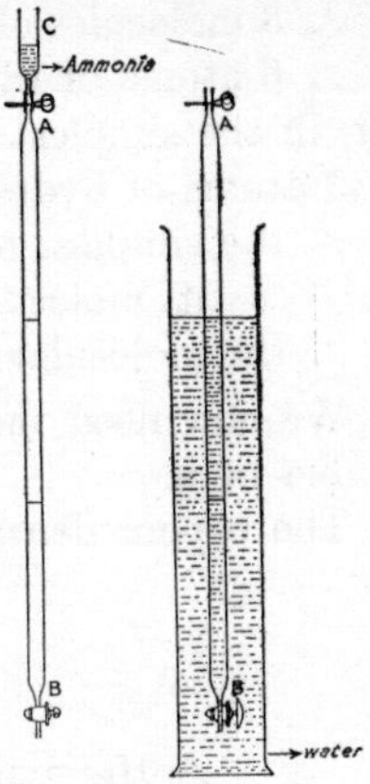

Fig. 21.

Formula of ammonia gas.

The original volume, AB, of chlorine combined with hydrogen from the ammonia to form hydrogen chloride. A volume, AB, of hydrogen from the ammonia must have been used up to combine with this chlorine (see (ii) above). At the same time, one-third of a volume AB of nitrogen was liberated from the ammonia.

∴ 3 volumes of hydrogen were combined with 1 volume of nitrogen in ammonia gas (temperature and pressure constant).

Applying Avogadro's Hypothesis, we may replace "volumes" by "molecules".

[1] To teachers. It is convenient to make this apparatus part of the delivery-tube when chlorine is being prepared as a demonstration experiment. The tube is then automatically filled with chlorine without extra trouble.

∴ 3 molecules of hydrogen combine with 1 molecule of nitrogen.

∴ 6 atoms of hydrogen combine with 2 atoms of nitrogen
or, in the simplest terms,

3 atoms of hydrogen combine with 1 atom of nitrogen.

∴ the simplest (empirical) formula for ammonia gas is NH_3 and
its molecular formula is $(NH_3)_n$ where n is a whole number.

∴ the molecular weight of ammonia gas is $(14 + 3)n$ or $17n$.

We now need the molecular weight of ammonia gas to find the
value of n.

The vapour density of ammonia gas is 8·5.

$$\therefore \text{ its molecular weight is } 17$$
$$\therefore 17n = 17$$
$$\therefore \quad n = 1$$

∴ the molecular formula of ammonia gas is NH_3

Equations.

$$2NH_3 + 3Cl_2 \rightarrow N_2 + 6HCl$$

Then $6HCl + 6NH_3 \rightarrow 6NH_4Cl$

Adding $8NH_3 + 3Cl_2 \rightarrow N_2 + 6NH_4Cl.$

Formula for Steam. The apparatus (see Fig. 22) consists of a
stout eudiometer tube surrounded by a jacket which contains
a vapour at 130° C. (amyl alcohol boils at 130° C. at 760 mm.
pressure). The other limb of the eudiometer tube serves as a
manometer, for mercury can be run into and out of this
tube, so altering the pressure. One
volume of oxygen is introduced and
then two volumes of hydrogen. The
open end of the tube is suitably
plugged so that the mercury is not
blown out. The mixture is exploded
by means of an electrical spark and
the plug is removed. On allowing
the gas to cool down to 130° C. and
equalising the mercury levels in the
two tubes it is found that there are
two volumes of steam left in the tube.
(All the above measurements of
volume are made at laboratory pressure and 130° C.) On cooling the
apparatus below 100° C. the steam
condenses to water and the mercury
rises to the top of the enclosed tube
showing that all the oxygen and

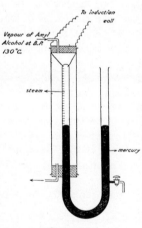

To induction coil

Vapour of Amyl
Alcohol at B.P.
130°C.

steam

mercury

FIG. 22.

Volume composition of steam.

hydrogen have been used up since they would not condense to a liquid as does the steam.

From this experiment

2 volumes of hydrogen and 1 volume of oxygen form 2 volumes of steam.

Applying Avogadro's Hypothesis we may substitute molecules for volumes, all the substances (at this temperature) being gaseous.

$\therefore$ 2 molecules of hydrogen and 1 molecule of oxygen form 2 molecules of steam

$\therefore$ 1 molecule of hydrogen and $\frac{1}{2}$ molecule of oxygen form 1 molecule of steam.

But the molecule of hydrogen contains two atoms and the molecule of oxygen contains two atoms.

$\therefore$ Formula for steam is H_2O.

Note. Since the reactants and the products are all gaseous under the conditions of the experiment the vapour density is not required.

Nitric Oxide. A suitable volume of nitric oxide is measured at atmospheric pressure (levels A and B equal) in the hard-glass tube (Fig. 23) The spiral of iron wire is then electrically heated to red

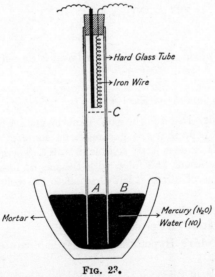

FIG. 23.

Volume composition of oxides of nitrogen.

heat. The metal combines with the oxygen of the nitric oxide, liberating nitrogen (the residual gas can be shown to be inactive). After about 20 minutes the electrical current is switched off and

D*

the tube allowed to cool. After the tube has been transferred to a deep vessel and lowered until the levels C and B are equal, the volume of nitrogen is measured and is found to be one-half of the original volume of nitric oxide.

That is, 1 volume of nitrogen is contained in 2 volumes of nitric oxide (temperature and pressure constant).

Using Avogadro's Hypothesis, we may substitute "molecules" for "volumes".

∴ 1 molecule of nitrogen is contained in 2 molecules of nitric oxide

∴ 2 atoms of nitrogen are contained in 2 molecules of nitric oxide

∴ 1 atom of nitrogen is contained in 1 molecule of nitric oxide

∴ the formula of nitric oxide is NO_x where x is a whole number

∴ the molecular weight of nitric oxide is $(14 + 16x)$

The vapour density of nitric oxide is 15.

The molecular weight of nitric oxide is 30.

$$∴ 14 + 16x = 30$$
$$x = 1$$

∴ formula of nitric oxide is NO

$$3Fe + 4NO \rightarrow Fe_3O_4 + 2N_2$$
triferric
tetroxide

Note. Pure nitric oxide for this experiment is conveniently prepared by half-filling a small flask with ferrous sulphate crystals, covering them with dilute sulphuric acid, warming and dropping sodium nitrite solution into the mixture from a tap-funnel.

Nitrous Oxide. Exactly the same experiment is performed as for nitric oxide except that the gas must be confined over mercury because nitrous oxide is fairly soluble in water. The hard-glass tube should be only about half-filled with the gas at first. It is found that the volume of nitrogen left is equal to the volume of nitrous oxide taken.

∴ 1 volume of nitrogen is contained in 1 volume nitrous oxide (temperature and pressure constant).

Using Avogadro's Hypothesis, we may substitute "molecules" for "volumes".

∴ 1 molecule of nitrogen is contained in 1 molecule of nitrous oxide.

∴ 2 atoms of nitrogen are contained in 1 molecule of nitrous oxide.

∴ the formula of nitrous oxide is N_2O_x (x is a whole number).

∴ the molecular weight of nitrous oxide is $(28 + 16x)$.

The vapour density of nitrous oxide is 22.

∴ Molecular weight of nitrous oxide is 44.

$$\therefore 28 + 16x = 44$$
$$\therefore x = 1$$

∴ the formula of nitrous oxide is N_2O

$$3Fe + 4N_2O \rightarrow Fe_3O_4 + 4N_2$$

Hydrogen Sulphide. A convenient volume of hydrogen sulphide is confined over mercury at atmospheric pressure (Fig. 24). By means of an induction coil, electric sparks are passed between the platinum wires for some time. This decomposes the hydrogen sulphide into its elements. Solid sulphur (of negligible volume) is deposited and hydrogen is left. It is found that, when the tube has cooled, the volume of hydrogen left is exactly equal to the volume of hydrogen sulphide taken (temperature and pressure constant).

∴ 1 volume of hydrogen is contained in 1 volume of hydrogen sulphide (temperature and pressure constant).

Applying Avogadro's Hypothesis, we may substitute "molecules" for "volumes".

∴ 1 molecule of hydrogen is contained in 1 molecule of hydrogen sulphide

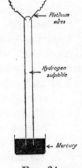

FIG. 24.
Volume composition of hydrogen sulphide.

∴ 2 atoms of hydrogen are contained in 1 molecule of hydrogen sulphide

∴ the formula of hydrogen sulphide is H_2S_x, where x is a whole number

∴ the molecular weight of the gas is $2 + 32x$.

The vapour density of hydrogen sulphide is 17.

∴ The molecular weight of hydrogen sulphide is 34

$$\therefore 2 + 32x = 34$$
$$x = 1$$

∴ the formula of hydrogen sulphide is H_2S

$$H_2S \rightarrow H_2 + S$$

Carbon Dioxide. The apparatus of Fig. 25 is used. A little *dry* powdered graphite (0·02 gm. is required for 40 c.c.) is placed in the *dry* tube, and *dry* oxygen is passed through the whole apparatus for 3–4 minutes. The clip is closed and mercury poured into the manometer. The clip is momentarily released to make the pressure in the tube atmospheric. The graphite is heated with a small flame, and it burns (not always obviously) to carbon dioxide. Expansion causes the level at C to fall, and the level at D to rise,[1] but, when the bulb has cooled, the levels at C and D return to their original positions, that is, the volume of carbon dioxide formed is equal to the volume of oxygen used.

∴ 1 volume of oxygen is contained in 1 volume of carbon dioxide (temperature and pressure constant).

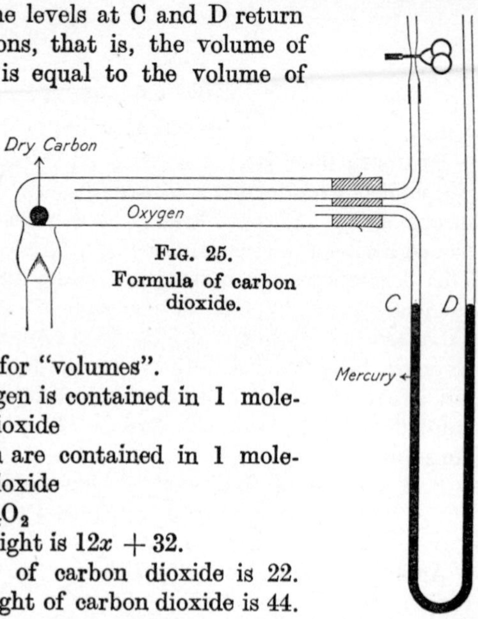

Dry Carbon

Oxygen

FIG. 25.
Formula of carbon dioxide.

Mercury

Applying Avogadro's Hypothesis, we may substitute "molecules" for "volumes".

∴ 1 molecule of oxygen is contained in 1 molecule of carbon dioxide

∴ 2 atoms of oxygen are contained in 1 molecule of carbon dioxide

∴ its formula is C_xO_2

∴ its molecular weight is $12x + 32$.

The vapour density of carbon dioxide is 22.

∴ The molecular weight of carbon dioxide is 44.

$$\therefore 12x + 32 = 44$$

$$x = 1.$$

∴ the formula of carbon dioxide is CO_2

$$C + O_2 \rightarrow CO_2$$

Sulphur Dioxide. The same experimental work is carried out as for carbon dioxide, substituting sulphur for carbon. As in the case of the carbon dioxide the volume of sulphur dioxide formed is equal to the volume of oxygen used.

The reasoning to obtain the formula, SO_2, is the same as for carbon dioxide, using the vapour density of sulphur dioxide, 32, and the atomic weight of sulphur, $S = 32$.

Formula of Ozone. Ozone can be made from oxygen and can be converted by heat into oxygen and no other product. It must therefore have the formula, O_n. The value of n is established as follows:

1. Ozone reacts with turpentine. Suppose on treatment with turpentine, 200 c.c. of ozonised oxygen shrink in volume by x c.c.

---

[1] If the level at C falls so that gas is in danger of being lost, remove the burner and close the mouth of tube D lightly with the finger.

This means that in the 200 c.c. of ozonised oxygen there are x c.c. of ozone.

2. Another 200 c.c. of the same sample of ozonised oxygen is heated, converting the ozone to oxygen. It will be found that there is an increase in volume of $x/2$ c.c. on cooling to the original temperature, pressure remaining constant. This means that the oxygen formed from the ozone occupies the x c.c. formerly occupied by the ozone, together with a further $x/2$ c.c. $i.e.$, $\dfrac{3x}{2}$ c.c. in all.

∴ x c.c. of ozone yield $\dfrac{3x}{2}$ c.c. oxygen at same temperature and pressure.

Or 2 volumes of ozone yield 3 volumes oxygen at same temperature and pressure.

∴ By Avogadro's Hypothesis,
2 molecules of ozone yield 3 molecules of oxygen,

$$i.e., \quad 2O_n = 3O_2$$
$$\therefore n = 3$$

and the formula of ozone is O_3.

Carbon Monoxide. A measured volume of carbon monoxide, confined over mercury in a eudiometer tube, is mixed with a measured volume of oxygen equal to several times its own volume. The mixture is exploded by a spark passed between platinum leads sealed through the glass. After cooling, the volume of residual gas is measured and the carbon dioxide is absorbed by allowing some concentrated caustic potash solution to rise above the mercury. (The potash solution is introduced at the bottom of the tube by means of a small pipette bent at the tip.) The diminution in volume caused by the potash represents the volume of carbon dioxide formed. The residual volume is the excess oxygen, and, by subtracting this from the original volume of oxygen taken, the volume of oxygen used up is obtained. (All measurements are taken at room temperature and atmospheric pressure.)

It will be found that:—

2 volumes of carbon monoxide combine with 1 volume of oxygen to form 2 volumes of carbon dioxide.

Using Avogadro's Hypothesis, we may substitute "molecules" for "volumes". Then, 2 molecules of carbon monoxide combine with 1 molecule of oxygen to form 2 molecules of carbon dioxide.

∴ 1 molecule of carbon monoxide contains $\frac{1}{2}$ molecule less oxygen than one molecule of carbon dioxide

∴ 1 molecule of carbon monoxide contains one atom of oxygen less than one molecule of carbon dioxide

But the formula of carbon dioxide is CO_2

∴ the formula for carbon monoxide is CO.

Note. Since the reactants and products are all gaseous the vapour density is not required.

EXPERIMENTAL FACTS AND DEDUCTIONS FROM THEM
(relating to Atomic Weights and Atomicity)

It is often a matter of some difficulty to understand the chain of reasoning which leads us to assume such statements as:—

The molecule of hydrogen contains *two* atoms.

The molecule of oxygen and chlorine contain *two* atoms.

The atomic weight of oxygen is 16.

The atomic weight of chlorine is $35\frac{1}{2}$.

These statements are used in the proof of the formulæ of the gases. Below is given (briefly) the line of argument which leads to the assumption of the above.

(For more complete explanation of the various steps used see the appropriate part of the theory.)

The formula of hydrogen is H_2.

(*a*) *Experiment.* 1 volume of hydrogen + 1 volume of chlorine → 2 volumes of hydrogen chloride.

(*b*) By Avogadro's Hypothesis: 1 molecule of hydrogen + 1 molecule of chlorine → 2 molecules of hydrogen chloride

∴ 1 molecule of hydrogen must contain *at least* two atoms.

Experiment. One sodium salt of hydrogen chloride is known

∴ the molecule of hydrogen chloride contains only ONE atom of hydrogen.

∴ the molecule of hydrogen which supplied ONE atom to each of two molecules of hydrogen chloride (see (*b*)) must have contained *two atoms*

∴ the formula is H_2.

The formula of oxygen is O_2 and the atomic weight 16.

Experiment. The equivalent of oxygen is 8

∴ (Atomic Theory) the atomic weight may be 8, 16, 24, 32, etc.

Experiment. 2 volumes hydrogen + 1 volume oxygen → 2 volumes steam.

By Avogadro's Hypothesis: 2 molecules hydrogen + 1 molecule steam → 1 molecule oxygen

∴ 1 molecule of oxygen contains *at least* two atoms.

Experiment. 1 volume of oxygen *never* produces more than two volumes of a gaseous oxide

∴ 1 molecule of oxygen contains *only* two atoms

∴ the formula is O_2.

Experiment. But the vapour density of oxygen is 16

∴ the molecular weight is 32

∴ the atomic weight is 16.

The formula for chlorine is Cl_2 and the atomic weight is 35.5.

Experiment. The equivalent weight of chlorine is 35·5

∴ (Atomic Theory) the atomic weight is 35·5, 71, 106·5, etc.

Experiment. The vapour density is 35·5.

∴ the molecular weight is 71.

But the molecule of chlorine contains at least two atoms (see (*b*) above)

∴ the atomic weight is 35·5.

QUESTIONS

1. How would you show experimentally that two volumes of hydrogen combine with one volume of oxygen to yield two volumes of steam? What deductions can be drawn from these facts as to the number of atoms in the oxygen molecule? (C.)

2. Complete the following statements:—
   (*a*) Two volumes of hydrogen unite with —— volume(s) of oxygen to give —— volume(s) of steam, all the substances being at 100° C. and atmospheric pressure.
   (*b*) Two volumes of hydrogen unite with —— volume(s) of nitrogen to give —— volume(s) of ammonia, all the gases being at the same temperature and pressure.
   State the law which these statements illustrate, and give the name of its author.
   Explain clearly how the formulæ of steam and ammonia follow from the statements you have made. (N.U.J.B.)

3. Describe two experiments from the results of which the formula CO_2 for carbon dioxide may be derived. Point out clearly what assumptions are made in the deduction of the formula. (B.)

4. Describe a eudiometer and explain shortly how it is used. Give an account of the experiments by which the formula of ammonia may be shown to be NH_3. (L.)

5. Describe the preparation and principal properties of carbon monoxide. What is the evidence on which the formula CO is assigned to this gas? (L.)

6. Give an account of the experimental evidence on which the accepted formula for hydrogen chloride is based. 223 c.c. of hydrogen chloride and 250 c.c. of gaseous ammonia, both measured at 13° C. and 770 mm., were mixed. Calculate the weight of the solid product. (Cl = 35·5. N = 14.) (L.)

7. State Gay-Lussac's Law of Gaseous Combination, illustrating your answer by reference to *four* examples.
   How would you show experimentally that a given volume of hydrogen sulphide contains twice as much hydrogen as an equal volume of hydrogen chloride? (L.)

8. Describe an experiment to show the volume composition of hydrogen chloride. State Avogadro's hypothesis, and apply it to the result of the above experiment so as to show that the molecule of hydrogen contains at least two atoms. (N.U.J.B.)

CHAPTER XI

NORMAL SOLUTIONS AND THEIR USE

THE EQUIVALENT OF A COMPOUND

THE conception of the equivalent of a compound is particularly important in the case of acids and compounds which react with them to produce salts; that is, bases (alkalis, especially) and some carbonates. We shall limit our definitions to these cases.

Acids. *Definition.* The **equivalent** of an acid is the number of grams of it which contain 1 gm. of hydrogen replaceable by a metal.

Thus:

1. HCl. Molecular weight is 36·5

   ↑

   1 gm. replaceable hydrogen in 36·5 gm. of acid
   ∴ equivalent of hydrochloric acid = 36·5.

2. H_2SO_4. Molecular weight is 98.

   ↑

   ∴ 2 gm. replaceable hydrogen in 98 gm. of acid

   $$\therefore \text{ equivalent of sulphuric acid} = \frac{98}{2} \text{ or } 49$$

Bases and Carbonates. *Definition.* The **equivalent** of a base (or carbonate) is the number of grams of it which react with an acid to replace 1 gm. of hydrogen by a metal.

It is desirable to write an equation to connect the base or carbonate with an acid in order to see clearly what its equivalent is.

For example:

1. $NaOH + HCl \qquad \rightarrow \qquad NaCl + H_2O$

   ↑   ↑

   40 gm. 1 gm. of hydrogen replaced by metal

   ↓   ↓

   $KOH + HCl \qquad \rightarrow \qquad KCl + H_2O$
   56 gm.

   ∴ equivalent of caustic soda = 40
   equivalent of caustic potash = 56

100

2. $Na_2CO_3 + H_2SO_4 \rightarrow Na_2SO_4 + H_2O + CO_2$

106 gm. 2 gm. of hydrogen replaced by metal

∴ equivalent of sodium carbonate $= \dfrac{106}{2} = 53$

3. $CaCO_3 + 2HCl \rightarrow CaCl_2 + H_2O + CO_2$

100 gm. 2 gm. of hydrogen replaced by metal

∴ equivalent of calcium carbonate $= \dfrac{100}{2} = 50$

4. $Ca(OH)_2 + 2HNO_3 \rightarrow Ca(NO_3)_2 + 2H_2O$

74 gm. 2 gm. of hydrogen replaced by metal

∴ Equivalent of slaked lime $= \dfrac{74}{2} = 37$

Standard Solution. **A standard solution is one which contains a known weight of a substance in a given volume of solution.**

For example: Solutions containing 8 gm. per litre or 2 oz. per gallon of certain substances are standard solutions.

NORMAL SOLUTIONS

The use of pure acids and alkalis in the laboratory is rarely possible for several reasons:

(*a*) Some, for example caustic soda and potash, and concentrated sulphuric acid, absorb water from the air, and to obtain them in a pure state would be very difficult. Others, for example concentrated hydrochloric acid and ammonia, are volatile.

(*b*) They are sometimes dangerous to handle.

(*c*) Many actions would be so vigorous as to be almost explosive in character.

Hence, acids and alkalis are very frequently used in solution. A very convenient concentration is obtained by **dissolving the equivalent weight in grams of a substance in water and making the solution up to one litre.**

This is termed a normal solution.

Definition. **A normal solution is one which contains the equivalent weight of a substance in grams in one litre of solution.**

Hence:

1 litre normal

| sulphuric acid contains 49 gm. per litre (see p. 100).
| hydrochloric acid contains 36·5 gm. per litre.
| nitric acid contains 63 gm. per litre.
| sodium hydroxide contains 40 gm. per litre.
| potassium hydroxide contains 56 gm. per litre.
| sodium carbonate contains 53 gm. per litre (see above).

Consider the action

$$NaOH + HCl \rightarrow NaCl + H_2O$$
$$40 \text{ gm.} \qquad 36·5 \text{ gm.}$$

That is: 40 gm. of caustic soda would neutralise exactly 36·5 gm. of hydrogen chloride.

But one litre of normal caustic soda contains 40 gm. per litre, and one litre of normal hydrochloric acid contains 36·5 gm. hydrogen chloride per litre.

Hence, one litre of normal caustic soda solution would exactly react with one litre of normal hydrochloric acid.

Similarly, if any two reagents, A and B, which have an action upon one another are made up into normal solutions,

one litre of normal A will react with exactly 1 litre of normal B

∴ 25 c.c. normal A will react with exactly 25 c.c. normal B and so on.

Normal solutions are equivalent to one another, volume for volume.

Normal solutions are very often too concentrated for ordinary use and hence decinormal solutions are employed. A decinormal solution is one-tenth as concentrated as a normal solution.

N/2 solution is half as concentrated as a N solution.

2N solution is twice as concentrated as a N solution.

5N solution is five times as concentrated as a N solution.

N/100 solution is one-hundredth as concentrated as a N solution, and so on.

Preparation of N/10 Sulphuric Acid. Sulphuric acid must not be directly weighed out because it is hygroscopic, and, therefore, of uncertain composition. Acid of accurate concentration is made as follows:

Method. A roughly N/10 solution is prepared and its true normality found by titration against an alkali which can be made up accurately. One common compound which reacts alkaline and can readily be obtained pure is sodium carbonate. When made by heating sodium bicarbonate to constant weight, it is very pure.

Preparation of roughly N/10 Sulphuric Acid.

$$H_2SO_4 + Na_2CO_3 \rightarrow Na_2SO_4 + H_2O + CO_2$$
$$98 \text{ gm.} \qquad 106 \text{ gm.}$$
$$2 \text{ litres N.} \quad 2 \text{ litres N.}$$

∴ 49 gm. of sulphuric acid are contained in 1 litre N, and 53 gm. sodium carbonate are contained in 1 litre N.

Hence 4·9 gm. of sulphuric acid are contained in 1 litre N/10, 5·3 gm. sodium carbonate are contained in 1 litre $\dfrac{N}{10}$.

1 c.c. concentrated sulphuric acid weighs 1·8 gm.

∴ 4·9 gm. occupies a volume of 2·7 c.c.

Pour some concentrated sulphuric acid through a funnel into a short burette **Take great care, as concentrated sulphuric acid is a most dangerous chemical.**

Run 3·0 c.c. of concentrated acid into water in a litre flask and make up to the mark with water. Shake well.

The acid is made slightly stronger than N/10 because it is then easy to dilute it by addition of water to exactly N/10.

Preparation of solution of sodium carbonate, EXACTLY N/10, that is, 5·3 gm. per litre.

Heat some pure sodium bicarbonate in a clean dish until the weight is constant.

$$2NaHCO_3 \rightarrow Na_2CO_3 + H_2O + CO_2$$

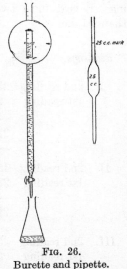

FIG. 26.
Burette and pipette.

Weigh out, on to a watch-glass, exactly 1·325 gm. Transfer the carbonate to a beaker containing a little hot water (shaking gently as the carbonate comes in contact with the water) and wash the watch-glass carefully by means of the wash-bottle, allowing the washings to drop into the beaker. Stir gently to dissolve, warming if necessary. Smear an almost imperceptible amount of vaseline on the lip of the beaker and pour the cooled solution down a glass rod into a funnel resting in the neck of a clean (but not necessarily dry) 250 c.c. flask. Wash the beaker out with further small quantities of water, pouring all washings down the rod and funnel into the 250 c.c. flask to ensure that no solution is left on the walls of the beaker. It is well to remember that once you have weighed out the sodium carbonate into the weighing bottle every particle of it, whether as solid or as a solution, must be transferred into the 250 c.c. graduated flask. Make up to the mark with water from a pipette, shake well or pour into a large dry beaker in order that the solution may become uniform.

Titration. Wash out a burette with water and then with a few c.c. of the acid solution which you have made up. (The burette is then left wet with the acid it is to contain, and there will be no water left to dilute the acid.)

Fill up the burette with the roughly N/10 acid and run out a drop or two to fill the jet below the tap.

Wash out a pipette first with water and then with the solution of sodium carbonate which it is to measure (again to avoid diluting it), and then draw up just past the mark, allow to run out until on the mark and then run this into a conical flask *which has been washed out with water only.*

Do not blow out the last drop of liquid from the pipette but merely allow the end of the tube to touch the surface of the liquid, after allowing a few seconds for the liquid to drain.

Add a few drops of methyl orange as an indicator (it will turn yellow); note the level of acid. Run in the acid until you observe a pink flash (you should be able to run in up to 20 c.c. without danger of over-running the end-point). Then run in more acid carefully drop by drop, shaking each time a drop is added, until the yellow colour just turns a permanent pink. Notice the reading. Repeat until two consecutive readings differ by no more than 0·1 c.c.

Readings.

I.	2nd reading	23·4 c.c.	}	TRIAL. Therefore not very
	1st reading	2·2 c.c.		accurate.
		22·2 c.c.		
II.	2nd reading	45·4 c.c.		
	1st reading	23·4 c.c.		
		22·0 c.c.		
				Mean 22·0 c.c.
III.	2nd reading	25·4 c.c.		
	1st reading	3·4 c.c.		
		22·0 c.c.		

∴ 22·0 c.c. of the acid were required to neutralise 25 c.c. of the N/10 sodium carbonate solution.

This is analogous to a situation in which a tug-of-war team of 22 men is just holding another team of 25 men. Which men individually are the stronger? Obviously the 22.

Similarly, since 22·0 c.c. of the acid neutralise 25 c.c. of the sodium carbonate solution, each c.c. of acid must be more concentrated than each c.c. of sodium carbonate solution, and the acid must be more concentrated than the carbonate sol. in the ratio $\dfrac{25}{22}$.

But the sodium carbonate solution was N/10

∴ the concentration of the acid is $\dfrac{25}{22} \times \dfrac{N}{10} = 0.114\ N$

$$Na_2CO_3 + H_2SO_4 \rightarrow Na_2SO_4 + H_2O + CO_2$$
$$98\ gm.$$
$$contain\ 2\ gm.$$
$$replaceable\ hydrogen$$

∴ 1 litre N contains 49 gm.

Normal sulphuric acid contains 49 gm. per litre

∴ concentration of acid is $\dfrac{25}{22} \times 4.9$ gm. per litre

$$= 5.57\ gm.\ per\ litre.$$

To make the acid N/10.
22 c.c. of acid neutralised 25 c.c. of N/10 alkali.
If the acid had been exactly N/10, 25 c.c. of it would have neutralised 25 c.c. of the sodium carbonate solution.

∴ 3 c.c. of water must be added to every 22 c.c. of acid left.
On measuring the acid in a large measuring cylinder, 920 c.c. were left.

Amount of water to add $= \dfrac{920}{22} \times 3$ c.c. $= \dfrac{2760}{22}$ c.c. $= 126$ c.c.

Add this volume of water to the acid and stir well. It will then be exactly N/10.

An accurately N/10 solution of an acid having been obtained in this way, it is possible to prepare roughly decinormal solutions of alkalis, *e.g.*, caustic soda (4 gm. per litre for N/10), caustic potash (5·6 gm. per litre for N/10), and standardise them, *i.e.*, find their exact concentrations by titrating against the acid as described in the last section. They can then be adjusted to N/10 by dilution as in the case of the sulphuric acid. Accurate solutions of the other common acids can also be prepared. With these acidic and alkaline solutions available, it is possible to carry out a great many estimations of acids and alkalis in solution and in mixtures. We cannot consider all such estimations here, but the lines on which they are carried out, and the calculations involved, are illustrated by the following examples and the questions which follow this chapter.

Examples of Use of Normal Solutions. Normal and decinormal solutions can be used for many estimations, of which the following are examples:

27·5 c.c. *of a solution of caustic soda neutralised* 25 c.c. *of* N/10 *hydrochloric acid. Calculate* (a) *the normality,* (b) *the strength of the caustic soda solution.*

Arrange the argument in your mind as follows:

(a) The object of the calculation is to fix the concentration of the caustic soda solution. We know the normality of the hydrochloric acid and hence we require to find neither the molecular weight of hydrogen chloride nor its concentration in grams per litre.

(b) Which is the more concentrated solution? The N/10 hydrochloric acid is more concentrated, since only 25 c.c. of it are needed to neutralise 27·5 c.c. of the caustic soda solution.

(c) What is the concentration of the caustic soda solution? Since it is weaker than N/10 in the ratio $\dfrac{25}{27\cdot5}$ the strength of the caustic soda solution will be $\dfrac{25}{27\cdot5} \times \dfrac{N}{10}$.

(d) Interchange for N the *equivalent weight* in grams of the substance whose solution we are considering.

$$NaOH + HCl \rightarrow NaCl + H_2O$$
$$40 \text{ gm.}$$

∴. Concentration of the caustic soda solution is

$$\frac{25}{27\cdot5} \times \frac{40}{10} \text{ gm. per litre}$$

$$= \frac{40}{11} \text{ gm. per litre} \qquad = 3\cdot64 \text{ gm. per litre.}$$

1 gm. *of pure ammonium chloride was boiled with* 20 c.c. *of a solution of caustic soda until the evolution of ammonia had ceased. If the resulting solution required* 11 c.c. *of* N/10 *hydrochloric acid for neutralisation, calculate* (a) *volume of ammonia gas evolved at N.T.P.,* (b) *the normality of the caustic soda solution.*

In a calculation of this kind, first write the equation. Then be careful to state the amounts of the substances in the equation in the same units as they are stated or required in the question, including only those with which the question is actually concerned.

Thus: ammonium chloride is stated in grams ("1 gm. of pure ammonium chloride"), ∴. ammonium chloride is stated in the equation in grams.

Caustic soda is required in terms of normality of its solution, ∴. caustic soda is stated in the equation in terms of N. caustic soda solution.

Ammonia is required as a volume of gas, ∴. it is stated in the equation in this form.

The required data are then:

$$NH_4Cl + NaOH \rightarrow NaCl + NH_3 + H_2O$$
$$53 \cdot 5 \text{ gm.} \quad 1 \text{ litre N} \qquad 22 \cdot 4 \text{ litres}$$
$$\text{at N.T.P.}$$

(a) From the equation:

53·5 gm. of ammonium chloride would liberate 22·4 litres ammonia gas at N.T.P.

1 gm. would liberate $\dfrac{22 \cdot 4}{53 \cdot 5}$ litres at N.T.P.

= 0·418 litres.

= 418 c.c. of ammonia gas at N.T.P.

(b) From the equation:

53·5 gm. of ammonium chloride react with 1,000 c.c. N. caustic soda.

1 gm. of ammonium chloride reacts with $\dfrac{1000}{53 \cdot 5}$ c.c. N. caustic soda.

= 18·7 c.c. N. caustic soda.

But the amount of caustic soda left was ≡ 11 c.c. N/10 acid
≡ 1·1 c.c. N. acid

∴ the 20 c.c. of caustic soda solution was equivalent altogether in 19·8 c.c. N. acid, ∴ to 19·8 c.c. N. caustic soda

∴ concentration of the caustic soda solution $= \dfrac{19 \cdot 8}{20}$ N

= 0·99 N

QUESTIONS

1. Describe how to perform the following operations, stating with reasons the precautions necessary to ensure accuracy:—
   (a) To transfer exactly 20 c.c. of a normal solution of sodium carbonate to a beaker, using a pipette;
   (b) To set up and fill a wet burette with a given solution of sulphuric acid;
   (c) To titrate this acid against the sodium carbonate solution, naming the indicator.

   What was the normality of the acid solution if 30 c.c. of it were used in (c)? (N.U.J.B.)

2. What is understood by the term "normal solution of hydrochloric acid"?

   1 gram of calcium carbonate having calcium sulphate as an impurity is dissolved in 250 c.c. of normal hydrochloric acid. 25 c.c. of the resulting liquid is found to require 31·2 c.c. of a solution of sodium hydroxide (containing 30 gm. of sodium hydroxide per litre) for exact neutralisation. Determine the percentage of $CaCO_3$ in

the original mixture (Ca = 40.   C = 12.   O = 16.   Na = 23.
Cl = 35·5.   H = 1).   (C.)

3. What is meant by the gram equivalent weight of a metal? 0·50 gm.
of a metal was dissolved in 25 c.c. of 2N sulphuric acid. Water
was added to bring the volume of the solution up to 100 c.c.   When
25 c.c. of the diluted solution were titrated with N/10 NaOH solution, 20·8 c.c., were required for neutralisation.
Calculate the gram equivalent weight of the metal. (N.U.J.B.)

4. The reaction between sodium bicarbonate and sulphuric acid is
represented by the equation

$$2NaHCO_3 + H_2SO_4 \rightarrow Na_2SO_4 + 2H_2O + 2CO_2$$

Calculate how many c.c. of normal sulphuric acid will be used
in the titration of 25 c.c. of a solution which contains 7 gm. of
sodium bicarbonate per 100 c.c. State the normality of the sodium
bicarbonate solution. (H = 1, C = 12, Na = 23, O = 16, S = 32.)
(N.U.J.B.)

5. What is meant by a normal solution?
Concentrated hydrochloric acid has a specific gravity of 1·16 and
contains 32 per cent by weight of hydrogen chloride. Calculate
the volume of this liquid which would be required to make 2 litres
of a normal solution of the acid. (Cl = 35·5.) (O. and C.)

6. What is meant by the term "equivalent" as applied to acids and
bases? What are the equivalents of hydrochloric acid, sulphuric
acid and caustic soda?
20 c.c. of an acid solution containing 12·25 gm. of the acid per
litre were allowed to react with excess of magnesium carbonate
$(MgCO_3)$. The carbon dioxide evolved measured 61·9 c.c. at 13° C.
and 720 mm. Find the equivalent weight of the acid. (Cl = 35·5,
S = 32, Na = 23, Mg = 24.) (L.)

7. Explain fully what is meant, in volumetric analysis, by the expression "a decinormal solution of sodium carbonate". A solution of
2·5 gm. of a sample of sodium carbonate, contaminated with salt,
was titrated with half-normal hydrochloric acid, of which 55·0 c.c.
were required for neutralisation. Calculate the percentage of anhydrous sodium carbonate in the sample. (N.U.J.B.)

8. Describe carefully how you would prepare 500 c.c. of normal sodium
carbonate solution if you were given an adequate supply of pure
sodium bicarbonate. 16·38 gm. of a dibasic acid containing two
molecules of water of crystallisation were dissolved in water and
the solution made up to 250 c.c.   25 c.c. of this solution required
for complete neutralisation 26 c.c. of normal sodium carbonate
solution. Find (a) the equivalent weight of the crystalline solid
acid, (b) the molecular weight of the anhydrous acid. (H = 1;
O = 16; Na = 23.   C = 12.) (B.)

9. Define (a) "equivalent weight of a metal", (b) "equivalent weight
of an acid", (c) "equivalent weight of an alkali". 0·48 gm. of a
metal is dissolved in 50 c.c. of normal sulphuric acid. This solution
now requires 10 c.c. of normal caustic soda for neutralisation. Find
the equivalent weight of the metal. (N.U.J.B.)

CHAPTER XII

THE ELECTROCHEMICAL SERIES AND ELECTROLYSIS

THE ELECTROCHEMICAL SERIES

Method of obtaining the Series. It is a well-known fact that certain metals will displace other metals from solutions of their salts in water. For example, iron will displace copper from copper sulphate solution, and zinc will displace silver from silver nitrate solution.

$$Fe + CuSO_4 \rightarrow FeSO_4 + Cu$$
$$Fe + Cu^{++} \rightarrow Fe^{++} + Cu$$
$$Zn + 2AgNO_3 \rightarrow Zn(NO_3)_2 + 2Ag$$
$$Zn + 2Ag^+ \rightarrow Zn^{++} + 2Ag$$

We can arrange the metals in a series such that any metal higher up in the series will displace from its salts any metal below it. The greater the gap separating the metals in the series, the more readily does displacement take place.

Again, if a plate of zinc and a plate of copper are immersed in dilute sulphuric acid, a current will flow from the copper to the zinc outside the cell and from the zinc to the copper inside the cell, if the plates are connected by a wire. Thus the copper and the zinc must be at different potentials when in contact with dilute sulphuric acid. These potentials can be measured and by arranging the metals according to this potential difference the same series is obtained as by the displacement method. The list obtained is as follows, omitting the less common metals :—

Metal.	Symbol.	
Potassium .	. **K**	Most electropositive element.
Sodium .	. **Na**	
Calcium .	. **Ca**	
Magnesium .	. **Mg**	
Aluminium .	. **Al**	
Zinc . .	. **Zn**	
Iron . .	. **Fe**	
Lead . .	. **Pb**	
(Hydrogen) .	. **H**	
Copper .	. **Cu**	
Mercury .	. **Hg**	
Silver . .	. **Ag**	
Gold . .	. **Au**	Least electropositive metal.

Hydrogen, although not a metal, is placed in the series to indicate the position it would occupy.

It will probably strike you at once that the metals occurring above hydrogen liberate that element from acids with an ease indicated by the interval separating the metal from hydrogen in the series. Thus magnesium and zinc liberate hydrogen readily (so would sodium and potassium, with such an " ease " that the experiment would be dangerous), whereas copper, which is below hydrogen in the series, does not liberate hydrogen from acids at all.

Chemical Activity of the More Electropositive Elements. Metals such as sodium and potassium, which occupy positions high up in the series, are said to be very electropositive. Metals high up in the series are very active chemically, and metals lower down less active. It is believed that all chemical reaction is closely connected with electrical charges, and so we shall not be surprised to find in general the chemical activity of a metal increases as its electropositive character becomes more pronounced.

Sodium and potassium, for example, are extremely active. They oxidise readily and react with water, and therefore they must be kept below the surface of petroleum oil. Copper, silver and gold, on the other hand, will be seen at the bottom of the series and they are comparatively inactive. They are practically unattacked by the atmosphere, and this is one reason why they are used as metals of the coinage. (Their progression in comparative value seems to have been a very fortunate coincidence !)

Gradation in Properties of Compounds of Metals according to Position in the Series. Not only does the series give us a good estimate of the chemical activity of the metal itself, but in many cases the properties of compounds of the metals are graded according to the position of the metal in the series. Thus the nitrates of sodium and potassium on heating decompose to the nitrite, the remainder of the metals of the series as far as copper (inclusive) form nitrates which decompose into the oxides on heating, liberating nitrogen peroxide and oxygen. The lowest members of the series, mercury, silver and gold, form nitrates which decompose to the metal on heating. (See p. 349.)

The following table shows some of these properties of the metals and their compounds. It will be noticed that, as a rule, a change occurs in the region of calcium and another change in the region of copper.

Be careful not to be too dogmatic about the properties as indicated in this way. It serves as a rough guide only, and as such it is invaluable as an aid to the memory. Do not think, however, that you can learn all the facts of Chemistry by a rigorous application

	Combustion.	Action on WATER.	Action on ACIDS.	Reduction of heated oxides by hydrogen.	Action of heat on oxides.	Action of water on oxides.	Character of hydroxides.	Character of carbonates.	Action of heat on nitrates.	Solubility of sulphides.
K	Burn in air or oxygen readily.	Decompose cold water.	Attacked by dilute acids.	NOT REDUCED.	Stable when heated.	Oxides react to form hydroxides.	Soluble in water therefore bases and alkalis.	Soluble and not decomposed by heat.	Nitrates decompose to nitrite.	Sulphides soluble in water.
Na										
Ca										
Mg		Decompose steam at red heat.								
Al	Oxidise when heated in air.					Oxides do not react with water.	Hydroxides insoluble bases only.	Insoluble and decomposed by heat.	Nitrates decompose to oxide.	Sulphides insoluble in water but soluble in dilute hydrochloric acid.
Zn				REDUCED.						
Fe										
Pb		Do not decompose water or steam at red heat.								
Cu			Attacked by oxidising acids.		Decompose.		Hydroxides not formed.	Carbonates unstable.	Nitrates decompose to metal.	Sulphides insoluble in water and dilute hydrochloric acid.
Hg										
Ag	Unaffected by oxygen.		Not attacked.							
Au										

Potassium
Sodium
Calcium
Magnesium
Aluminium
Zinc
Iron
Lead
Copper
Mercury
Silver
Gold

of the electrochemical series. You would be doomed to disappointment.

It is reproduced at the heading of any chapter where it is useful, and the metals in these cases are represented by their symbols.

The Place of Non-Metals in the Series. You might ask if the non-metals can be included in the series in some way. A complete list of all elements has been worked out and a modified list to include only the common ones is given here :

Electropositive

METALS
- Potassium   K
- Sodium   Na
- Calcium   Ca
- Magnesium   Mg
- Aluminium   Al
- Zinc   Zn
- Iron   Fe
- Lead   Pb
- (Hydrogen)   H
- Copper   Cu
- Mercury   Hg
- Silver   Ag
- Gold   Au

NON-METALS
- Carbon   C
- Nitrogen   N
- Phosphorus   P
- Sulphur   S
- Oxygen   O
- Chlorine   Cl
- Fluorine   F

Electronegative

In this complete series, the further apart two elements are, the more likely they are to form a stable compound. Thus oxygen combines very readily with sodium and potassium. Elements close to one another either do not combine at all or form unstable compounds. Thus chlorine dioxide, ClO_2, is an unstable explosive substance. Metals do not form stable compounds with each other.

ELECTROLYSIS

ELECTROLYSIS is the decomposition of a compound by the passage through it of an electric current.

Electrolytes and Non-electrolytes.

Consider the apparatus of Fig. 27. By varying the liquid in the beaker, three results can be obtained.

1. If the liquid in the beaker is alcohol, ether, chloroform, benzene or turpentine (to select a few from thousands of similar liquids)

the ammeter will show no current passing, whatever increase may be made in the voltage used, and no chemical action will occur at the electrodes. These substances are called *non-electrolytes*.

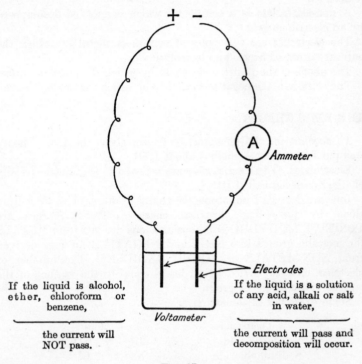

If the liquid is alcohol, ether, chloroform or benzene, ────── the current will NOT pass.

Electrodes

If the liquid is a solution of any acid, alkali or salt in water, ────── the current will pass and decomposition will occur.

Voltameter

FIG. 27.

Experiment to show the difference between an electrolyte and a non-electrolyte.

2. If the liquid in the beaker is an aqueous solution of any mineral acid, caustic alkali or salt, the ammeter will indicate the passage of a large current and chemical decomposition will take place at the electrodes. These solutions are called *strong electrolytes*.

3. If the liquid in the beaker is pure water and a very high voltage is applied, a sensitive ammeter will register a current but it will be very small and the corresponding chemical decomposition at the electrodes will be very slight. There also exist a large number of compounds which, if dissolved in the water, will increase its conductivity, relative only, to a very small extent. Water, and substances of this type, are called *weak electrolytes*.

DEFINITIONS.

An **electrolyte** is a solution or a molten compound which will conduct electric current with decomposition at the electrodes as it does so.

A **non-electrolyte** is a compound which cannot be decomposed by an electric current.

The **electrodes** are two poles of carbon or metal by which the current enters or leaves an electrolyte.

The **anode** is the positive electrode by which the current enters.

The **cathode** is the negative electrode by which the current leaves.

THE IONIC THEORY.

To account for the phenomena of electrolysis the Ionic Theory was put forward by Arrhenius about 1880.

Electrolytes. These substances are believed to contain electrically charged particles called IONS.

Ions are derived from atoms (or groups of atoms) but differ from them by possessing electrical charges. These charges are POSITIVE for HYDROGEN ions and ions derived from METALS (or metallic groups like NH_4), and NEGATIVE for ions derived from NON-METALS or ACIDIC RADICLES. The number of electrical charges carried by an ion is equal to the valency of the corresponding atom or group.

Some examples of ionisation are :—

Compound	Ions	
Sulphuric acid	$2H^+$	SO_4^{--}
Sodium chloride	Na^+	Cl^-
Sodium hydroxide	Na^+	OH^-
Copper sulphate	Cu^{++}	SO_4^{--}
Lead nitrate	Pb^{++}	$2NO_3^-$
Hydrochloric acid	H^+	Cl^-

It is very important to notice that an ion is fundamentally different from the corresponding atom or group. For example, a chlorine ion is not the same thing as a chlorine atom. It possesses a negative electric charge, while the chlorine atom is electrically neutral. This electrical charge gives to the ion properties quite different from those of the electrically neutral chlorine atom.

For example, by dissolving ordinary electrically neutral molecular chlorine in water, a solution is produced which is yellow in colour and is a vigorous bleaching agent, but a solution containing chlorine ions has neither of these properties. Similarly, ordinary metallic sodium, made up of neutral sodium atoms, attacks water liberating hydrogen, but sodium ions carrying a positive electrical charge have no such action upon water.

Note also that the electrical charges carried by an ion are equal in number to the valency of the corresponding element or group. Thus, ions of metals and metallic groups (for example, the ammonium group) always possess a positive charge, while ions of non-metals and non-metallic groups (for example, the carbonate, sulphate, and nitrate ions) possess a negative charge. Those charges are equal to the valency of the atom or group from which the ion is derived. The charge of electricity possessed by the sodium ion is the same in quantity as that possessed by the chlorine ion, both elements being univalent, but the charge on the hydrogen ion is positive and that on the chlorine ion negative. The ions of bivalent copper, zinc, lead and ferrous iron carry a positive charge whose magnitude is twice that of the charge on the sodium ion, while bivalent sulphate ion (SO_4^{--}) and carbonate ion (CO_3^{--}) carry negative charges which are twice as great as the charge carried by the chlorine ion. In all cases, the total charges carried by the positive ions are equal in magnitude to the total charges carried by the negative ions, making the solution as a whole, electrically neutral.

In **strong electrolytes,** the ionisation is complete. Thus, there exist in a solution of common salt no molecules, NaCl, but only ions, Na^+ and Cl^-. All strong electrolytes, *i.e.*, SALTS, THE MINERAL ACIDS and the CAUSTIC ALKALIS, are in this state of complete ionisation in solution.

In **weak electrolytes,** ionisation is only slight and most of the electrolyte exists in solution in the form of unionised molecules; for example, in ordinary bench (2N) acetic acid, out of every 1000 molecules present, three are ionised and 997 are unionised.

$$CH_3COOH \rightleftharpoons CH_3COO^- + H^+.$$

A solution of ammonia in water is also a weak electrolyte, containing a relatively small proportion of ammonium and hydroxyl ions.

$$NH_4OH \rightleftharpoons NH_4^+ + OH^-.$$

Most of the organic acids are weak electrolytes, *e.g.*, tartaric, citric and carbonic. It is not possible to draw an absolutely sharp dividing line between strong and weak electrolytes, *e.g.*, trichloracetic acid is more highly ionised than acetic acid but is much less highly ionised than hydrochloric acid, and so lies between them in strength. For your present purpose, the strong electrolytes are the only group of considerable importance.

Non-electrolytes exist only in the form of molecules and are incapable of ionisation, for example,

Chloroform	$CHCl_3$.
Cane sugar	$C_{12}H_{22}O_{11}$.
Alcohol	C_2H_5OH.
Urea	CON_2H_4.

Water as an electrolyte. Water is an electrolyte but is very weak.

$$H_2O \rightleftharpoons H^+ + OH^-$$

Exact measurement shows that in pure water, for every molecule of water ionised, furnishing one hydrogen ion and one hydroxyl ion, there are 600,000,000 molecules of water not ionised. The electrical conductivity of water, arising from these quantities of ions, is very small, but, even so, it must be clearly borne in mind that water is an electrolyte and has a small, but measurable, electrical conductivity.

Further, if by electrical or chemical action, hydrogen or hydroxyl ions are removed, more water molecules can ionise. So, while at any moment, H^+ and OH^- concentrations in water are very small, the water is potentially capable of yielding more of either ion as circumstances may demand.[1]

Mechanism of Electrolysis. Electrolysis of Conc. Hydrochloric Acid. The apparatus of Fig. 28 is suitable. The products are collected over calcium chloride solution because both are insoluble in it.

When the current is switched on, gas will be found to collect in both tubes, which were full of saturated calcium chloride solution at the beginning. Equal volumes of gas will collect in the two tubes.

When sufficient gas has accumulated, disconnect the U-tube after switching off the current.

---

[1]The exact position is as follows:
In pure water,

$$[H^+] = [OH^-] = 10^{-7} \text{ gm. ions per litre (at } 25° \text{ C.).}$$
$$\therefore [H^+][OH^-] = 10^{-14} = Kw \text{ (a constant).}$$

Kw is called the ionic product of water and is always maintained in aqueous liquids.

If H^+ or OH^- is withdrawn, water will ionise further to restore the value of Kw. When $[H^+] = [OH^-] = 10^{-7}$, the liquid is in the same condition as pure water, i.e., neutral; if $[H^+]$ is greater than 10^{-7}, it is acidic; if $[H^+]$ is less than 10^{-7}, it is alkaline. But the product $[H^+] \times [OH^-]$ is always 10^{-14}.

At the *cathode*, the gas will be colourless and can be tested by applying a light to it when it will explode in air. The gas is *hydrogen*.

At the *anode*, the gas will be pale yellowish-green. This gas can be tested by damp litmus paper, which will be bleached. It is *chlorine*.

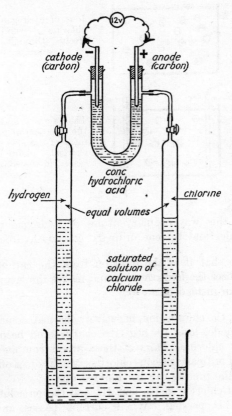

FIG. 28.

Explanation of Electrolysis by the Ionic Theory. So far we have seen that hydrochloric acid contains hydrogen ions and chlorine ions. The concentration of hydroxyl ion from water is so small that it plays no significant part in this electrolysis.

When no current is passing, the ions are wandering aimlessly about in the solution (Fig. 29). The electrical circuit is closed and, immediately, the cathode becomes charged negatively, and the anode positively. The cathode attracts to itself the positive ions (that is, the hydrogen ions) whilst the anode attracts the negative

E

ions (that is, the chlorine ions). A procession begins, hydrogen ions to the negative pole, chlorine ions to the positive pole.

The positive hydrogen ions strike the negative pole and acquire from it a charge[1] which makes them electrically neutral, and they

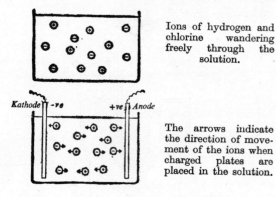

Ions of hydrogen and chlorine wandering freely through the solution.

The arrows indicate the direction of movement of the ions when charged plates are placed in the solution.

FIG. 29.

become in this way ordinary atoms of hydrogen which link up into molecules and become ordinary gaseous hydrogen.

Note that it is the electron from the cathode which neutralises the hydrogen ion and makes the latter become an atom instead of an ion.

Similarly, the chlorine ion, negatively charged, comes into contact with the anode, loses its negative charge[2] and becomes an atom of ordinary chlorine. Pairs of these atoms combine and become molecules of ordinary gaseous chlorine, which comes off as a greenish gas. Thus the process can be summed up :—

Hydrogen chloride yields ions H^+ and Cl^- on solution in water; no current is passing. When current passes and electrolysis begins,

H^+ + electron $\rightarrow$ H	Cl^- - electron $\rightarrow$ Cl
ion atom	ion atom
uncharged	uncharged
$H + H \rightarrow H_2$	$Cl + Cl \rightarrow Cl_2$
molecule	molecule
At CATHODE	At ANODE
Hydrogen 1 vol.	Chlorine 1 vol.

[1] That is, an electron is gained.
[2] That is, an electron is lost.

SELECTIVE DISCHARGE OF IONS.

When two or more ions of similar charge are present under similar conditions in a solution, *e.g.*, H^+ and Na^+, or OH^- and SO_4^{--}, one is preferentially selected for discharge and the selection of the ion discharged depends on the following factors :—

1. Position of the metal or group in the Electrochemical Series.

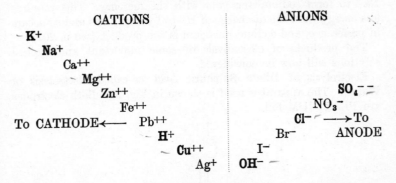

Consider the arrangement given above which is the same as that of the electrochemical series. If all other factors (see below) are constant, any ion will be discharged from solution in preference to those above it, positive ions at the cathode and negative ions at the anode. For example, in caustic soda solution, containing positive ions H^+ (from water) and Na^+, H^+ discharges in preference to Na^+; in copper sulphate solution, containing OH^- (from water) and SO_4^{--} as negative ions, OH^- is discharged in preference to SO_4^{--}.

The more important ions are printed in heavy type in the table.

2. Concentration.

Increase of concentration of an ion tends to promote its discharge, *e.g.*, in concentrated hydrochloric acid, containing OH^- (from water) and Cl^- as negative ions, the concentration of Cl^- is overwhelmingly the greater of the two. In these circumstances, Cl^- is discharged in preference. But, if the acid is very dilute, some discharge of OH^- may also occur.

This is the only case you will meet at present in which the order of discharge stated by the electrochemical series is reversed by a concentration effect. The same case arises in the electrolysis of sodium chloride solution, because the same anions are involved.

3. Nature of the Electrode.

This factor may sometimes influence the choice of ion for discharge. The most important contrast is electrolysis of a solution of sodium chloride, with mercury cathode and with platinum cathode.

With platinum cathode, H^+ is discharged in accordance with the order of the electrochemical series, Na^+ being higher in the series. The cathode product is hydrogen gas (see p. 122).

If a mercury cathode is used, there is the possibility of discharging Na^+ to form sodium amalgam with the mercury. This requires less energy than the discharge of H^+ to hydrogen gas and so occurs in preference, and sodium amalgam is the product (see p. 207).

The products of electrolysis of some important and typical solutions will now be considered.

Electrolysis of Dilute Sulphuric Acid (so-called **Electrolysis of Water**). The apparatus used is shown in Fig. 30. Both electrodes are PLATINUM foil.

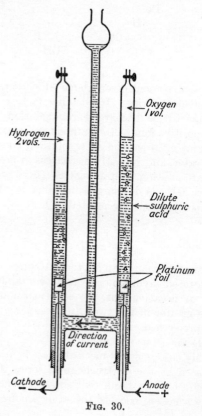

Fɪɢ. 30.

The following ions are present :—

From sulphuric acid	H^+ and SO_4^{--}
From water	H^+ and OH^-

CATHODE

$$H^+$$

migrates to the cathode, gains an electron and becomes a hydrogen atom

$$H^+ + e \rightarrow H$$

Hydrogen atoms combine in pairs to give molecules.

$$H + H \rightarrow H_2$$

Migration of SO_4^{--} to the anode and discharge of H^+ are equivalent to decrease of concentration of sulphuric acid.

Summary.
Hydrogen, 2 vols.
Acidity decreasing.

ANODE

$$\boxed{SO_4^{--} \text{ and } OH^-}$$

both migrate to the anode, where OH^-, being lower in the E.C. series, is discharged in preference to SO_4^{--}, in spite of the high concentration of the latter.

$$OH^- - e \rightarrow OH$$

By interaction between the OH groups, water and oxygen are produced

$$OH + OH \rightarrow H_2O + O$$
$$O + O \rightarrow O_2$$

Discharge of OH^- disturbs the ionic equilibrium of water. More water ionises to restore it.

$$H_2O \rightleftharpoons H^+ + OH^-$$

Excess H^+ so produced, with incoming SO_4^{--} is equivalent to increased concentration of sulphuric acid.

Summary.
Oxygen, 1 vol.
Acidity increasing.

The *total acidity* at anode and cathode together remains *constant*. The final result, 2 vols. of hydrogen at the cathode and 1 vol. of oxygen at the anode, is equivalent to the electrolysis of water.

Electrolysis of Caustic Soda Solution. The apparatus is the same as for the electrolysis of dilute sulphuric acid (p. 120). The electrodes are again PLATINUM foil.

The ions present are :—

From caustic soda	Na^+	OH^-
From water	H^+	OH^-

CATHODE

both ions migrate to the cathode. H^+, being lower in the E.C. series, is discharged in preference to Na^+, in spite of the high concentration of the latter.

$$H^+ + e \rightarrow H$$

The hydrogen atoms then combine in pairs to give molecules.

$$H + H \rightarrow H_2$$

Discharge of H^+ disturbs the ionic equilibrium of water. More water ionises to restore it.

$$H_2O \rightleftharpoons H^+ + OH^-.$$

Excess OH^- so produced, with incoming Na^+, is equivalent to increase of concentration of caustic soda.

Summary.
Hydrogen, 2 vols.
Alkalinity increasing.

ANODE

$$OH^-$$

ions migrate to the anode and discharge by loss of an electron.

$$OH^- - e \rightarrow OH$$

By interaction between the OH groups, water and oxygen are produced.

$$OH + OH \rightarrow H_2O + O$$
$$O + O \rightarrow O_2$$

Migration of Na^+ to the cathode and discharge of OH^- are equivalent to fall of concentration of caustic soda.

Summary.
Oxygen, 1 vol.
Alkalinity decreasing.

The total alkalinity at anode and cathode together is constant. The process is equivalent to the electrolysis of water.

Electrolysis of Sodium Chloride Solution. The apparatus is the same as for concentrated hydrochloric acid (p. 117) or dilute sulphuric acid (p. 120). The CATHODE may be PLATINUM (or carbon), but the ANODE must be CARBON to resist attack by chlorine.

The ions present are :—

From sodium chloride	Na^+	Cl^-
From water	H^+	OH^-

CATHODE	ANODE
Na^+ H^+	Cl^- OH^-

CATHODE	ANODE
both migrate to cathode. H^+, being lower in the E.C. series, discharges in preference to Na^+. $$H^+ + e \rightarrow H$$ Hydrogen molecules are then formed by combination of the atoms in pairs. $$H + H \rightarrow H_2$$ Discharge of H^+ disturbs the ionic equilibrium of water. More water ionises to restore it. $$H_2O \rightleftharpoons H^+ + OH^-$$ Excess OH^- so produced, with incoming Na^+, is equivalent to the presence of caustic soda. *Summary.* Hydrogen, 1 vol. Solution becomes alkaline by presence of caustic soda.	both migrate to the anode. Cl^- is discharged because present in much greater concentration than OH^- (see p. 119). $$Cl^- - e \rightarrow Cl$$ The atoms then combine in pairs to give molecules. $$Cl + Cl \rightarrow Cl_2$$ *Summary.* Chlorine, 1 vol.

Hydrogen and chlorine are produced in equal volumes. (If the three-limbed voltameter is used, chlorine will have to saturate the brine first.)

Electrolysis of Copper Sulphate Solution.

The ions present are :—

From copper sulphate	Cu^{++}	SO_4^{--}
From water	H^+	OH^-

CATHODE	ANODE

Cu^{++}
H^+

SO_4^{--}
OH^-

CATHODE side:

both migrate to the cathode. Cu^{++}, being lower in the E.C. series, discharges in preference to H^+.

$$Cu^{++} + 2e \rightarrow Cu$$

The copper deposits as a brown layer.

Summary.
Copper deposited.

ANODE side:

Platinum anode.
See the exactly similar case of dilute sulphuric acid (p. 121).

Summary.
Oxygen given off.
Solution becomes acidic with sulphuric acid.

Copper anode.
With this anode, there are three possibilities :—
1. Discharge of SO_4^{--} ⎫ by
2. Discharge of OH^- ⎪ loss of
3. Conversion of Cu ⎬ elec-
   atom to Cu^{++} ⎪ trons
The last of these occurs most readily. SO_4^{--} and OH^- are not discharged. Copper passes into solution from the anode as Cu^{++} ions.

$$Cu - 2e \rightarrow Cu^{++}$$

Summary.
Copper passes into solution as ions. The total concentration of the solution in SO_4^{--} (not discharged) and Cu^{++} (copper is depositing on the cathode) is constant. The electrolysis merely transfers copper from anode to cathode.

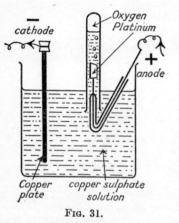

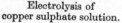

FIG. 31.
Electrolysis of
copper sulphate solution.

SUMMARY OF THE EFFECTS OF ELECTROLYSIS

Solution electrolysed	Cathode of	Anode of	At Cathode	At Anode
Hydrochloric acid (conc.)	Carbon or platinum	Carbon	Hydrogen one volume	Chlorine one volume
Sulphuric acid (dil.)	Platinum	Platinum	Hydrogen 2 volumes; decrease of acidity	Oxygen 1 volume; increase of acidity
Caustic soda (sodium hydroxide)	Platinum	Platinum	Hydrogen 2 volumes; increase of alkalinity	Oxygen 1 volume; decrease of alkalinity
Common salt (sodium chloride)	Platinum or carbon	Carbon	Hydrogen 1 volume; caustic soda solution	Chlorine 1 volume
Copper sulphate (1)	Copper	Platinum	Copper deposited	Oxygen and sulphuric acid
Copper sulphate (2)	Copper	Copper	Copper deposited	Copper dissolved

Laws of Electrolysis. The laws expressing the quantitative results of electrolysis were first stated by Faraday. They assert that the weight of an ion liberated during electrolysis is proportional to

(1) the time of passing the current
(2) the magnitude of the current passed
(3) the chemical equivalent of the ion.

The third statement is the most difficult to understand. It asserts, for example, that, if by passing a certain quantity of electricity through different electrolytes, hydrogen, copper, silver, chlorine and oxygen are liberated, then, if the weight of hydrogen liberated is x gm., the weight of copper will be $31·8x$ gm., of silver $108x$ gm., of chlorine $35·5x$ gm., and of oxygen $8x$ gm., these figures being proportional to the respective chemical equivalents of the elements.

If a current of one ampere flows for one second the quantity of electricity conveyed is called one "coulomb". It has been found that the passage of one coulomb of electricity liberates $\dfrac{1}{96,000}$ gm. of hydrogen. Therefore, 1 gm. of hydrogen is liberated by passing 96,000 coulombs; this amount of electricity is called one "faraday". It follows from Faraday's Laws, that one faraday of electricity also liberates the equivalent weight in grams of any other ion.

QUESTIONS ON CHAPTER XII WILL BE FOUND ON PAGE 133.

E*

CHAPTER XIII

TYPES OF REACTIONS

Combination.
Decomposition.
Displacement.
Catalysis.
Reversible Reactions.
Thermal Dissociation.
Oxidation and Reduction.
Double Decomposition.

CHEMICAL reactions are recognised by certain phenomena which accompany them. (See Chapter I.) They can again be subdivided into classes of reactions, each of which has its own peculiarities.

Combination takes place when two or more substances combine to form a single substance.

Example 1. Iron and sulphur *combine* when heated to form ferrous sulphide.

$$Fe + S \rightarrow FeS$$

Example 2. If warm lead dioxide is lowered into a gas jar of sulphur dioxide, the two compounds *combine* and lead sulphate is formed.

$$PbO_2 + SO_2 \rightarrow PbSO_4$$

Decomposition occurs when a compound splits up into simpler substances. This change usually takes place without the necessity for the presence of a second substance, and very often the action of heat is sufficient to cause the reaction to take place.

Example 1. If calcium carbonate (for example, marble) is heated in an *open* crucible to bright red heat, the calcium carbonate *decomposes* into calcium oxide (lime) and carbon dioxide.

$$CaCO_3 \rightarrow CaO + CO_2$$

Example 2. If potassium chlorate is heated strongly it *decomposes* into potassium chloride and oxygen.

$$2KClO_3 \rightarrow 2KCl + 3O_2$$

Displacement occurs when one element (or group) takes the place of another element (or group) in a compound.

126

Example 1. If zinc is placed in copper sulphate solution, copper is *displaced* by the zinc and zinc sulphate is left in solution.

$$Zn + CuSO_4 \rightarrow ZnSO_4 + Cu$$

Example 2. If chlorine is bubbled into potassium bromide solution, the chlorine *displaces* bromine and a red bubble of bromine is formed. A solution of potassium chloride is left.

$$2KBr + Cl_2 \rightarrow 2KCl + Br_2$$

Catalysis. Catalysis takes place when a small amount of substance alters the speed of a chemical reaction without being changed in weight or chemical composition *at the end* of the reaction. There are certain peculiarities about catalysis:

(*a*) A catalyst may increase the rate of a chemical change (this is its usual use) or decrease it. For example, the presence of acid considerably retards the decomposition of hydrogen peroxide into water and oxygen.

(*b*) A catalyst is usually specific in action. Thus many catalysts will help only *one* particular reaction and it must not be taken for granted that a catalyst which catalyses one reaction will catalyse another. (Platinum, especially in a finely divided state, and water, it is true, do catalyse a large number of reactions.)

(*c*) A catalyst cannot affect the total amount of substance decomposed. It merely speeds up the action.

Example 1. Manganese dioxide will catalyse the decomposition of potassium chlorate into potassium chloride and oxygen. (See p. 223.)

$$2KClO_3 \rightarrow 2KCl + 3O_2$$

Example 2. Finely divided platinum will catalyse the combination of oxygen with sulphur dioxide to form sulphur trioxide. (See p. 320.)

$$2SO_2 + O_2 \rightarrow 2SO_3$$

Example 3. Nitric oxide will catalyse the combination of sulphur dioxide, oxygen and steam to form sulphuric acid. (See p. 320.)

$$2H_2O + 2SO_2 + O_2 \rightarrow 2H_2SO_4$$

Reversible Reactions. A reversible reaction is one which can be made to proceed in either direction by the alteration of the conditions of the experiment. It is indicated thus:

$$A + B \rightleftharpoons C + D$$

Example 1. By passing steam over heated iron, hydrogen can be obtained and triferric tetroxide formed.

$$3Fe + 4H_2O \rightarrow Fe_3O_4 + 4H_2 \quad . \quad . \quad . \quad . \quad (X)$$

If, however, hydrogen is passed over heated triferric tetroxide (magnetic oxide of iron) the products are iron and steam.

$$Fe_3O_4 + 4H_2 \rightarrow 3Fe + 4H_2O \quad \ldots \quad (Y)$$

Or, combining these equations, the above reactions may be stated:

$$3Fe + 4H_2O \rightleftharpoons Fe_3O_4 + 4H_2$$

The above equations do not tell the whole story. For reaction X to go to completion, the steam must be continually in excess and for reaction Y to go to completion, the hydrogen must be in excess.

The explanation is (Case X) that the current of steam sweeps away some of the hydrogen without allowing it to come into contact with any iron oxide formed, while fresh steam is always available to react with iron. In Case Y, the steam formed tends to be driven from contact with the iron by the stream of hydrogen, while fresh hydrogen is always available to react with any iron oxide. Thus, under appropriate conditions, the reaction will go to completion in either direction.

If iron and water are heated in a closed vessel, an equilibrium mixture containing iron, iron oxide, steam and hydrogen will be obtained.

Example 2. If carbon dioxide is bubbled into lime water, calcium carbonate is formed, and finally if sufficient carbon dioxide is bubbled in, a solution of calcium bicarbonate is formed.

$$CaCO_3 + H_2O + CO_2 \rightarrow Ca(HCO_3)_2$$

If, however, this solution of calcium bicarbonate is heated to boiling, the calcium bicarbonate decomposes forming calcium carbonate (which is observed as a white precipitate) and carbon dioxide escapes into the atmosphere.

$$Ca(HCO_3)_2 \rightarrow CaCO_3 + H_2O + CO_2$$

Or

$$Ca(HCO_3)_2 \rightleftharpoons CaCO_3 + H_2O + CO_2$$

Thermal Dissociation is the decomposition of a substance by the action of heat such that if the products are allowed to cool in contact with one another the original substance is entirely reformed. It is a special form of a reversible reaction in which the temperature is the sole factor governing the change.

Example 1. If ammonium chloride is heated it becomes ammonia gas and hydrochloric acid gas, but if these two gases are allowed to cool in contact with one another the original substance is entirely re-formed.

$$NH_4Cl \rightleftharpoons NH_3 + HCl$$

The vapour from ammonium chloride would be expected to have a vapour density equal to half the molecular weight of ammonium chloride or 26·75 ($NH_4Cl = 53·5$). Actually its vapour density is 13·38, one-half of the expected value. This is because, in the vapour state, ammonium chloride molecules no longer exist. They are broken up, as explained above, into molecules of ammonia and hydrogen chloride.

$$NH_4Cl \rightleftharpoons NH_3 + HCl$$

Each molecule of ammonium chloride yields two molecules, one of ammonia and one of hydrogen chloride, therefore, by Avogadro's Hypothesis, the vapour must occupy twice the volume it would have occupied if the ammonium chloride molecules had remained intact. The total weight of vapour is unaltered, therefore the vapour density is only half the expected value.

Example 2 (see p. 198). If calcium carbonate is heated in a *closed* vessel so that none of the products can escape, the carbon dioxide and quicklime formed by the action of heat combine to form calcium carbonate again when the temperature is allowed to fall.

$$CaCO_3 \rightleftharpoons CaO + CO_2$$

Thermal dissociation is reversible; decomposition is not. Compare the dissociation of ammonium chloride, as described above, with the decomposition of ammonium nitrite into water and nitrogen.

$$NH_4NO_2 \rightarrow N_2 + 2H_2O$$

However long the nitrogen and water are left in contact, they will never recombine to give back the original ammonium nitrite, but the products of dissociation of ammonium chloride give back the original compound on cooling.

Double Decomposition. This name is given to reactions in which two compounds take part, both are decomposed and two new substances formed *by an exchange of radicals*. Double decomposition reactions are always of the type:

$$A.B + C.D \rightarrow A.D + C.B$$

For example: $$Cu.SO_4 + H_2.S \rightarrow Cu.S + H_2.SO_4$$

Commonly, both the original compounds used in the reaction are soluble in water, while, of the products formed, one (sulphuric acid) is soluble and one (copper sulphide) is not. Usually the precipitated compound is the one which is wanted, for it can easily be separated and purified by filtration and washing. Less frequently, the important product of a double decomposition reaction is more volatile than the other compounds concerned and is driven off either as a gas or, by heating, as the vapour of a volatile liquid. For example:

$$NaCl + H_2SO_4 \rightarrow NaHSO_4 + HCl \uparrow$$
$$\text{gas}$$
$$KNO_3 + H_2SO_4 \rightarrow KHSO_4 + HNO_3$$
$$\text{volatile}$$
$$\text{liquid}$$

Oxidation and Reduction. It is necessary to discuss the way in which the use of these terms has developed before it is possible to give a concise definition of them.

Originally, reduction was a reaction in which some compound was deprived of all, or part, of the oxygen it contained, and an oxidation was a reaction in which a substance combined with oxygen. In the reaction represented by the equation:

$$CuO + H_2 \rightarrow Cu + H_2O$$

the hydrogen is oxidised to water and the copper oxide reduced to copper. This is the simplest possible use of the terms.

The readiness with which hydrogen combines with oxygen to form water caused hydrogen to be regarded as a kind of "chemical opposite" of oxygen; so the term oxidation was extended to include reactions in which a compound gave up some or all of its hydrogen as well as those in which it combined with oxygen. (This idea of oxidation is analogous to the idea of enriching a man by relieving him of his debts.) By this extension a reaction like the conversion of concentrated hydrochloric acid to chlorine is called an oxidation because two molecules of hydrogen chloride (2HCl) are converted to a molecule of chlorine (Cl_2) by loss of hydrogen.

$$2HCl + (O) \rightarrow H_2O + Cl_2$$

The oxygen for this reaction is commonly supplied from manganese dioxide (p. 272). A similar case is the oxidation of hydrogen sulphide to sulphur by, say, chlorine.

$$H_2S + Cl_2 \rightarrow 2HCl + S$$

A further extension of the idea of oxidation arose from the fact that certain elements exercise two or more different valencies. One of the most important of these is iron, which exerts a valency of 2 in ferrous compounds and 3 in ferric compounds. Now the conversion of ferrous oxide, FeO, to ferric oxide, Fe_2O_3, is a clear and simple case of oxidation.

$$2FeO + O \rightarrow Fe_2O_3$$

But all ferrous salts, for example ferrous chloride, $FeCl_2$, and ferrous sulphate, $FeSO_4$, correspond to, and can theoretically be obtained by neutralisation from ferrous oxide; similarly, all ferric salts, for example, ferric chloride, $FeCl_3$, ferric sulphate, $Fe_2(SO_4)_3$, correspond to and can theoretically be obtained by neutralisation, from ferric oxide. So the term oxidation was extended to include not only the conversion of ferrous oxide to ferric oxide, but also the conversion of *any* ferrous compound to a ferric compound. Thus, the conversion of ferrous chloride to ferric chloride by chlorine

$$2FeCl_2 + Cl_2 \rightarrow 2FeCl_3$$

is spoken of as being an oxidation, although oxygen is not involved. Similar cases of oxidation are:

$$2FeSO_4 + H_2SO_4 + O \rightarrow Fe_2(SO_4)_3 + H_2O$$

ferrous   ferric
sulphate   sulphate

$$2Fe(OH)_2 + H_2O + O \rightarrow 2Fe(OH)_3$$

ferrous   ferric
hydroxide   hydroxide

In such cases it will be noted that the oxidation always involves an increase in the proportion of those groups which are electronegative, that is, which migrate to the anode when the compound is electrolysed (p. 118). Thus, there is a higher proportion of the electronegative Cl' group in ferric chloride, $FeCl_3$, than in ferrous chloride, $FeCl_2$, and a higher proportion of the electronegative SO_4'' group in ferric sulphate, $Fe_2(SO_4)_3$, than in ferrous sulphate, $FeSO_4$. This conclusion brings us to the point of being able to give a full definition of the term "oxidation".

Definition. **An oxidation is a reaction during which the proportion of the electronegative constituent in a substance is increased.**

A reduction is a reaction during which the proportion of the electronegative constituent in a substance is decreased.

Examples.
1. $2Cu + O_2 \rightarrow 2CuO$ (oxidation of copper to copper oxide).
2. $Fe + S \rightarrow FeS$ (oxidation of iron to ferrous sulphide).
3. $Mg + Cl_2 \rightarrow MgCl_2$ (oxidation of magnesium to its chloride).
4. $4HCl + MnO_2 \rightarrow MnCl_2 + 2H_2O + Cl_2$ (oxidation of hydrogen chloride to chlorine).
5. $2FeCl_2 + Cl_2 \rightarrow 2FeCl_3$ (oxidation of ferrous chloride to ferric chloride).
6. $2HgO \rightarrow 2Hg + O_2$ (reduction of mercuric oxide to mercury).
7. $H_2 + S \rightarrow H_2S$ (reduction of sulphur to hydrogen sulphide).
8. $Fe_2O_3 + 3CO \rightarrow 2Fe + 3CO_2$ (reduction of ferric oxide to iron).
9. $Fe_2(SO_4)_3 + H_2S \rightarrow S \downarrow + H_2SO_4 + 2FeSO_4$ (reduction of ferric sulphate to ferrous sulphate; oxidation of hydrogen sulphide to sulphur).
10. $3Cu + 8HNO_3 \rightarrow 3Cu(NO_3)_2 + 4H_2O + 2NO$ (oxidation of copper to copper nitrate; reduction of nitric acid to nitric oxide).

Oxidising Agent. An oxidising agent is a substance which brings about *oxidation* (defined above).

Reducing Agent. A reducing agent is a substance which brings about *reduction* (defined above).

Some common simple oxidising and reducing agents are:

Oxidising Agents.	*Reducing Agents.*
Oxygen (p. 227).	Hydrogen (p. 58).
Chlorine (p. 278).	Hydrogen sulphide (p. 309).
Ozone (p. 234).	Sulphur dioxide (p. 314).
Hydrogen peroxide (p. 232).	Carbon (p. 237).
Nitric acid (p. 343).	Carbon monoxide (p. 248).

Examples of the use of each will be found on the page quoted.

Ionic Reactions. Many reactions (in fact, the majority) in Inorganic Chemistry take place between ions rather than between molecules, and the properties of the solutions are those of its ions. For example, copper sulphate solution contains the copper ion (Cu^{++}) and the sulphate ion (SO_4^{--}). The copper ion is blue and will react with many other ions:—

$$Cu^{++} + S^{--} \rightarrow CuS \downarrow$$

(or more usually, $CuSO_4 + H_2S \rightarrow CuS \downarrow + H_2SO_4$). It is important to note that in this reaction the hydrogen and sulphate group are in the form of ions both before and after the precipitation of the copper sulphide. This precipitation will take place if *any* soluble copper salt in solution (nitrate, chloride, acetate, etc.) is added to any soluble sulphide in solution (sodium, potassium, etc.).

Exothermic and Endothermic Reactions. The great majority of chemical reactions are accompanied by a marked heat change. The above two types are distinguished.

An exothermic reaction is one during which heat is liberated to the surroundings

e.g. the burning of hydrogen

$$H_2 + \tfrac{1}{2}O_2 \rightarrow H_2O + 68,400 \text{ cals.}$$

the burning of carbon

$$C + O_2 \rightarrow CO_2 + 94,400 \text{ cals.}$$

Heat energy can be derived from coal, coke, coal-gas, petrol and paraffin, in the home or in industry, because the combustions of all these substances are exothermic reactions.

An endothermic reaction is one during which heat is absorbed from the surroundings.

e.g. formation of nitric oxide from its elements

$$\tfrac{1}{2}N_2 + \tfrac{1}{2}O_2 \rightleftharpoons NO - 21,600 \text{ cals.}$$

conversion of oxygen to ozone

$$1\tfrac{1}{2}O_2 \rightleftharpoons O_3 - 34{,}000 \text{ cals.}$$

Notice that *heat liberated* is indicated by a $+$ sign, *heat absorbed* by a $-$ sign.

QUESTIONS ON CHAPTER XII

1. What do you understand by the term "electrolyte"? Describe experiments to demonstrate the products formed in the electrolysis of solutions of (a) sulphuric acid, (b) sodium sulphate, (c) copper sulphate. (O. and C.)
2. State Faraday's Laws of Electrolysis. Describe carefully what happens when copper sulphate solution is electrolysed between (a) platinum and (b) copper electrodes, and when sodium chloride solution is electrolysed between (a) platinum, and (b) carbon electrodes. (L.)
3. Give a general but concise account of the phenomena which occur when a salt is dissolved in water and the solution is electrolysed.
   Describe briefly two instances of the practical application of electrolysis. (L.)

QUESTIONS ON CHAPTER XIII

1. Give an account of catalysis, briefly referring to (a) the catalytic oxidation of ammonia, (b) Deacon's process for the preparation of chlorine. Describe an experiment to show that the manganese dioxide used in the ordinary laboratory preparation of oxygen from potassium chlorate has not changed appreciably in weight during the reaction. (B.)
2. What is a reducing agent? Give *three* examples of common reducing agents. Describe and explain any experiment in which sulphuric acid is reduced. (O. and C.)
3. Describe and explain experiments in which the following substances play the part of oxidising agents: (a) nitric acid, (b) copper oxide, (c) chlorine. How would you show practically that oxidation has occurred in *two* of the cases you select? (O. and C.)
4. Define *reversible reaction, thermal decomposition* and *thermal dissociation.* Describe any experiment you have seen to demonstrate thermal dissociation.
   What happens when (a) lead nitrate, (b) mercuric oxide, (c) nitrogen peroxide, (d) ammonium nitrate are heated? In each case state to which of the above classes the reaction belongs, giving your reasons. (N.U.J.B.)
5. State what type of reaction—combination, double decomposition, replacement, oxidation—takes place when: (a) sulphur is boiled with nitric acid, (b) ammonia gas and hydrogen chloride are mixed, (c) chlorine is passed into potassium iodide solution, (d) hydrogen sulphide is passed into a solution of copper sulphate, (e) excess of carbon dioxide is passed into lime water. (N.U.J.B.)
6. Explain and illustrate by one example in each case, the meaning of the terms: (a) reversible reaction, (b) catalyst, (c) allotropy, (d) double decomposition, (e) deliquescence, (f) synthesis. (L.)

CHAPTER XIV

AIR, COMBUSTION AND RUSTING

A STUDY of the air begins naturally with an examination of that most familiar of all chemical reactions—burning. Most of the common combustible materials (coal, wood, petrol) are complex compounds which are unsuitable as the starting point of our investigation. We shall fall back upon the metals, which are all elements, and, therefore, the simplest materials known.

Effect of Heating Certain Metals in Air.

Copper. Take up a piece of copper foil in a pair of tongs and hold it in a bunsen flame. The metal becomes red hot and, on cooling, is covered with a black layer. This is **black copper oxide.** If the metal is scraped, the surface layer is obtained as a powder and the fresh copper exposed can be similarly treated. In time, a quantity of the black powder can be obtained.

Lead. Heat a little lead foil on a crucible lid. It melts to shining beads of molten lead. Stir the beads. The metal gradually changes to a yellow powder called **litharge.**

Magnesium. Hold one end of a length of magnesium ribbon in tongs and place the other end in a bunsen flame. The ribbon burns with a dazzling flame (it is rather dangerous to look at it for any length of time) and leaves a white ash—**magnesium oxide.**

These experiments leave no doubt that the metals concerned have undergone a drastic change. The products left after heating them are quite different from the original metals.

The Nature of the Change. It is hardly necessary to describe experiments to prove that air is concerned in this change. This can, however, quite readily be shown by taking the most combustible of these metals, magnesium, placing it in a crucible, filling the crucible with sand, well pressed down to exclude air, and heating the crucible to redness. In cooling, the magnesium is unchanged.

Since air is concerned in the change, two possibilities have to be considered. The metals may have combined with something from the air or they may have lost something, which has been taken up by the air. (A third possibility is that the change in the metals may be due to some rearrangement of their material without loss or gain, but this is unlikely since such a change could presumably occur without air.) Clearly, in the first case, the material which had combined would make the weight of the product greater than that of the metal, while, in the second case, the material lost would have the reverse effect. We have only to weigh the metal before burning and the product after burning to decide this point.

To Find whether there is any Change in Weight when Magnesium burns in Air. Weigh a crucible (with lid) containing about 0·5 gram of magnesium. Set up the apparatus as in Fig. 32. Remove the lid and heat the crucible. When the magnesium begins to burn, put the lid on the crucible. Raise it occasionally to allow air to enter to burn the magnesium but, as far as possible, avoid losing any "smoke" (fine particles of magnesium oxide) which would tend to make the final weight too low. When all the magnesium has burned allow the crucible and lid to cool. Then weigh them again. There will be a *gain* in weight.

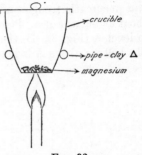

FIG. 32.

Burning magnesium in a crucible.

The products of combustion of a substance always weigh more than the original substance.

This is even true for coal. If we could collect all the ash, soot, smoke and the gases (carbon dioxide and steam) which escape up the chimney, they would weigh more than the original coal. (See p. 28.) This gain in weight, which occurs no matter what the substance is that burns, at once establishes the point that, during burning, the burning material combines with something. We now have to show whether the "something" comes from the air.

To do this, it will be necessary to find whether, when a substance burns in air, the air decreases in amount. We must devise an experiment to test this point. It would be absurd to carry out the experiment in the open laboratory into which air could leak from outside to replace loss; we must secure a sample of air in a confined space, that is, in a closed vessel, and, if possible, any change in the amount of air should be automatically shown to us by the apparatus. A very simple arrangement satisfies this requirement. We shall confine the sample of air in a bell-jar over water (see Fig. 33). The water forms a flexible base to the bell-jar and will move up or down inside the jar to show us what is happening to the amount of air inside. As a matter of mere convenience we shall choose yellow phosphorus for our burning substance this time. (Yellow phosphorus takes fire very readily and must be treated with great care. Never touch it with your fingers. The heat of them may start it burning and the burns it will cause are very severe and difficult to heal. Yellow phosphorus is always kept under water because of the ease with which it takes fire.)

To Find whether there is a Diminution in the Volume of the Air when Phosphorus burns in it. Float a small porcelain dish on water in a pneumatic trough and put in it a piece of yellow phosphorus about as big as a pea. Place over it a bell-jar and adjust the water to level A (Fig. 33, I), the stopper of the bell-jar being removed. The bell-jar above A is graduated into five equal portions. Heat a

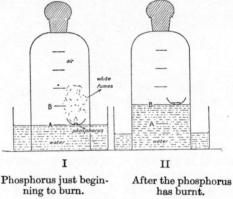

I
Phosphorus just begin-
ning to burn.

II
After the phosphorus
has burnt.

Fig. 33.

The burning of phosphorus in air.

long iron needle in a bunsen flame, touch the phosphorus with it, withdraw the needle quickly and insert the stopper of the bell-jar. The phosphorus burns with a bright yellow flame, giving off dense white fumes of phosphorus pentoxide, which fill the jar. After a time the phosphorus no longer burns. The water level inside the bell-jar will then be found to *rise*[1] and, when the bell-jar is cold, the water level will stand at mark B on the jar (Fig. 33, II). Clearly, the rise of water inside the bell-jar means that, during the burning of the phosphorus, some of the air was used up to combine with the phosphorus.

After a time, the white fumes dissolve in the water, leaving the

[1] While the phosphorus is burning, the level of water inside the bell-jar will fall. This is an expansion effect of the heated air. It is also necessary to pour water into the trough until the levels of water inside and outside the bell-jar are equal. If this is omitted we are not measuring the volumes under the same conditions.

bell-jar clear. It will then be seen that some unburnt phosphorus remains in the porcelain dish. This is very significant. **The flame was not extinguished for lack of phosphorus.** We can see that some gas still remains in the bell-jar from the mark B upwards. This gas must be different from ordinary gas because it will not allow phosphorus to burn in it; it must also be different from the part of the air which has combined with the phosphorus because it will not do this. **If a lighted splint is plunged into the residual gas the splint is extinguished.** We are forced to conclude, therefore, that the air is not a single substance. It must contain at least two gases—one which supports the combustion of phosphorus and one which does not. Further, we may conclude that the gas which is active in supporting the combustion of the phosphorus constitutes about one-fifth of the air by volume (this represents the rise of the water from A to B) and the other gas about four-fifths. These two gases have names. The one which supports the combustion of phosphorus is called **oxygen**, the other **nitrogen**. Lavoisier's experiment (p. 148) clearly shows the presence of oxygen in air.

Let us sum up in a few sentences what we have learnt so far.

The principal gases in air are *OXYGEN* and *NITROGEN*. Oxygen constitutes about one-fifth of the air by volume and nitrogen about four-fifths. During the combustion of a substance, it combines chemically with the oxygen of the air and the chemical combination is accompanied by the evolution of light and heat. The combination with oxygen causes a gain in weight. Nitrogen will not support combustion.

By an experiment similar to the above, it can be shown that the material of a burning candle combines with oxygen and causes the water-level inside the bell-jar to rise. The candle will not, however, remove all the oxygen.

We may now give the equations for the chemical reactions considered in this chapter.

$$2Cu + O_2 \rightarrow 2CuO$$
copper oxide

$$2Pb + O_2 \rightarrow 2PbO$$
lead oxide

$$2Mg + O_2 \rightarrow 2MgO$$
magnesium oxide

$$P_4 + 5O_2 \rightarrow P_4O_{10}$$
phosphorus pentoxide

The Smouldering of Phosphorus. Phosphorus smoulders in air. The chemical effects of the smouldering are very similar to those of the active burning of phosphorus except for the time factor. This

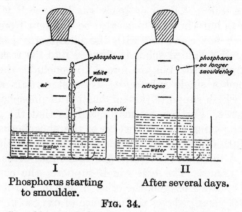

I
Phosphorus starting
to smoulder.

II
After several days.

FIG. 34.
Smouldering of phosphorus in an enclosed space.

can be shown by an experiment for which Fig. 34 is sufficient explanation.

More Accurate Determination of the Proportion of Oxygen in Air by Volume. In this experiment, we make use of the smouldering of phosphorus to absorb the oxygen from a measured volume of air. (See also p. 155.)

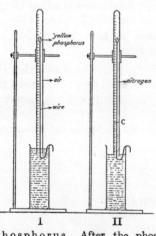

I
Phosphorus
beginning   to
smoulder.

II
After the phos-
phorus has ceased
to smoulder.

FIG. 35.
To find the percentage by volume of
oxygen in the air.

Take a graduated glass tube, closed at one end, fill it to a depth of about 2 inches with water, close the open end with the thumb and invert the tube in a deep jar of water. (If possible, allow the tube to stand like this for several hours so that the air is saturated with water-vapour.) Adjust the level of water in the graduated tube to be the same as the level in the jar. The air inside the tube is then at atmospheric pressure. Read off the volume of air. Now push up inside the tube a flexible wire carrying a piece of yellow phosphorus (Fig. 35, I). Read the temperature of the laboratory and the barometer and set the apparatus aside until the phosphorus no longer smoulders. The water level inside the tube will have risen to C, the remaining gas being nitrogen (Fig. 35, II). Remove the phosphorus and then lower the graduated tube until C is at the level of water in the jar, giving atmospheric pressure again inside the tube. Read off the volume of nitrogen. Take the temperature of the laboratory and read the barometer.

The calculation of the percentage of oxygen in the air by volume is given below.

Original volume of air	= 70·5 c.c.
Temperature 14° C.	Pressure 755 mm.
Final volume of nitrogen	= 55·0 c.c.
Temperature 12° C.	Pressure 760 mm.

The volume of nitrogen must first be converted to the volume it would occupy at the same temperature and pressure as that of the original air.

Volume of nitrogen at 14° C. and 755 mm. pressure.

$$= 55 \cdot 0 \times \frac{287}{285} \times \frac{760}{755} \text{ c.c.}$$

$$= 55 \cdot 8 \text{ c.c.}$$

$$\therefore \text{ volume of oxygen} = (70 \cdot 5 - 55 \cdot 8) \text{ c.c.}$$

$$= 14 \cdot 7 \text{ c.c.}$$

$$\therefore \text{ percentage of oxygen in the air by volume}$$

$$= \frac{14 \cdot 7}{70 \cdot 5} \times 100\%$$

$$= 20 \cdot 8\%$$

In dry air, the correct percentage of oxygen is 20·9% by volume.
Other Gases Present in Air.   *Carbon Dioxide.* Carbon dioxide is present in air to the extent of 0·03% by volume. It is formed during the combustion of all the common fuels—coal, coke, coal-gas, water-gas, petrol, paraffin oil—all of which contain carbon.

$$C + O_2 \rightarrow CO_2$$

It is also breathed out as a waste product by all animals.

In spite of the enormous quantities poured into the atmosphere in this way, the proportion of it remains constant, partly because carbon dioxide is taken up by the leaves of plants and converted to complex starchy compounds (for a more complete discussion of this subject, see p. 148) and partly because it dissolves in the water of the oceans.

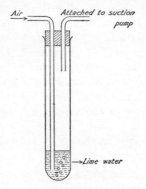

FIG. 36.
Method of showing the presence of carbon dioxide in the atmosphere.

The presence of carbon dioxide in the air can be shown by aspirating air through a boiling-tube containing a little lime-water. After a time the lime-water will go turbid, showing the presence of carbon dioxide (Fig. 36).

$$Ca(OH)_2 + CO_2 \rightarrow CaCO_3 + H_2O$$

Water-vapour. This substance is always present in the air in varying quantities. It is given off by evaporation from the oceans, rivers and lakes.

Its presence may be demonstrated by exposing some deliquescent substance, say calcium chloride, to the air on a clock-glass. A solution of the compound will be obtained after a day or two. If this is distilled (see p. 153), the colourless liquid obtained may be proved to be water by the tests given on pp. 153–4.

The Rare Gases. About 1% of the air by volume is made up of the rare gases. The most abundant of them is argon, the others being neon, xenon, krypton and helium. The proportion of each of the last four is very minute. Argon and neon have found a use in "gas-filled" electric light bulbs and coloured "neon" electrical signs. They are obtained from liquid air.

Impurities. The air always contains small traces of many gases —hydrogen sulphide, sulphur dioxide and others—especially in industrial areas. They are given off during the combustion of coal and fuels derived from it. The tarnishing of silver is chiefly due to the formation of a layer of black silver sulphide on it by the action of traces of atmospheric hydrogen sulphide.

The following diagram summarises the composition of the air.

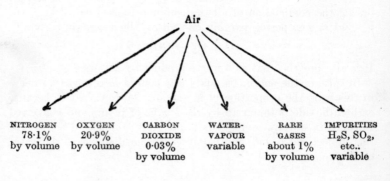

Air					
NITROGEN 78·1% by volume	OXYGEN 20·9% by volume	CARBON DIOXIDE 0·03% by volume	WATER-VAPOUR variable	RARE GASES about 1% by volume	IMPURITIES H_2S, SO_2, etc.. variable

PLATE II.

Photographs of Hanley (above), by courtesy of *The Times*, and
Barcelona, by courtesy of *Wide World Photos*, showing the effect
of industries upon the atmosphere above a town.

Composition of Air by Weight. This estimation was carried out
by Dumas, 1841. Air was drawn through the following apparatus
in the order shown (Fig. 37).

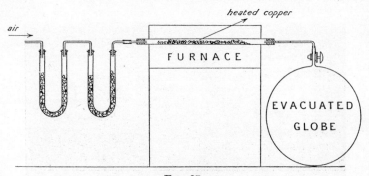

FIG. 37.

Gravimetric composition of the air.

1. U-tubes containing caustic potash to remove carbon dioxide (only one shown in the figure).
2. U-tubes containing concentrated sulphuric acid (on pumice) to remove water-vapour (only one shown in the figure).
3. A heated, weighed tube containing finely-divided copper to absorb oxygen;

and, finally, the remaining "atmospheric nitrogen" (still containing the rare gases) entered a weighed evacuated globe.

The increase in weight of the copper gave the weight of oxygen, and the increase in weight of the globe, the weight of nitrogen (and rare gases).

Neglecting carbon dioxide, the percentage of oxygen by weight in dry, pure air is 23·2%, the remainder being nitrogen and rare gases.

Air—Mixture or Compound? The evidence on which a decision on this question can be reached is given below:

(1) The composition of air is very nearly, but not quite, constant. Small, but definite, differences of composition have been detected when samples of air from different parts of the earth have been analysed.

(2) (a) If air is dissolved in water and boiled out again (see p. 155), the percentage by volume of oxygen in the air boiled out is increased from 21% to about 30%. No chemical reaction is involved here; the composition of air has been altered by a physical method, which depends merely on the fact that oxygen is twice as soluble in water as is nitrogen.

(b) If liquid air is allowed to evaporate, nitrogen evaporates more quickly, leaving almost pure oxygen. Here again, the gases of air are separated by a purely physical process.

This evidence alone is sufficient to decide that **air is a mixture.**

Confirming it are the following facts:

(3) If nitrogen, oxygen, carbon dioxide, water-vapour and the rare gases are mixed in appropriate proportions, there is no explosion, evolution of heat, volume change or other evidence of chemical combination, but the product resembles ordinary air in every way.

(4) The composition of air corresponds to no simple chemical formula such as it would be expected to possess if it were a compound.

The Combustion of a Candle.   The products of combustion of a candle can be shown by the apparatus of Fig. 38.

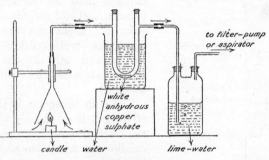

FIG. 38.

To show the products of combustion of a candle.

The products from the burning candle are drawn up the funnel and through the apparatus.

Drops of liquid will condense in the U-tube and the anhydrous copper sulphate will change to blue hydrated crystals. This proves that one of the products from the candle is *water*. The lime water will rapidly turn milky (the milkiness is caused by a fine precipitate of chalk.). This proves that *carbon dioxide* is also given off from the candle.

Candle-wax contains carbon and hydrogen. During the burning, these elements combine with oxygen of the air, forming carbon dioxide and water.

$$C \; + \; O_2 \rightarrow CO_2$$
$$2H_2 \; + \; O_2 \rightarrow 2H_2O$$

Then $$\underset{\text{white}}{CuSO_4} + 5H_2O \rightarrow \underset{\substack{\text{hydrated crystals;}\\\text{blue}}}{CuSO_4.5H_2O}$$

$$Ca(OH)_2 + CO_2 \rightarrow \underset{\text{chalk}}{CaCO_3} \downarrow + H_2O$$

Most of the common fuels—coal, coke, coal-gas, petrol, paraffin oil, water-gas—contain one or both of the same elements as candle-wax and their products of combustion consist mainly of carbon dioxide and water.

Though they pass off as gases, the products of combustion of a candle should weigh more than the candle-wax, which has burnt.

To show that the Products of Combustion of a Candle weigh more than the Candle-wax Burnt. The apparatus is described by Fig. 39.

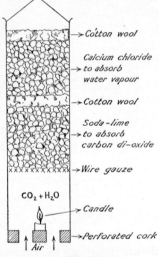

Cotton wool

Calcium chloride to absorb water vapour

Cotton wool

Soda-lime to absorb carbon di-oxide

Wire gauze

$CO_2 + H_2O$

Candle

Perforated cork

Air

Fig. 39.

To show the increase in weight when a candle burns.

Suspend the apparatus from the balance hook of a large, rough balance, and add weights to counterpoise it. Light the candle. The apparatus will quickly gain in weight and will depress the pan of the balance to which it is attached.

The gain in weight is the weight of oxygen from the air with which the carbon and hydrogen of the candle-wax have combined during burning.

Other Kinds of Combustion. Combustions in oxygen or air are so common that it becomes almost habitual to use the word "combustion" as if it referred to this kind of reaction alone. Actually, it may be applied to any chemical combination accompanied by light and heat in which one or more of the reactants are gaseous. You will find, for example, in this book, accounts of the combustion of hydrogen, phosphorus and copper in chlorine gas.

Oxygen of the Air burning in Coal-gas. An interesting reversal of the usual state of affairs, in which air is acting as the combustible material, may be secured by using apparatus as in Fig. 85. (See p. 249.)

THE RUSTING OF IRON

The important facts connected with the rusting of iron may be ascertained by the following experiments.

To find if there is any Change in Weight when Iron Rusts. Weigh a clock-glass containing some iron borings. Damp the borings and set them aside to rust. When rusted, place them in an oven to dry thoroughly, then weigh the clock-glass again. There will be a *gain* in weight. **In this respect rusting is analogous to burning.** We may now try an experiment to see whether the air is similarly concerned in both.

To find whether Iron combines with anything from the Air while Rusting. This experiment is described by Fig. 40.

To show the character of the gas left in the bell-jar in Fig. 40 (II), fill up the trough till level B rises to level A. Then remove the stopper of the bell-jar and insert a lighted taper. It will be extinguished; the remaining gas is *nitrogen*. During rusting the iron has combined with the *oxygen* of the air. This accounts for the rise

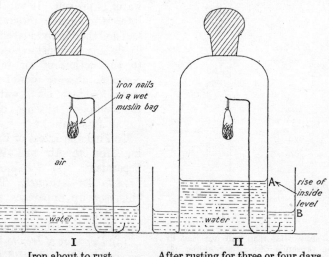

I	II
Iron about to rust.	After rusting for three or four days.

FIG. 40.   The rusting of iron.

in the water level (Fig. 40) and the gain in weight (see p. 137).

Rusting and Burning are Similar. It is important to understand clearly that, from the chemical standpoint, rusting and burning are the same process. During burning, magnesium combines with oxygen of the air, forming magnesium oxide.

$$2Mg + O_2 \rightarrow 2MgO$$

During rusting, iron combines with oxygen of the air in the presence of water to form brown hydrated ferric oxide, "rust".

$$4Fe + 3O_2 \rightarrow 2Fe_2O_3$$

The only difference is in the time required for the two processes. Heat is generated during rusting just as it is during burning, but it is dissipated to the surroundings without attracting notice because of its much slower rate of production.

It is very unfortunate for mankind that iron, which possesses so many useful properties, should be so readily attacked by the oxygen of the air. To protect iron from rusting, it is painted or galvanised (see p. 378). The various protective processes probably cost at least fifty million pounds annually over the whole world.

We will now investigate further the conditions under which iron rusts. We have already seen that during rusting, iron combines with oxygen of the air, and it is common knowledge that iron rusts more readily when plenty of water is present. It will be of interest to separate these agents and find their individual effects. To do this, we must expose iron to the action of air in the complete absence of water (to water-free air) and to water in the complete absence of air (to air-free water).

To Find the Effect of Exposing Iron to Air and Water Separately. (1) *Exposure of Iron to Air separately.* To do this, set up apparatus as in Fig. 41, I. The figure sufficiently explains the experiment.

(2) *Exposure of Iron to Water separately.* Boil about 350 c.c. of water rapidly in a beaker

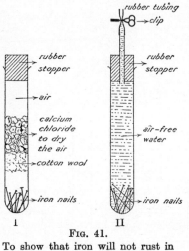

Fig. 41.

To show that iron will not rust in the presence of : I, air alone; II, water alone.

for at least half an hour. This will boil all the air out of it. Put a few iron nails into a test-tube and fill it to the brim with the boiled water. Press into the mouth of the test-tube a rubber stopper carrying a glass tube and rubber tube as shown in Fig. 41, II. (Note that the glass tube must be flush with the bottom of the stopper.) The water will rise into the rubber tube. Place a clip in position to exclude all air.

Leave the test-tubes for several days. In neither case will rusting occur. This means that iron will not rust in the presence of air alone or of water alone; both are needed together to rust the iron.

To make sure that the nails you have used are actually capable

of rusting, put them into a test-tube with a little water, leave the
test-tube open to the air and notice the result after a day or two.

What we have done in the above experiment is to take two
substances, air and water, which normally act on iron *together* and
test the effect of each *singly*. This is the favourite device of
scientists. It is only by finding out the effects produced by one
agent at a time that reliable information can be obtained.

EARLY IDEAS ABOUT BURNING

A theory of burning which was generally accepted by scientists
for about 150 years was developed by Stahl (1660-1734). The
theory supposed there existed a "fiery matter" called "phlogiston"
and that a substance would burn in air if the substance contained
phlogiston, but would not burn if no phlogiston was contained in
it. Thus carbon, phosphorus and magnesium, which burn very
readily, would have been supposed to contain a very high proportion
of phlogiston, while materials like sand, water and slate, which
do not burn at all, would have been supposed to contain no
phlogiston.

The process of burning was simply the escape of phlogiston from
the burning substance into the air. The known fact that a substance cannot burn without air was explained by saying that, unless
air was present to absorb it, phlogiston could not escape from a
substance containing it.

The name "calx" was applied to the residue left after burning a
metal. According to the Phlogiston Theory, the calx differed from
the metal simply by having less phlogiston; thus,

$$\text{Metal} - \text{phlogiston} = \text{calx}$$

The theory had a plausible explanation for certain chemical facts,
but its weakness was exposed as soon as the chemical balance came
into common use. It was then noticed that the products of combustion of a substance are always heavier than the original substance,
not lighter, as would be expected if burning was accompanied by
a *loss* of phlogiston.

In 1774, Priestley discovered the gas we now call "oxygen" (see
p. 405) by heating "red calx of mercury" and noted the brilliance
and rapidity of combustions in oxygen. He explained these by
supposing that oxygen contained no phlogiston and was so ready
to absorb it that burning substances lost their phlogiston with very
great rapidity. His name for oxygen was, therefore, "dephlogisticated air"—air containing no phlogiston.

Lavoisier realised the very great importance of Priestley's dis-
covery and in a famous experiment settled, once and for all time,

the nature of combustion, and gave the death blow to the phlogiston theory. His experiment was carried out with the apparatus shown (Fig. 42).

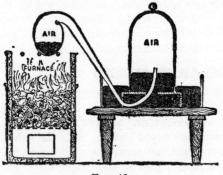

FIG. 42.
Lavoisier's experiment.

The mercury level in the bell-jar was marked and the retort was heated for several days, so that the mercury was kept just below its boiling-point. "Red calx of mercury" (mercuric oxide) appeared on its surface and the mercury level in the bell-jar rose as air was used to combine with the mercury in the retort. After a time, there was no further rise. Lavoisier found that about one-fifth of the air had been absorbed. He then collected all the red calx of mercury and, on heating it, obtained from it a volume of oxygen equal to the diminution in volume of the air in the bell-jar. On mixing the oxygen with the gas left in the bell-jar, a product exactly like air was obtained. The only reasonable explanation of these facts was that oxygen was contained in the air, that it combined with the heated mercury to form the red calx, leaving behind another constituent of the air which would not combine with mercury. To this constituent, Lavoisier gave the name "azote". We now call it nitrogen.

This experiment (1774) finally settled the nature of combustion as a combination of the burning substance with the oxygen of the air. By 1800, the phlogiston theory was abandoned, and, with its departure, modern chemistry begins.

Oxygen and Carbon Dioxide in Life-Processes. Photo-synthesis.
It can readily be shown that carbon dioxide is present in the air expelled from the lungs of a human being. Use the apparatus of Fig. 43.

With the clip A open and the clip B closed, breathe in air through the mouthpiece M. The air bubbles through the lime water in C. Then close clip A, open clip B and breathe out the air so that it passes through the lime-water in D. Repeat this several times. The lime-water in C remains unaffected while that in D is rapidly turned milky. This must mean that during its occupation of the lungs, the air has

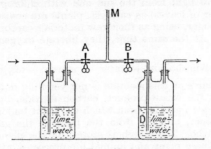

FIG. 43.

To show the presence of carbon dioxide in respired air.

increased its proportion of carbon dioxide, which is absorbed by the lime-water in D with formation of a precipitate of chalk.

$$Ca(OH)_2 + CO_2 \rightarrow CaCO_3 + H_2O$$

At the same time, oxygen is absorbed from the air into the blood, forming a loose compound with the hæmoglobin (the red colouring matter) of the red blood corpuscles.

The use of the oxygen and the presence of carbon dioxide may be explained briefly as follows. The process of digestion converts our food materials into compounds which are either soluble in water or easily emulsified with it. The soluble compounds are absorbed into the blood as the food passes through the small intestine. They are carried round by the blood stream and used either to replace wastage and maintain growth in the body-tissues or to supply energy for movement of the body and to maintain its temperature at about 98·4° F., a temperature usually considerably higher than that of surrounding objects. This energy is supplied by oxidation of the soluble products of digestion. Consider, for example, a sugar. It is well known that if a sugar is thrown on to the fire it burns vigorously, giving off heat, and forming, as products of combustion, carbon dioxide and water. The same oxidation process, giving the same products, occurs in the body, the oxygen being taken from its loose combination with hæmoglobin to oxidise the dissolved sugar. For a given quantity of sugar oxidised, the same amount of heat is given out whether it is burnt rapidly on the fire or oxidised more slowly in the body.

$$C_6H_{12}O_6 + 6O_2 \rightarrow 6CO_2 + 6H_2O + \text{a definite quantity of heat}$$

This is the source of the body's heat. The waste product, carbon dioxide, is carried round in the blood (chiefly as bicarbonate) and is liberated as the blood passes through the lungs, from which it is breathed into the air. The breathing process of animals is similar.

It has already been pointed out that all common fuels give off carbon dioxide when burnt. Living animals also discharge carbon dioxide as we have just seen. There must obviously be some agency at work using up these vast quantities of carbon dioxide and restoring the oxygen

F

absorbed from the air during combustion, for otherwise the composition of the air would change appreciably.

Actually, the plant life of the world is at work restoring the balance. With the help of light from the sun and with chlorophyll (the green colouring matter of leaves) as catalyst, plants are continually building up starch and sugar, using as their raw materials carbon dioxide of the air and water. At the same time, they liberate oxygen, which passes into the air.

carbon dioxide + water → starch + oxygen

The actual course of this reaction is not yet fully understood, but it is obvious that the waste product, carbon dioxide, breathed out by animals, is the raw material from which the plant builds up its starch. The waste product, oxygen, from the plant is the gas essential for animals to breathe. The starch is stored by the plant as a reserve, food supply. These plant and animal life-processes, at work together maintain a balance and keep the composition of the air constant.

In addition to carrying on the above feeding process, plants also breathe in the same way as animals, but, relatively, their breathing process is of small account. On balance, a plant uses up carbon dioxide and liberates oxygen. It may be mentioned that, biologically, the characteristic difference between animals and plants is not connected with size or movement or similar factors, but lies in the fact that plants build up (synthesise) complex starchy food materials from the simple compounds, carbon dioxide and water, while animals must have these complex materials available as food and break them down by digestion into simpler substances.

Experiments illustrating the above brief outline will be found described in any elementary text-book of biology.

QUESTIONS

1. What happens when the following substances are exposed to the air: (a) quicklime, (b) solid sodium hydroxide, (c) washing soda, and (d) anyhdrous calcium chloride? How would you confirm experimentally your answer in ONE case? (N.U.J.B.)
2. What do you understand by the term combustion? Give two examples of combustion in which oxygen plays no part. Describe experiments which illustrate the resemblance between the combustion of a candle and the respiration process in an animal, giving sketches of any apparatus you would use. (D.)
3. An ordinary paraffin candle consists of carbon and hydrogen in combination. State what becomes of the candle when it burns in air, and describe an experiment in support of your statement. Make a sketch of the apparatus you would use to show that the weight of the products of combustion is greater than the weight of the candle consumed. (N.U.J.B.)
4. Explain concisely the chemical meaning of the terms *combustion* and *rusting*. Describe the experiments you would make to show what reactions take place when iron rusts in moist air. (O. and C.)
5. When copper is heated in air, a black substance is formed. How

would you prove that the copper had combined with another element to form this new substance, and how could you determine what this element is? (N.U.J.B.)

6. If a green plant is placed in a closed volume of air in daylight, what changes would you expect to result in the composition of the air? How would you demonstrate that these changes occur? To what do you attribute them? (O. and C.)

7. (a) Give briefly *three* reasons for regarding air as a mixture and not a compound.

   (b) How would you determine the weight of oxygen in a given volume of air? Sketch the apparatus you would use and show, using an imaginary case, how you would work out the calculation.

   (c) Describe briefly how you would determine the *volume* of oxygen in a sample of air confined over water in an eudiometer tube. (N.U.J.B.)

8. Describe in detail how you would proceed in order to remove completely the oxygen, carbon dioxide, and water-vapour from ordinary air. How would you prove that the residual gas was really free from these substances? (L.)

9. How would you find by experiment the percentage, by volume, of oxygen in the air? What other gases are always present in the air?

   What is a physical change? Describe a simple laboratory experiment in which some "air" is obtained of different composition from the ordinary air as the result of a physical change. (L.)

10. Give two reasons in each case for considering that (a) air is a mixture and not a chemical compound, (b) water is a compound and not a mixture.

    How did Lavoisier prove that oxygen is a constituent of the air? How may oxygen be produced from liquefied air? (L.)

CHAPTER XV

WATER AND SOLUTION

Water is Essential to Life. Water is of fundamental importance to all kinds of plants and animals and therefore to man. It is of equal importance with the air we breathe in maintaining the vital processes necessary to life and growth, but since it is not everywhere available its provision has, from the earliest times, limited the setting up of villages and towns to the places where a water supply existed. Not only is water used all over the world in vast quantities for drinking purposes, but it is used in even greater quantities for washing, bleaching, dyeing, raising steam to drive engines, and as a solvent in industrial processes far too numerous to mention. It is the concern of the chemist to ensure that a supply of water is maintained which is suitable for all these purposes.

If the water is too soft (see p. 162) it will attack the lead of the pipes in which it may be carried. If acids are present from decaying organic matter, sufficient lead may be dissolved by the water to cause harm to those who drink it. If the water supply for a town is too hard, because of the high percentage of dissolved solid matter which it contains, no firm will consider establishing a new industry there because of the enormous extra expense which they will incur in softening the water.

Purification plants used in swimming baths, by the use of chloride of lime, keep the water comparatively free from the bacteria which carry many infectious diseases. The development of the high pressure steam boiler, for the driving of machinery of all kinds, would have been impossible but for the solving of the problem of how to obtain water of a sufficiently high degree of purity for use in these boilers. The above are a few examples of how Chemistry is of use in the service of man.

Occurrence of Water. Pure water does not exist in a natural state, but supplies of water are obtainable all over the world, varying in degrees of purity from rain water from clean districts (which contains ·0005% of solid impurities) to sea water, in which the impurities reach the comparatively high proportion of 3·6%. (In certain lakes the proportion of solid matter is even higher.)

152

Purification. A sample of fairly pure water can be made from rain water, tap water, or river water by the process of distillation.

The impure water is placed in the distilling flask and is boiled (Fig. 44). The steam comes off (together with gaseous impurities)

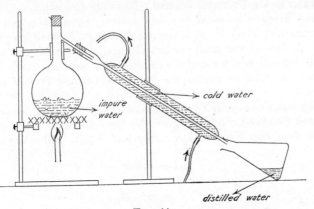

Fig. 44.
Distillation of impure water.

whilst the solid impurities are left behind. The steam is condensed to water by the cold jacket of water in the condenser. The distillate, which collects in the receiver, is termed distilled water. It has a flat and insipid taste.

Pure Water. The preparation of perfectly pure water (or as near to perfectly pure water as its unusual solvent powers will allow) is a matter of much difficulty. It is prepared for conductivity experiments by as many as twenty successive distillations from a pure tin or platinum retort into a receiver which has been cleaned by having the purest water then obtainable kept in it for ten years! Potassium permanganate is added to the impure water in the earlier stages to oxidise organic impurities.

Properties. Water is a clear colourless liquid with an insipid taste. It is usually recognised in the laboratory by its capacity to turn anhydrous copper culphate (white) to a blue colour.

$$CuSO_4 + 5H_2O \rightarrow CuSO_4.5H_2O$$

copper   water   hydrated copper
sulphate   sulphate (blue)

This test, of course, merely denotes the **presence** of water and not the **absence** of everything else except water; *e.g.*, a dilute solution of sulphuric acid would turn anhydrous copper sulphate from white to blue. *PURE* water has the following properties:

(*a*) It freezes at 0° C.

(*b*) It boils at 100° C., when the barometer stands at 760 mm., and pure water will boil away completely with no change in temperature.

(*c*) Its maximum density is 1 gm. per c.c. at 4° C.

(*d*) It is neutral to litmus.

Water as the Universal Solvent. There are few substances which do not dissolve in water to some extent. Even when you drink your morning glass of water you are drinking a little of the glass as well. It is true you need not get alarmed, for the amount is very small indeed, but for certain experiments ordinary glass vessels cannot be used as containers for water because of this solvent effect.

Tap water can easily be shown to contain a considerable quantity of both dissolved solids and gases by the following experiments.

To show Tap Water contains Dissolved Solids. Fill a large clean

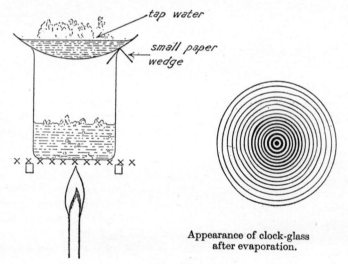

Appearance of clock-glass
after evaporation.

FIG. 45.

To show tap water contains dissolved solids.

clock-glass with tap water and evaporate it down to dryness on a steam-bath as shown in Fig. 45. On holding the glass up to the light or against a sheet of white paper, you will observe a large number of concentric rings of solid matter left as the water gradually evaporated.

To Show that Tap Water contains Dissolved Gases. Fill a flask with water and put in a few pieces of porous pot. Insert a two-holed rubber stopper to which are fitted a delivery-tube and a short piece of glass tubing which can be closed by a rubber tube and clip and attached to the tap in the initial stages (the lower ends of both tubes should not project beyond the surface of the stopper). By attaching the small piece of glass tubing to the tap by means of a rubber tube the whole apparatus (including the delivery-tube) is filled with

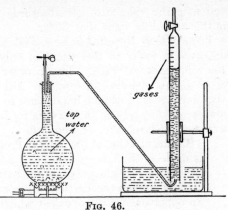

FIG. 46.
To show tap water contains dissolved gases.

water. (Fig. 46.) As the water is heated, bubbles of gas are seen to rise and these will collect and be carried over into the burette. Boil the water until no more gas is given off. The gas can be shown to differ from air in that its oxygen content is much higher, and the gas boiled out will rekindle a glowing splint.

To determine the volume of oxygen in the air boiled out of water. Use in the last experiment a burette into which will fit the absorption cup (G. Fowles) shown in Fig. 47.

Fill the cup with crystals of pyrogallic acid and add water to fill up the air spaces. (See Fig. 47.) Have ready a piece of solid caustic soda (make certain that it will be able to enter the burette), insert it into the burette and follow it quickly with the absorption cup. Invert the tube several times and release the cup under water. Transfer the tube to a deep gas-jar, lower it until the levels are the same inside and out,

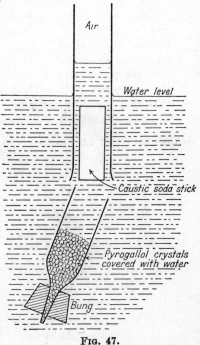

FIG. 47.
Absorption cup.

and note the volume of gas absorbed. The percentage of oxygen in this air will be more than 30%.

Value of these Dissolved Gases to Fish Life. The oxygen of the air dissolves in water to the extent of only 4 volumes of oxygen in 100 volumes of water (*i.e.*, 1 litre of water contains only a maximum of 40 c.c. (or ·06 gm.) of oxygen). Although this amount is only very small it is of utmost importance to fish life. The fish (with a few exceptions) rely on this oxygen for breathing, in just the same way as we rely on the air around us.

Chemical Value of the Solvent Properties of Water. Use is made in the laboratory of this exceptional property to bring into very close contact the particles of reacting substances. When the particles dissolve in water they have an opportunity for movement which they do not have in the solid state. Under these circumstances many reactions take place which do not take place if the reactants are solids (see ionisation), *e.g.*,

$$AgNO_3 \quad + \quad NaCl \quad \rightarrow \quad AgCl \quad + \quad NaNO_3$$

| solution of silver nitrate | solution of common salt | precipitate of silver chloride | solution of sodium nitrate |

The above reaction will not take place if common salt and silver nitrate are ground together in a mortar. because the average distance of the particles from one another is too great.

In the above cases the water acts as a medium in which the action takes place. It does not as a rule react with the substances. The chemical actions of water, however, as an oxide and as a hydroxide producer are extensive.

Actions of Water on Metals

K Na Ca	Attack water.
Mg Al Zn Fe	Attack steam.
Pb Cu Hg Ag Au	Do not attack water or steam.

By an examination of the electrochemical series it is easily shown that water attacks the metals to a degree varying with their position in the series.

Potassium. Place a **small**[1] piece of potassium on water in a large dish (notice the silvery gleam of the unoxidised metal as it is cut with a knife). The potassium melts to a silvery ball, darts about the water and a gas is given off (hydrogen) which burns spontaneously with a violet flame (the colour is due to the burning of small quantities of potassium vapour). Fig. 48.

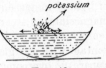

Fig. 48.

Action of potassium on water.

$$2K + 2H_2O \rightarrow 2KOH + H_2$$
potassium   water   potassium   hydrogen
                      hydroxide

If a piece of red litmus is placed in the dish it will turn blue because of the presence of potassium hydroxide, which is an alkali.

Sodium. Perform the above experiment with sodium. The sodium melts to a silvery ball, but does not light unless it is restricted in movement. Effervescence occurs, a gas is liberated, and if a light is applied it burns with a yellow flame (the yellow colour is from the sodium). If the sodium is packed tightly into a sodium spoon (see Fig. 49) the gas can be collected and shown to be hydrogen.

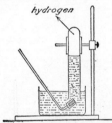

Fig. 49.

Action of sodium on water

$$2Na + 2H_2O \rightarrow 2NaOH + H_2$$
sodium   water   sodium   hydrogen
                  hydroxide

Calcium. Drop a piece of calcium (a grey metal) into a dish of water and invert over it a boiling-tube full of water. There is effervescence, and a gas (hydrogen) is given off which explodes if mixed with air and a flame is applied (Fig. 50). The calcium dissolves, and if carbon dioxide is bubbled into a sample of this solution (blow into it down a glass tube), a milkiness due to a suspension of calcium carbonate in water is obtained. The solution is, in fact, lime-water, *i.e.*, calcium hydroxide (slaked lime) dissolved in water.

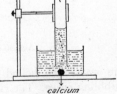

Fig. 50.

Action of calcium on water.

[1] Under no circumstances should the piece of potassium be larger than a small pea, as the action is very vigorous. Stand well back from the dish as the action proceeds.

F*

$$Ca + 2H_2O \rightarrow Ca(OH)_2 + H_2$$

calcium   water   calcium   hydrogen
                       hydroxide

Magnesium. This metal will not act appreciably on cold water but is attacked by boiling water. Steam vigorously attacks a piece of lighted magnesium ribbon. The demonstration of the action of magnesium on steam is beset with the practical difficulty that the temperature is so high that if the burning magnesium comes into contact with any glass, cracking immediately ensues. The following apparatus overcomes this difficulty in a simple way.

A stout, very wide short-necked flask is partly filled with water and a piece of red litmus paper is dropped into the water and the water heated to boiling (Fig. 51). Meanwhile a piece of magnesium ribbon is attached to the piece of apparatus by pulling the cork away from the glass tube a little, and pushing the ribbon in parallel with the glass. Over the glass tube is placed a boiling-tube. When

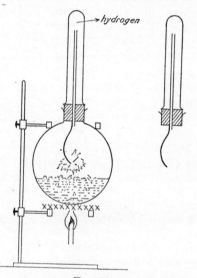

FIG. 51.
Action of burning magnesium on steam.

the water has boiled for a minute, remove the bunsen and let bubbling cease. The ribbon is lighted and plunged into the steam, the cork fitting into the neck of the flask. The magnesium continues to burn, forming a white ash (magnesium oxide) which drops off into the water. When the action has ceased, remove the boiling-tube and apply it immediately to a flame, when there will be an explosion due to the combination of the hydrogen produced with oxygen of the air which is not completely displaced from the tube.

The piece of litmus paper will, after a time, turn blue. The magnesium oxide is only slightly soluble in water, but it will dissolve sufficiently to turn the litmus blue, showing the presence of a hydroxide.

$$Mg + H_2O \rightarrow MgO + H_2$$

magnesium   water   magnesium   hydrogen

oxide

(*N.B.* The above experiment shows that steam contains both oxygen and hydrogen.)

Alternative Method. (See Fig. 52.)

Blow a small hole in a *hard-glass* test-tube by applying a small blow-pipe flame until the tube is soft and blowing at the open end whilst the glass is being heated. Put a coil of 6 in. magnesium ribbon in the tube, add two or three c.c. of water, insert the cork and clamp the apparatus by the cork at the angle shown (Fig. 52). Heat, gently at first, with a bunsen burner, keeping the latter moving to maintain an atmosphere of steam. Finally heat strongly when the magnesium will burn and simultaneously the liberated hydrogen will burn as it meets the outside air.

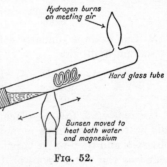

Fig. 52.

Zinc does not attack hot or cold water. If zinc is heated to redness in a current of steam hydrogen is formed.

$$Zn + H_2O \rightarrow ZnO + H_2$$

zinc oxide

Iron does not attack water (rusting takes place only when air is present as well) but is readily attacked by a **quantity** of steam. This method is often used as a method of preparing hydrogen in quantity. See p. 216.

$$3Fe + 4H_2O \rightarrow Fe_3O_4 + 4H_2$$

iron   steam   triferric   hydrogen

tetroxide

black oxide

of iron

The above reaction can be made to proceed in the reverse direction by passing a **quantity** of hydrogen over heated black oxide of iron (see p. 127).

Action of Water on Non-Metals

Carbon attacks steam at a bright red heat, forming carbon monoxide and hydrogen.

$$C + H_2O \rightarrow CO + H_2$$

carbon   steam   carbon   hydrogen
(coke)   monoxide

Chlorine acts on water to form hypochlorous acid.

$$Cl_2 + H_2O \rightarrow HClO + HCl$$

chlorine   water   hypochlorous   hydrochloric
                    acid   acid

Action of Water on Oxides

Potassium oxide is attacked by water with the formation of potassium hydroxide.

$$K_2O + H_2O \rightarrow 2KOH$$

potassium   water   potassium
oxide   hydroxide

Sodium oxide is similarly attacked by water with the formation of sodium hydroxide.

$$Na_2O + H_2O \rightarrow 2NaOH$$

sodium   water   sodium
oxide   hydroxide

Calcium oxide (*lime*). Place a piece of quicklime in a dish and add water a few drops at a time. For a little while nothing is observed and then water-vapour is seen to come off, whilst a hissing sound as the water drops on indicates that the mass is becoming hot. It commences to expand and crack, and finally crumbles to a powder, slaked lime.

$$CaO + H_2O \rightarrow Ca(OH)_2$$

calcium   water   calcium
oxide   hydroxide
(lime)

The above three hydroxides are soluble in water (slaked lime only slightly) and together with ammonium hydroxide form the common alkalis.

Sulphur dioxide reacts readily with water to form sulphurous acid.

$$SO_2 + H_2O \rightarrow H_2SO_3$$

sulphurous
acid

Similarly, other acidic oxides form acids with water, *e.g.*,

$$SO_3 + H_2O \rightarrow H_2SO_4$$

sulphur   sulphuric
trioxide   acid

$$2NO_2 + H_2O \rightarrow HNO_2 + HNO_3$$

nitrogen   nitrous   nitric
dioxide   acid   acid

$$CO_2 + H_2O \rightarrow H_2CO_3$$

carbon   carbonic
dioxide   acid

Action of Water on Chlorides. See Chlorides, p. 286.

Action of Water on certain Metallic Carbides. Calcium and aluminium carbides react with water forming the hydroxide of the metal and hydrocarbons.

$$CaC_2 + 2H_2O \rightarrow Ca(OH)_2 + C_2H_2$$

acetylene

$$Al_4C_3 + 12H_2O \rightarrow 4Al(OH)_3 + 3CH_4$$

methane

Composition of Water. The results of experiments already performed indicate clearly that water contains hydrogen and oxygen. If hydrogen is burnt in oxygen or exploded with it, water is produced (see p. 221) and nothing else. It remains to find the number of atoms of each element which is present in the molecule.

Volume Composition of Steam. The experiment described on p. 92 shows two volumes of steam to be formed from one volume of oxygen and two volumes of hydrogen. It follows that the formula for steam is H_2O.

Electrolysis of Water. The above is the synthesis of water from its elements whilst electrolysis is the analysis. On electrolysis of water (see p. 121) it is found that the volume of hydrogen liberated is twice that of the oxygen liberated, thus confirming the above experiment.

Gravimetric Composition of Water. Hydrogen was at first taken to be the standard $(H = 1)$ for the determination of Atomic Weights. Now the first step in a determination of an atomic weight is usually a determination of the equivalent weight, and since many elements do not combine with or displace hydrogen readily, their equivalents have been determined by finding the weight of the element which combined with the equivalent of oxygen. Hence it is necessary to know with great accuracy the equivalent of oxygen.

This is determined by passing purified hydrogen through several U-tubes of calcium chloride to dry it, and then through a tube containing pure dry copper oxide which is heated strongly. The latter tube and its contents are first weighed (Fig. 53). The water which passes over is collected in another set of calcium chloride tubes which are weighed before and after the experiment.

$$CuO + H_2 \rightarrow Cu + H_2O$$

copper   hydrogen   copper   water
oxide

The loss in weight of the tube containing the copper oxide gives the weight of oxygen, and the difference between the increase in weight of the absorption apparatus and the weight of oxygen gives

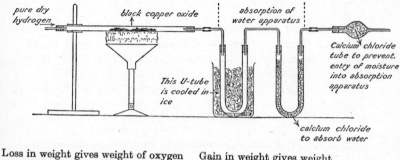

Loss in weight gives weight of oxygen which has combined with the hydrogen.

Gain in weight gives weight of water formed.

Difference gives weight of hydrogen.

Fig. 53.

Gravimetric composition of water.

the weight of hydrogen which has combined with the oxygen to form water.

By an experiment involving the combination of the element themselves it was found that

1 gm. of hydrogen combined with 7·9396 gm. of oxygen.

This accurate figure was obtained by Morley (1890–95) who succeeded in weighing the hydrogen, oxygen and also the water formed. The latter, of course, introduces a check on any error made. The difficulty of weighing a volume of hydrogen (because of the very small weight of even a large volume) was overcome by absorbing the hydrogen in the metal palladium. The hydrogen was expelled by heating the palladium to redness.

HARDNESS OF WATER

There are many types of natural water found on the earth's surface.

Rain water is the purest natural water, and if collected in a country district contains oxygen, nitrogen, carbon dioxide (dissolved as the rain drops pass through the atmosphere) and only a small amount of dissolved solids (·0005%).

River water, from which many domestic supplies are obtained, will obviously contain the same gaseous impurities and also any solids which the water has dissolved as it passed over the soil. The amount and kind of impurity will depend, therefore, on the type of soil over which the water runs. If the water runs over impervious material such as granite, the river water may be nearly as pure as rain water. In actual practice many springs and rivulets feed the large river from which a town's water supply is obtained, and hence the impurities are often the same as those of spring water.

Spring water is water which has made its way downwards through the soil and contains solid impurities.

Sea water is the reservoir into which all the impurities eventually go, and hence the solid content of sea water is usually high (3·6%).

The solids which are found in the natural waters are mainly the sulphates and bicarbonates of calcium and magnesium together with smaller amounts of sodium chloride, silicates, nitrates, ammonium salts, as well as the gaseous impurities already mentioned as being present in rain water, *i.e.*, oxygen, nitrogen and carbon dioxide.

Of the solid impurities the most important are calcium sulphate and calcium bicarbonate.

Calcium sulphate is present because many rocks and soils contain gypsum ($CaSO_4.2H_2O$) which is slightly soluble in water (1 : 500) and hence some of it dissolves in any water with which it comes in contact.

Calcium bicarbonate is present because water which contains carbon dioxide is capable of dissolving small quantities of limestone or chalk (which is found in large quantities in some soils and in small quantities in practically all soils).

$$CaCO_3 \;+\; H_2O \;+\; CO_2 \;\rightarrow\; Ca(HCO_3)_2$$

limestone	water	carbon	calcium bicarbonate
(insoluble)		dioxide	(slightly soluble)

It will be obvious that all the more soluble substances present on the surface of the earth were washed away in the course of past ages.

Definition. **A hard water is one which will not readily form a lather with soap.**

The Nature and Method of Manufacture of Soap. Soap is the sodium salt of an organic[1] acid. One of the commonest soaps is the sodium salt of stearic acid, $C_{17}H_{35}CO_2H$, and has the formula, $C_{17}H_{35}CO_2Na$, sodium stearate. It is important to notice that, for all its complex formula, soap is of exactly the same chemical nature

[1] An organic compound is a compound of carbon. The chemistry of carbon is so complex that it is convenient to treat it separately from that of other elements as "organic chemistry".

as common salt, NaCl. Both are sodium salts of acids. The complex group, $C_{17}H_{35}CO_2$—, of sodium stearate corresponds to the Cl of sodium chloride. For convenience, the formula of sodium stearate is often written NaSt, the St being used as a substitute for the stearate group, $C_{17}H_{35}CO_2$—.

Soap is manufactured by heating vegetable oils (such as palm oil or olive oil) or animal fats with caustic soda solution. The oils or fats are compounds formed from glycerine and certain complex organic acids, such as stearic acid, mentioned above. The caustic soda liberates glycerine from the fat and forms the sodium salt of the acid, which is the soap.

$$\text{Fat or oil } + \text{ caustic soda } \rightarrow \text{ soap } + \text{ glycerine}$$

Soap is manufactured by steam-heating the fat and caustic soda solution in large pans. Common salt is added later and assists in the separation of the soap which, when cool, sets as a hard cake on the surface of the liquid. It is removed and purified, dyes and perfumes being added to produce toilet soaps.

The manufacturing process can be illustrated in the laboratory, using mutton fat or lard. Put the lard into an evaporating dish and add to it a solution of caustic soda to which methylated spirit has been added to quicken the action. Heat the dish on a steam-bath. When all the liquid has evaporated off, a yellowish solid will be left. It is impure soap.

The soap cleanses by dissolving in the water, loosening the particles of dirt, and the whole (soap, water and dirt) can then be washed away.

Cause of Hardness. Now if there happens to be a calcium compound dissolved in the water the soap is precipitated in the form of calcium stearate (which appears as a "curd"), the latter being insoluble, *e.g.*,

$$2\text{NaSt} + \text{CaSO}_4 \rightarrow \text{Na}_2\text{SO}_4 + \text{CaSt}_2$$

sodium stearate (soluble)	calcium sulphate (soluble)	sodium sulphate (soluble)	calcium stearate (**insoluble**)

Until the whole of the calcium compound has been acted upon by the soap, none of the latter can form a lather. Thus with a hard water a large amount of soap is used to precipitate and remove the calcium, and only a small extra amount to cause a lather.

In this way the valuable stearate group, which loosens the dirt, is lost completely, since it would be just as useful to try to wash with insoluble calcium stearate as any other substance insoluble in water, *e.g.*, marble, or iron.

This is not the only reason why hardness must be removed. Where water is used for boilers, certain of these solid substances (calcium sulphate and magnesium silicate being the worst offenders) are left behind as scale on the inside of the pipes of the boiler as the

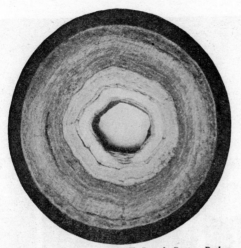

From a photograph by Mr. H. Pocock Repton, Derby.

PLATE III

Hot-water pipe (3-inch) nearly blocked by deposits of calcium carbonate.

water is evaporated off. As this scale increases in thickness the bore of the pipe becomes smaller, and the walls of which the pipes are made become heated to a higher temperature than is normal, causing the pipes to weaken and finally burst.

Removal of Hardness. *Distillation* will remove all solid matter. This method is, as a rule, far too costly to be employed.

Many high pressure boilers supply steam to drive turbines, and the steam which comes from the turbines is condensed to water, which is actually distilled water. In some works the water is fed back again into the boiler and small amounts of distilled water artificially prepared are added to make up the losses which are inevitable.

Removal of Calcium as Calcium Carbonate (Chalk). Many of the methods of rendering a hard water soft have as their object the conversion of a soluble calcium salt into the insoluble carbonate. In this way the calcium is removed, since the calcium carbonate, being insoluble, takes no further part in the reaction. An insoluble calcium salt cannot cause hardness.

Temporary Hardness. Hardness which is due to the presence of calcium bicarbonate can be removed by heating the water to boiling

By courtesy of Messrs. Cox's Cave, Cheddar; from a photograph by Messrs. Frith, Reigate

PLATE IV

Stalagmites and stalactites.

for a few minutes. Heat decomposes the calcium bicarbonate into calcium carbonate (chalk) and carbon dioxide is expelled.

$$Ca(HCO_3)_2 \rightarrow CaCO_3 + H_2O + CO_2$$

calcium   calcium   water   carbon
bicarbonate   carbonate   dioxide
(slightly soluble) (insoluble)

Because it can be removed merely by boiling, the name "temporary" is given to this type of hardness. This method would be expensive on the large scale.

Furring of Kettles. In a district where the water contains calcium bicarbonate the insides of kettles become coated with a layer of calcium carbonate caused by the decomposition of the bicarbonate according to the equation shown above.

Stalagmites and Stalactites. These pillars of almost pure calcium carbonate are made by water containing dissolved calcium bicarbonate dripping from the roof on to the floor of a cavern. Some of the calcium bicarbonate decomposes, giving off carbon dioxide into the atmosphere of the cave, and depositing calcium carbonate a little at a time on the roof and floor. This deposition causes a stalactite to grow downwards from the top of the cave and a stalagmite to grow upwards from the floor of the cave until after many years the two meet. The growth varies very much from small fractions of an inch to 10 feet or more per year.

Removal of Temporary Hardness by Addition of Lime. Temporary hardness can also be removed by the addition of the calculated quantity of lime (excess of lime would cause hardness on its own account). The amount of lime is calculated from a knowledge of the hardness of the water and of the capacity of the reservoir (Clark's method). The lime first attacks the water to form slaked lime which dissolves in the water to a slight extent.

$$Ca(OH)_2 + Ca(HCO_3)_2 \rightarrow 2CaCO_3 + 2H_2O$$

slaked lime	calcium	calcium	water
(slightly soluble)	bicarbonate (slightly soluble)	carbonate (insoluble)	

A third method of removal of temporary hardness is to add sodium carbonate. (Permanent hardness is also removed at the same time.)

$$Na_2CO_3 + Ca(HCO_3)_2 \rightarrow 2NaHCO_3 + CaCO_3 \downarrow$$

Permanent hardness is due mainly to the presence of dissolved calcium sulphate. This cannot be decomposed by boiling and hence the name "permanent" is given to this type of hardness.

It is most easily removed by the addition of washing soda crystals to the water, when a precipitate of insoluble calcium carbonate is thrown down and thus prevents the calcium from interfering.

(You should make yourself quite certain of the reason why soluble calcium sulphate can cause hardness, whereas insoluble calcium carbonate cannot. See p. 164.)

$$CaSO_4 + Na_2CO_3 \rightarrow CaCO_3 + Na_2SO_4$$

calcium sulphate (soluble)	sodium carbonate	calcium carbonate (insoluble)	

PRACTICAL DETERMINATION OF APPROXIMATE DEGREE OF HARDNESS AND ILLUSTRATION OF THE ABOVE FACTS

To make temporarily Hard Water. Bubble carbon dioxide into lime-water in a flask for about 20 minutes. The precipitate at first formed will have dissolved to form a temporarily hard water.

$$Ca(OH)_2 + CO_2 \rightarrow CaCO_3 + H_2O$$

| lime water | carbon dioxide | calcium carbonate | water |

$$CaCO_3 + H_2O + CO_2 \rightarrow Ca(HCO_3)_2$$

| calcium carbonate | water | carbon dioxide | calcium bicarbonate |

To make permanently Hard Water. Add a little gypsum or anhydrous calcium sulphate to water in a flask. Shake and allow to stand, decant off the clear liquid; you will find it will be permanently hard water.

To make a Soap Solution. Scrape shavings off a tablet of pure Castile soap. Weigh out about 6 gm. of shavings and add to about 100 c.c. of methylated spirit in a beaker on a water bath. Warm and stir. When dissolved, transfer to a litre flask and add water to make up about one litre. Shake and allow to stand.

N.B. Since the composition of soap is variable the above solution need not be made up with great accuracy, nor are the readings to be taken as a mathematical comparison of hardness. **In these experiments the hardness of various waters is being compared.**

Fill a burette with the soap solution and place 25 c.c. of distilled water by means of a pipette into a conical flask. Run in 1 c.c. of the soap solution at a time and, between additions, cork up the flask and shake. **When a lather is obtained, which persists unbroken for two minutes, the titration is completed.** You will easily see the difference between a "curd" (which is formed when soap solution is run into a hard water) and a lather, as the former breaks very quickly and the latter consists of many tiny bubbles which reflect the light from the windows. When you have run 30 c.c. of soap solution into a hard water, you need not proceed further. The water is hard. Having obtained the result for distilled water perform the following experiments.

To show that Boiling softens Temporarily Hard Water. Take 25 c.c. of the temporarily hard water made as indicated above and titrate against soap solution. Notice the curd which forms.

$$Ca(HCO_3)_2 + 2NaSt \rightarrow CaSt_2 + 2NaHCO_3$$

calcium
stearate
(curd)

Take *another* 25 c.c. and heat to boiling on a tripod and gauze. Notice that a milkiness appears (chalk). Titrate against soap solution again and note your result when a lather is obtained which remains unbroken for two minutes.

$$Ca(HCO_3)_2 \rightarrow CaCO_3 + H_2O + CO_2$$

To show that Washing Soda Crystals soften Permanently Hard Water. Titrate 25 c.c. of the permanently hard water and record your result. Take *another* 25 c.c. of the hard water, add a few crystals of washing soda, and shake until they dissolve. Again you will notice a turbidity due to a precipitate of chalk.

$$Na_2CO_3 + CaSO_4 \rightarrow Na_2SO_4 + CaCO_3 \downarrow$$

Titrate again and notice your results. They should speak for themselves. A typical set of results is given here.

Amount of soap solution necessary to produce a lather to last unbroken for two minutes.

25 c.c. distilled water
  2nd reading   3·0 c.c.⎫
  1st reading   1·0 c.c.⎭   2·0 c.c.

25 c.c. temporarily hard water
  2nd reading   33·0 c.c.⎫
  1st reading   3·0 c.c.⎭   30·0 c.c.[1]

25 c.c. temporarily hard water after boiling
  2nd reading   40·0 c.c.⎫
  1st reading   33·0 c.c.⎭   7·0 c.c.

25 c.c. permanently hard water
  2nd reading   31·0 c.c.⎫
  1st reading   1·0 c.c.⎭   30·0 c.c.[1]

25 c.c. permanently hard water to which washing soda was added
  2nd reading   36·0 c.c.⎫
  1st reading   31·0 c.c.⎭   5·0 c.c.

Permutit Method of Softening Water. The above methods of softening water (*i.e.*, boiling and adding soda) are used mainly in the home for softening small amounts of water. In the treatment of larger supplies of water (but not so large as to be treated by the lime method) the permutit process is used. Many "water softeners" sold for domestic use work on this principle.

Permutit is a complex substance (hydrated sodium aluminium silicates) but we can regard it as Na_2Y ($Y = Al_2Si_2O_8xH_2O$). When a dissolved calcium salt runs over it there is double decomposition.

$$\underset{\text{insoluble}}{Na_2Y} + CaSO_4 \rightarrow \underset{\text{insoluble}}{CaY} + Na_2SO_4$$

[1] Indicates no lather produced. No more soap solution was added—the water is extremely hard.

The sodium permutit will finally become a calcium permutit, and it can be made fresh again by running strong salt solution over it and washing away the soluble calcium chloride formed.

$$CaY + 2NaCl \rightarrow Na_2Y + CaCl_2$$

WATER OF CRYSTALLISATION

Place a few crystals of copper sulphate into a test-tube and heat gently. There will be a copious evolution of water-vapour (which will condense and run back and crack the tube if the mouth of the tube is not held lower than the bottom). The colour and shape of the crystals will disappear, and in place of blue crystals of hydrated copper sulphate you will observe a white powdery mass of anhydrous copper sulphate.

$$CuSO_4 \ . \ 5H_2O \rightarrow CuSO_4 + 5H_2O$$

copper ↑ sulphate   anhydrous   water
crystals | copper sulphate

This dot denotes loose chemical combination between the water and the copper sulphate.

If the same experiment is performed with pure common salt or potassium chloride there will be no evolution of water-vapour and a crystalline mass will still remain.

Water of crystallisation is necessary to the crystalline shape of some crystals, and is that definite amount of water with which the substance is associated on crystallising out from an aqueous solution. The crystals cannot form in these cases without the presence of water with which to form a loose compound. It is sometimes termed "water of hydration".

These contain water of crystallisation.	These do not contain water of crystallisation.
Sodium carbonate crystals ($Na_2CO_3 \ . \ 10H_2O$).	Sodium chloride NaCl.
Sodium sulphate crystals ($Na_2SO_4 \ . \ 10H_2O$).	Potassium permanganate $KMnO_4$.
Copper sulphate crystals ($CuSO_4 \ . \ 5H_2O$).	Potassium nitrate KNO_3.
Ferrous sulphate crystals ($FeSO_4 \ . \ 7H_2O$).	Ammonium sulphate ($(NH_4)_2SO_4$).

SOLUTION

Many solids possess the property of dissolving in water. For instance, if we shake up a few small crystals of copper sulphate (crush them in a mortar first) with water in a test-tube, the water will turn blue and the crystals will finally disappear.

The particles of copper sulphate in the solution must be very small, for we cannot see them with the naked eye, nor even with the most powerful microscope made. Furthermore, they will pass through the pores of a filter-paper with ease. The solution (as this mixture is called) of copper sulphate in water appears to be just as blue in one part of the test-tube as it does in another. If we were to fill a long tube with the solution, cork up the tube and leave it for years, it would still appear as blue at the top as at the bottom, and equal volumes taken from any part of the solution would be found to contain equal weights of copper sulphate. We say that the solution is homogeneous (that is, the same throughout) or in other words, the particles of copper sulphate have been "shared out" evenly to all parts of the liquid.

Water is not the only liquid which will dissolve solids, nor is copper sulphate the only solid to dissolve in water. There are many other liquids such as ether, carbon disulphide, benzene, in which many solids, liquids and gases dissolve. The dissolved substance is usually called the SOLUTE and the liquid in which it dissolves the SOLVENT.

To obtain the Solute from a Solution. Into a porcelain evaporating dish pour a solution of common salt in water, and heat the contents on a tripod and gauze. Water-vapour will be seen to come off and finally there will be left a white solid, common salt.

This method can be used to purify rock salt, since earthy impurities and dirt will not dissolve and can be removed by filtration.

To obtain the Solvent from a Solution. If we could catch the water-vapour coming off in the previous experiment and cool it, we could recover the water free from common salt, since the solid does not come off with the vapour. The method of catching the vapour and cooling it is called *condensation* and the apparatus employed is a distilling flask, condenser and receiver (see Fig. 44). The condenser consists of a long tube surrounded by a wider tube through which water can flow, to cool the vapours and convert them into a liquid again. The whole process of boiling off the liquid as vapour and then cooling it again so that it is received as liquid in another vessel is called *distillation*. The product obtained here is called "distilled water". It is free from dissolved solids but may contain gases in solution. It has a "flat" taste which makes it unpalatable. Distilled water is used in electric accumulators because the solids present in ordinary tap-water are injurious to the plates.

We can now sum up the properties of a solution:—

(a) The particles of solute in a solution are so small as to be invisible and will pass through the pores of the finest filter.

(b) The solution is homogeneous.

(c) The solute can be recovered from the solution by the process of evaporation to dryness and the solvent by the process of distillation.

Chemical Solution. This is a term often employed to indicate the apparent solution of a solute in a solvent, together with chemical action. For example, zinc appears to dissolve in dilute sulphuric acid and neither zinc nor dilute sulphuric acid can be recovered by evaporation or distillation, since the solid residue on evaporation would be zinc sulphate. Actually the processes of chemical action and solvent action follow one another. The zinc attacks the acid to form zinc sulphate, which then dissolves in the water present.

Suspension. The above properties of a solution help us to differentiate between a solution and a suspension. A solid is said to be in suspension in a liquid when small particles of it are contained in the liquid but are not dissolved in it.

If the mixture is left undisturbed the solid particles will slowly settle to the bottom of the containing vessel, leaving the pure liquid above them.

Muddy water is a typical suspension. The mud would settle after a time if left undisturbed, leaving a brown residue on the bottom of the containing vessel and clear water above. The particles of mud would be retained by a filter-paper whilst the water (and any solids in solution) would pass through.

Saturated Solution. If we add half a gram of common salt to 100 gm. of water in a beaker the salt will dissolve. We could go on for a time adding salt half a gram at a time and, by stirring vigorously between each addition, bring about solution of the common salt, but with increasing difficulty. Finally, there would come a time when no more common salt would dissolve **at that particular temperature,** and no matter how long we left it or how vigorously we stirred no more common salt would dissolve. The solution is then said to be saturated with common salt at the particular temperature.

Definition. **A saturated solution of a solute at a particular temperature is one which contains as much solute as it can dissolve at that temperature, in the presence of the crystals of the solute.**

The concentration of a saturated solution varies with the solute, the solvent and also with the temperature. Thus sulphur is almost insoluble in water yet readily dissolves in carbon disulphide and a rise in temperature will cause more to dissolve.

This is generally true for solids; for example, nitre is at least seven times more soluble in water at 80° C. than it is in water at 10° C.

Determination of Solubility. To give a quantitative meaning to solubility, it is necessary to fix the amount of the solvent and to state the temperature under consideration. The amount of solvent is usually fixed at 100 gm.

Definition. **The solubility of a solute in a solvent at a particular temperature is the number of grams of the solute necessary to saturate 100 gms. of the solvent at that temperature.**

It denotes a limit, that is, the *maximum* amount which can normally be held in solution. Solubility is also sometimes expressed in grams of solute per litre of solution.

To Determine the Solubility of Nitre (Potassium Nitrate) in Water at the Temperature of the Laboratory

This determination must be carried out in two stages. It is first necessary to prepare a saturated nitre solution at laboratory temperature and then to find the proportions of nitre and water in it.

To make the Saturated Solution. The rate of solution of a solid in cold water is generally so slow that it is almost impossible to obtain a saturated solution of it in a reasonable time by merely shaking the solid with the water. The quicker and more certain way is to crystallise from a warm solution by cooling.

Half-fill a boiling-tube with water and dissolve in it some nitre. Warm and shake well. Pour off a small sample into a test-tube and cool it under the tap. If no crystals appear, return the sample to the boiling-tube and add more nitre. Test another sample and continue in this way till a sample gives crystals. Then cool the whole solution. When the crystals have separated and the solution is quite cold, take the temperature of it. Then filter it through a *dry* filter-paper and funnel into a *dry* receiver to avoid diluting it. The filtrate is a saturated solution of nitre at the observed temperature.

To obtain the Solubility of Nitre, using this Solution. Weigh a clean dry dish and add some of the saturated solution to it. Weigh again. **Once having weighed be careful not to lose any portion of the solution.** Place the dish on a steam bath (Fig. 45), and evaporate until the nitre is left quite dry. (The dish on a gauze may be warmed very gently over the bunsen flame for a few minutes to complete the removal of water.) Allow the dish to cool and weigh it. Calculate the weight in grams of the nitre which would have dissolved in 100 gm. of water as in the following calculation.

Alternative method of evaporation to dryness. The following method is quicker than the one suggested above with little loss of accuracy if carefully performed. Weigh a dish (3 inch diameter is suitable) with a clock-glass to fit over it. Weigh again having added some saturated solution of nitre and replaced the clock-glass. Evaporate to dryness over a medium flame increasing the size of the flame towards the end. Do not heat the solid sufficiently strongly to decompose it. Allow to cool and weigh.

Weighings.

> Weight of dish   .   .   .   . 14·32 gms. = a gms.
> Weight of dish and solution .   . 35·70 gms. = b gms.
> Weight of dish and nitre   .   . 18·60 gms. = c gms.
>
> Temperature of the saturated solution = 15° C.

Hence:

$$\underset{(b-c)}{17\cdot 10 \text{ gm. of water dissolve}} \underset{(c-a)}{4\cdot 28 \text{ gm. nitre}}$$

$$\therefore \quad 1 \text{ gm. of water dissolves } \frac{4\cdot 28}{17\cdot 10} \text{ gm. nitre}$$

$$\frac{(c-a)}{(b-c)}$$

$$\therefore \quad 100 \text{ gm. of water dissolve } \frac{4\cdot 28}{17\cdot 10} \times 100 \text{ gm. nitre}$$

$$\frac{(c-a)}{(b-c)} \times 100$$

$$= 25\cdot 0 \text{ gm. nitre per 100 gm. water at 15° C.}$$

As a general rule an increase in temperature brings about an increase in the solubility of a solid solute.

Some common exceptions are calcium sulphate, calcium hydroxide and sodium sulphate (over a certain range of temperature).

By finding the solubilities of a solute at varying temperatures a graph can be plotted to show how the solubility alters with increase of temperature, with many interesting results. This is called a *solubility curve* of the solute.

To Determine the Solubility of Nitre at 50° C. This is the method employed to determine the solubility at any temperature above laboratory temperature. At these higher temperatures, the rate of solution of the nitre is greatly increased, and a saturated solution may be made directly.

Crush some crystals of nitre in a mortar, place some of them in a
boiling-tube and add a little water (to make the tube about half-full).
Put the boiling-tube in a beaker of water and warm the latter up
to a temperature of about 55° C. (Fig. 54). Whilst warming the

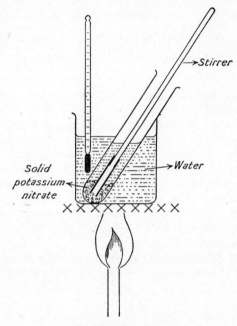

FIG. 54.

Solubility of nitre at 50° C.

solution keep adding nitre crystals to the boiling-tube, and stir
all the time. Add nitre until some remains undissolved at the
bottom of the tube. Remove the flame when the temperature, as
read by the thermometer, reaches 55° C., and allow the apparatus
to cool, stirring all the while and always maintaining some undissolved nitre at the bottom of the tube. Just before the temperature
falls to 50° C., remove the stirrer, allow the solid nitre to settle,
and put the dry thermometer into the nitre solution. When the
temperature is exactly 50° C., rapidly decant a little of the saturated
solution into a weighed dish, leaving all solid nitre behind. Weigh
the dish again and evaporate to dryness as in the previous experiment. Calculate the weight of nitre dissolved in 100 gm. of water
at 50° C. in a similar way.

By repeating the experiment at varying temperatures several

values can be obtained from which a curve can be plotted. Below is a table of values obtained in this way. Plot the graph on squared paper. The following figures were actually obtained by a middle school form. (The figures in brackets are the accepted accurate values.)

Temperature .	11° C.	15° C.	30° C.	40·5° C.	50° C.	57° C.
Gm. nitre per 100 { gm. water {	23·6 gm. (10° C.; 20 gm.)	25·1 gm. (25 gm.)	43·3 gm. (45 gm.)	63 gm. (40° C.; 63 gm.)	84 gm. (85 gm.)	102 gm. (106 gm.)

Alternative method (using any substance which does not exhibit supersaturation).

Weigh 4·5 gm. of potassium chlorate into a boiling-tube and run in 10 c.c. (gm.) of water from a burette. Warm until dissolved, remove from the flame, insert a thermometer and allow to cool, stirring with the thermometer. Note the temperature at which crystals appear. This will be the temperature at which the solubility is 45 gm. Add a further 10 c.c. of water and repeat the experiment. Continue the addition, determining the temperature at which the solution is just saturated until 60 c.c. of water have been added. Construct the graph.

Graph of Solubilities. Look at the accompanying graph of the solubilities of a few common salts. (Fig. 55.) Answer the following questions.

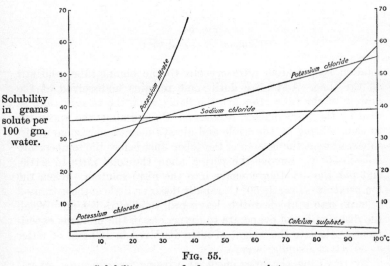

Fig. 55.
Solubility curves of a few common substances.

(a) *For which salt does the solubility increase most rapidly with rise in temperature?*

(b) *If a solution containing potassium chlorate and potassium chloride is cooled, which salt will deposit first?*

(c) *For which salt is there a decrease in solubility with increase in temperature?*

Super-saturation. Fill a 6 × 1 inch boiling-tube to a depth of about an inch with water, then fill it up with crystals of "hypo", sodium thiosulphate, $Na_2S_2O_3 . 5H_2O$. Heat the tube gently and shake until the crystals are all dissolved. Holding the boiling-tube quite still, cool the solution under the tap. Even when the solution is quite cold, no crystals separate (Fig. 56, I). Now select a single pin-head size crystal of "hypo" and drop it into the solution. At once, white crystals separate, growing slowly downwards through

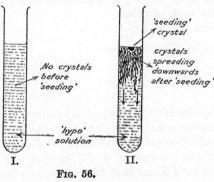

FIG. 56.
Super-saturation.

the solution and starting from the added crystal as centre (Fig. 56, II). The contents of the boiling-tube become almost a solid mass of "hypo" crystals and only a very little solution can be poured off. Note the rise of temperature as the crystals separate.

After the crystals have separated, the solution left must be still saturated with "hypo". Before they separated, it must have been "more than saturated", or "super-saturated", as it is called.

Definition. **A solution is said to be super-saturated when it contains in solution more of the solute than it can hold at that temperature in the presence of the crystals of the solute.**

It is important to notice that "super-saturated" solutions are in an unstable condition. They can only be obtained to any marked extent:

(a) From a few compounds, for example: Glauber's salt, $Na_2SO_4 . 10H_2O$, "hypo", $Na_2S_2O_3 . 5H_2O$.

(*b*) By excluding all dust. The dust particles might act as centres of crystallisation,

(*c*) By cooling the solution slowly. "Hypo" is exceptional in giving a super-saturated solution when cooled quickly.

(*d*) By avoiding all shaking or disturbance of the solution.

A solution cannot be super-saturated if in contact with crystals of the solute.

Effect of Dissolved Solids on the Boiling-Point of a Solution.
Put about 200 c.c. of water into a distilling flask ($\frac{1}{2}$ litre) fitted with a sensitive thermometer, which should read to tenths of a degree. Add a few pieces of porous pot, clamp the flask at a suitable height and heat the water to boiling-point and notice at what temperature the water boils. Now add a weighed amount of common salt, say 5 gm., and again determine the boiling-point. Repeat this experiment, adding exactly 5 gm. of salt each time and noting the boiling-point after each addition.

Specimen Readings:—

Temperature of boiling water	99·7° C
,, ,, ,, ,, with 5 gm. of salt added	100·2° C
,, ,, ,, ,, ,, 10 gm. ,, ,, ,,	100·7° C
,, ,, ,, ,, ,, 15 gm. ,, ,, ,,	101·2° C

It will be observed that equal quantities of salt dissolved in the water produce equal elevations in the boiling-point of the solution.

Effect of Dissolved Substances on the Freezing-Point of Solutions.
Water, if pure, freezes at 0° C., but if it contains some dissolved substance, it is found that the solution no longer freezes at 0° C., but at a lower temperature. It is also found that equal additional quantities of the dissolved solid cause equal depressions of the freezing-point. Hence, the depression of the freezing-point of a solvent is proportional to the amount of a substance dissolved in a given mass of the solvent.

QUESTIONS

1. Explain the difference between (*a*) temporary, and (*b*) permanent hardness in water. Give the names of ONE substance causing temporary and of TWO substances causing permanent hardness in water. Explain how permanent hardness may be removed, giving equations for the chemical changes involved. How would you test for the presence of a chloride in tap water? (N.U.J.B.)
2. What are solubility curves? Of what use are they? What experiments would you make in order to construct a solubility curve for potassium chlorate? (O. and C.)

3. What are the substances which cause (a) temporary, (b) permanent "hardness" in water?

Explain the effect of adding the following substances to "hard" water: (a) soap, (b) lime-water, (c) washing soda.

What is the "fur" deposited in the kettle? Briefly explain how stalactites and stalagmites are formed in caves. (B.)

4. What are the conditions, and what are the products, for the reaction of the following substances with water or steam: (a) iron, (b) calcium, (c) charcoal, (d) chlorine, (e) calcium carbide? (D.)

5. Imagine that you wish to prove experimentally to someone that 18 gm. of water contain 2 gm. of hydrogen and 16 gm. of oxygen. Give a labelled sketch of the apparatus you would use; indicate the two chief precautions you would adopt to ensure an accurate result; show how you would use the data you obtain to prove the above statement. (N.U.J.B.)

6. Ordinary tap water always contains some air in solution. Describe in detail how you would collect a quantity of this air from tap-water. How could you find the proportion by volume of oxygen in such air? Explain why the composition of this dissolved air will be different from that of ordinary air. (N.U.J.B.)

7. State and explain what happens when carbon dioxide gas is passed for a long time through lime-water. State and explain what happens when soap solution is shaken up with the final product (a) before it has been boiled, (b) after it has been boiled. (N.U.J.B.)

8. What is meant by the terms "saturated solution" and "supersaturated solution"? Describe exactly how you would proceed to determine the solubility of potassium nitrate in water at 15° C. (N.U.J.B.)

9. What experiments would you make to find out whether (a) a given sample of water is hard or soft, (b) a gas jar contains nitrous oxide or a mixture of nitrogen and oxygen, (c) a given solid is sodium sulphide or sodium sulphate? (O. and C.)

10. Choose either (a) or (b), but not both:

   (a) Write an essay on "combustion", giving a brief historical introduction.

   (b) Define the term solubility. What are the effects of temperature and pressure on the solubility of (a) gases, (b) solids, in water? Give the requisite practical details for constructing a solubility curve of a salt, e.g., nitre. State two of the uses of a solubility curve. (B.)

11. A colourless liquid (X) is either pure water, or water containing some dissolved solid. Describe carefully how to discover which it is by observations of the temperature at which it (a) boils, (b) freezes. Sketch the apparatus you would use in each case. Assume that a supply of pure water is provided. (N.U.J.B.)

12. What do you observe when carbon dioxide is passed for a long time through lime-water? Give equations representing the reactions which take place.

What happens when the final solution obtained is (a) treated with soap solution, (b) boiled, (c) treated with a solution of sodium carbonate

Describe the "permutit" process for softening water and state how the permutit is restored (or revivified). (C.W.B.)

CHAPTER XVI

ACIDS, BASES AND SALTS

ACIDS

In Chapter VII, an acid (dilute sulphuric acid) was used for the preparation of hydrogen by bringing it into contact with a metal (zinc). In this reaction free hydrogen was liberated from the acid, and the zinc, formerly present as the free metal, entered into chemical combination to form the salt, zinc sulphate. We shall define the term salt later.

$$Zn + H_2SO_4 \rightarrow ZnSO_4 + H_2$$

The significant point to grasp about this reaction is that **the hydrogen of the acid has been replaced by a metal.** In making this point, we have laid our finger on the characteristic property of acids—that property which distinguishes them from other compounds—the fact that they contain hydrogen which can be replaced by a metal. (Acids, also, of course, turn litmus red.) The compound formed is called a salt, and we can regard salts provisionally as compounds obtained by replacing the hydrogen of an acid by a metal.

This process of replacing the hydrogen of an acid by a metal cannot always be carried out directly. The hydrogen of dilute sulphuric acid, H_2SO_4, for example, cannot be directly replaced by copper to form copper sulphate, $CuSO_4$, by the action of the acid on copper, for the very good reason that copper simply will not act upon dilute sulphuric acid. In this case, we have to fall back upon an indirect method of replacement such as the action of the acid upon cupric oxide.

$$CuO + H_2SO_4 \rightarrow CuSO_4 + H_2O$$

Though this is an indirect replacement of hydrogen by a metal, the final result is the same, that is, the relation between copper sulphate and sulphuric acid is that the copper sulphate is produced by replacing the hydrogen of sulphuric acid by copper.

Definition. **An acid is a substance which will turn blue litmus red and contains hydrogen, which may be replaced, directly or indirectly, by a metal.**

There are, actually, some tens of thousands of acids. All contain hydrogen, which can be replaced by a metal, and, in addition, certain other properties are found to be fairly commonly shared by them.

Some other Properties of Acids. *Taste.* Most dilute acids have a sour taste. This is true of the three common mineral acids, sulphuric, hydrochloric and nitric, and of many others. The sour taste of many unripe fruits, lemons and sour milk is caused by the acids in them.

Action on Litmus. Most acids turn blue litmus to red. Some of the weaker acids, however, for example carbonic acid, H_2CO_3, are so feebly acidic that they can only turn the litmus to claret colour.

Corrosive Action. The man in the street connects the term "acid" with the idea of a corrosive, "burning" liquid. This is because two of the commonest acids—sulphuric acid (oil of vitriol) and nitric acid ("aqua fortis")—are actually corrosive liquids. Acids are not, however, generally corrosive, and the great majority of them are solids.

Action on Carbonates. Almost all acids (only the very weakest are exceptions) liberate carbon dioxide from a carbonate; for example

$$CaCO_3 + 2HCl \rightarrow CaCl_2 + H_2O + CO_2$$
dilute hydro-
chloric acid

$$CuCO_3 + 2HNO_3 \rightarrow Cu(NO_3)_2 + H_2O + CO_2$$
dilute
nitric acid

To find whether a given substance has acidic properties, a test frequently used is to add some of it to sodium carbonate solution; if effervescence occurs, the substance is an acid.

Methods of Preparation of Acids

1. *By the reaction between an anhydride (the acid oxide of a non-metal) and water.*

For example $\qquad SO_2 + H_2O \rightarrow H_2SO_3$
sulphurous acid

$$P_4O_{10} + 6H_2O \rightarrow 4H_3PO_4$$
phosphoric acid

2. *By displacing a weaker or more volatile acid from its salt by a stronger or less volatile acid.*

For example, (a) displacement of the more volatile hydrogen chloride from a metallic chloride by the less volatile sulphuric acid.

$$NaCl + H_2SO_4 \rightarrow NaHSO_4 + HCl \uparrow$$

G

(b) Displacement of the weaker boric acid from borax by sulphuric acid.

$$Na_2B_4O_7 + H_2SO_4 + 5H_2O \rightarrow Na_2SO_4 + 4H_3BO_3$$

borax   boric
acid

The action of acids upon carbonates is a special case of this general reaction. Carbonic acid is a very weak acid and also very readily decomposes into the gas, carbon dioxide, and water.

For example, $Na_2CO_3 + H_2SO_4 \rightarrow Na_2SO_4 + [H_2CO_3]$

carbonic acid

$$[H_2CO_3] \rightarrow H_2O + CO_2 \uparrow$$

3. *By precipitating an insoluble sulphide from a metallic salt by hydrogen sulphide.*

For example, $Pb(C_2H_3O_2)_2 + H_2S \rightarrow PbS + 2C_2H_4O_2$

lead acetate   acetic acid

BASES

We have seen (p. 180) that, where it is not possible to replace the hydrogen of an acid by a metal directly, the same result can often be achieved by acting upon the oxide of the metal with the dilute acid. Here are some cases of this kind of reaction, which is quite general.

$$CuO + H_2SO_4 \rightarrow CuSO_4 + H_2O$$

copper oxide   copper sulphate

$$Na_2O + 2HCl \rightarrow 2NaCl + H_2O$$

sodium oxide   sodium chloride

$$ZnO + H_2SO_4 \rightarrow ZnSO_4 + H_2O$$

zinc oxide   zinc sulphate

$$Fe_2O_3 + 6HCl \rightarrow 2FeCl_3 + 3H_2O$$

ferric oxide   ferric chloride

$\uparrow$

All these compounds are "salts".

The above four reactions can all be carried out using the dilute acids. Whenever this type of reaction can be performed with a metallic oxide, it is also given by the corresponding metallic hydroxide. For example:

$$Cu(OH)_2 + H_2SO_4 \rightarrow CuSO_4 + 2H_2O$$
copper
hydroxide

$$NaOH + HCl \rightarrow NaCl + H_2O$$
sodium
hydroxide

$$Zn(OH)_2 + H_2SO_4 \rightarrow ZnSO_4 + 2H_2O$$
zinc
hydroxide

$$Fe(OH)_3 + 3HCl \rightarrow FeCl_3 + 3H_2O$$
ferric   All these
hydroxide   compounds
             are "salts".

Notice that, in each case, the products are the same—a salt and water—whether an oxide or hydroxide of a metal is employed.

Compounds which react in this way with acids to produce a salt and water and no other product are included in the very important class of substances called **bases**.

If a metallic oxide or hydroxide will react with an acid to give a salt and water only, it is a base.

All the oxides and hydroxides concerned in the eight equations given above are *bases*.

The terms *basic oxide* and *basic hydroxide* are frequently used. They are defined in a similar way. Thus:

Definition. **A basic oxide (hydroxide) is a metallic oxide (hydroxide) which will react with an acid to form a salt and water only.**

It is important to realise the significance of the word "only" in these definitions. If it was omitted, certain compounds, which are quite different from metallic oxides and hydroxides, would be included under the definition of a "base". Thus, lead dioxide reacts with hydrochloric acid to produce lead chloride (a salt) and water, but the word "only" excludes it from the class of "bases" because chlorine is also produced.

$$PbO_2 + 4HCl \rightarrow PbCl_2 + 2H_2O + Cl_2$$

Compare this with the equations above. Lead dioxide is clearly not a base.

A name is also given to these very important reactions between bases and acids. They are called "neutralisations".

Definition. **A neutralisation is a reaction between an acid and a base producing a salt and water only.**

All the eight reactions given above are examples of neutralisations. Full experimental details of some neutralisations are given later in this chapter, when methods of making salts are discussed.

Alkalis. A very important division can be made inside the general class we have called "bases", according to whether they are, or are not, soluble in water. The great majority of the bases are insoluble in water, and they are just "bases". A few are soluble in water, and to them the name *"alkalis"* is given. The common ones are sodium hydroxide (caustic soda) NaOH, potassium hydroxide (caustic potash) KOH, calcium hydroxide (slaked lime) $Ca(OH)_2$, and ammonium hydroxide NH_4OH. This property of solubility in water is the only difference between the select little group of alkalis and the bases generally, but what a difference! It puts the alkalis at our service in hundreds of reactions in solution and for hundreds of purposes for which the insoluble bases are quite useless.

Definition. **An alkali is a base which is soluble in water.**

We must make it quite clear that all alkalis are bases and have

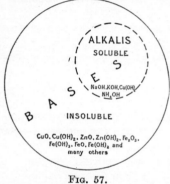

all the properties of bases together with the property of dissolving in water, while the insoluble bases are—just bases. A diagram may make the point clearer (Fig. 57).

Every compound inside the big, continuous circle is a base; the compounds inside the dotted circle are alkalis and bases; the compounds inside the big circle, but outside the dotted one, are bases but not alkalis.

FIG. 57.

Properties of Alkalis. In addition to neutralising acids, the alkalis all have a bitter taste and possess the property of turning red litmus blue. Further, the two strong or "caustic" alkalis, caustic soda and potash, have a powerful corrosive action on the skin and should be handled with care. Just as a non-volatile acid displaces a volatile acid from its salts, a non-volatile alkali displaces the volatile ammonia from ammonium salts. If an ammonium compound is warmed with an alkali, ammonia gas is liberated.

For example:

$$NaOH + NH_4Cl \rightarrow NH_3 \uparrow + H_2O + NaCl$$
sodium   ammonium   ammonia
hydroxide chloride

$$Ca(OH)_2 + (NH_4)_2SO_4 \rightarrow 2NH_3 \uparrow + 2H_2O + CaSO_4$$
slaked   ammonium   ammonia
lime   sulphate

SALTS

We have seen (p. 180) that the characteristic of an acid is that it contains hydrogen which can be replaced by a metal. The compound which is obtained as a result of this replacement is called a salt.

The following table compares the formulæ of a few salts with those of the acids from which they are derived. Notice carefully how, in each case, a metal has replaced the hydrogen of the acid.

Acid.	Salt.	
HCl	NaCl	Sodium chloride
HCl	KCl	Potassium chloride
H_2SO_4	$ZnSO_4$	Zinc sulphate
H_2SO_4	$FeSO_4$	Ferrous sulphate
HNO_3	$NaNO_3$	Sodium nitrate
HNO_3	$AgNO_3$	Silver nitrate
H_2CO_3	$CaCO_3$	Calcium carbonate
H_2CO_3	$BaCO_3$	Barium carbonate

Normal and Acid Salts. When an acid contains more than one hydrogen atom per molecule, it is possible for the replacement of it by a metal to take place by stages.

Thus, one of the hydrogen atoms of sulphuric acid may be replaced by a sodium atom to give sodium hydrogen sulphate, $NaHSO_4$, after which a second sodium atom may replace the remaining hydrogen atom to give sodium sulphate, Na_2SO_4.

Salts like sodium hydrogen sulphate, $NaHSO_4$, partake of the nature of a salt because they are obtained by replacing some of the hydrogen of an acid by a metal, and they partake also of the nature of an acid because they still contain hydrogen, which can be replaced by a metal. Having this dual nature, they are appropriately called "acid salts". Salts, like sodium sulphate, Na_2SO_4, to form which *all* the hydrogen of an acid has been replaced by a metal, are called "normal salts".

Definition. A salt is a compound obtained by replacing the hydrogen of an acid by a metal; if all the hydrogen of the acid is replaced, the salt is called a "normal" salt; if only part of the hydrogen is replaced, the salt is called an "acid" salt.

Examples:

Acid.	Acid Salt.		Normal Salt.
H_2SO_4	$NaHSO_4$	sodium hydrogen sulphate	Na_2SO_4
H_2CO_3	$NaHCO_3$	sodium hydrogen carbonate	Na_2CO_3
H_2S	NaHS	sodium hydrogen sulphide	Na_2S

A method of preparing the normal and acid sodium salt of sulphuric acid is given on p. 321, of the normal and acid sulphides of sodium on p. 311, and of sodium carbonate and bicarbonate on p. 103 and p. 259.

Basicity of an Acid. We have seen that the characteristic of an acid is that it contains hydrogen which can be replaced by a metal. The number of hydrogen atoms per molecule of the acid which can be replaced by a metal is called the basicity of the acid.

Definition. **The basicity of an acid is the number of hydrogen atoms per molecule of it which can be replaced by a metal.**

The basicity of hydrochloric acid, HCl, which contains only one hydrogen atom per molecule, is one. Sulphuric acid has a basicity of two, phosphoric acid, H_3PO_4, a basicity of three, these being the number of replaceable hydrogen atoms per molecule.

Basic Salts. A salt may also be regarded as derived from a basic oxide or hydroxide by replacing the oxygen atoms or the hydroxyl (OH) groups of the base by an acid radical, thus:

Base.	Salt.
NaOH	NaCl
$Zn(OH)_2$	$ZnSO_4$
$Al(OH)_3$	$AlCl_3$
Fe_2O_3	$Fe_2(SO_4)_3$

If the replacement of the oxide or hydroxyl groups by acid radicals is not complete, the salt is known as a *basic salt.*

Thus:

Base.	Basic Salt.	Normal Salt.	
$Zn(OH)_2$	$Zn(OH)Cl$	$ZnCl_2$	zinc chloride
$Al(OH)_3$	$Al(OH)_2Cl$	$AlCl_3$	aluminium chloride
Bi_2O_3	$BiOCl$	$BiCl_3$	bismuth chloride

Alternatively, a basic salt may be regarded as a compound produced by the combination of one or more molecules of a base with one or more molecules of the corresponding normal salt.
Thus:

Base.	Normal Salt.	Basic Salt.
$Zn(OH)_2$	$ZnCl_2$	$Zn(OH)_2.ZnCl_2$ basic zinc chloride or $2Zn(OH)Cl$
$Cu(OH)_2$	$CuCO_3$	$CuCO_3.Cu(OH)_2$ basic copper carbonate
$Pb(OH)_2$	$PbCO_3$	$Pb(OH)_2.2PbCO_3$ basic lead carbonate (white lead)

Practical details of the more important methods of making salts are given in the following pages.

METHODS OF PREPARING SALTS

Rules of Solubility of Salts in Water.

SOLUBLE.	INSOLUBLE.
1. All common *salts* of *sodium, potassium* and *ammonium*.	
2. All common *nitrates* of metals,	
3. All common *chlorides* except	silver chloride, mercurous chloride and lead chloride.
4. All common *sulphates* except	barium sulphate and lead sulphate. (Calcium sulphate sparingly soluble.)
	5. All common *carbonates* except those of sodium, potassium and ammonium (see Rule 1).

Several general methods are available for preparing salts. The method chosen for preparing any particular salt depends largely on whether it is soluble in water or not. It is necessary, therefore, for you to become quite familiar with the simple rules of solubility on p. 187. Knowing the solubility of the salt, you will then be able to decide at once what type of method to use.

Soluble salts usually are prepared by methods which involve **crystallisation**. **Insoluble** salts are usually prepared by methods which involve **precipitation**.

PREPARATION OF SALTS BY THE ACTION OF AN ACID UPON A METAL

This is usually carried out using a *dilute* acid and a metal. The salt formed then passes into solution in the water of the dilute acid and can be obtained, with the necessary precautions to give purity, by crystallisation. This method is suitable for preparing *soluble* salts.

To Prepare a Sample of Crystalline Zinc Sulphate (White Vitriol) from Metallic Zinc. Half-fill a beaker with bench dilute sulphuric acid and add granulated zinc. Effervescence occurs; if it is slow, add a little copper sulphate to quicken the action and warm gently. The gas is hydrogen (test: explosion on applying a lighted taper). If the action ceases because of the disappearance of zinc, add more zinc to make sure that the acid is not left in considerable excess. The reason for this is that later we shall evaporate the solution and any excess acid would then tend to become concentrated. When the effervescence slows down and there is still plenty of zinc left, filter to remove insoluble impurities such as excess zinc and particles of carbon which were an impurity in it.

The colourless solution will contain zinc sulphate together with a little sulphuric acid. There will probably be too much water present to allow the crystals to separate, so we must remove some of it. Place the solution in an evaporating dish and heat. At intervals, pour a little of the solution into a test-tube and cool it under the tap, shaking well. After evaporating for a time, you will see small crystals in one of the cooled samples. This shows that the solution will give crystals when cool, for the small sample is typical of the whole. Pour the solution into a beaker and allow it to cool and crystallise. In this case the crystals will be colourless needles.

Filter off the crystals, wash them two or three times with a small quantity of cold distilled water and place them on a porous plate or between filter-papers to dry. The washing with distilled water is to remove the surface solution from the crystals and replace it with pure water which, as it dries off, will not deposit impurities as would the solution. The porous plate or filter-papers are used to absorb water from the surfaces of the crystals. To purify still further, dissolve the crystals in a little very hot water and repeat the crystallisation process. The impurities will then be carried off dissolved in the filtrate and a smaller quantity of purer crystals will be left.

$$Zn + H_2SO_4 \rightarrow ZnSO_4 + H_2$$
$$ZnSO_4 + 7H_2O \rightarrow ZnSO_4 . 7H_2O$$

Other salts may be similarly prepared, for example, ferrous sulphate and magnesium sulphate.

Preparation of Ferrous Sulphate Crystals (green vitriol). Use iron filings or wire and excess dilute sulphuric acid. The solution and crystals are green.

$$Fe + H_2SO_4 \rightarrow FeSO_4 + H_2$$
$$FeSO_4 + 7H_2O \rightarrow FeSO_4 . 7H_2O$$
(ferrous sulphate crystals)

Preparation of Magnesium Sulphate Crystals (Epsom salt). Use magnesium rod and dilute sulphuric acid. The solution and the crystals are colourless.

$$Mg + H_2SO_4 \rightarrow MgSO_4 + H_2$$
$$MgSO_4 + 7H_2O \rightarrow MgSO_4 . 7H_2O$$
(magnesium sulphate
crystals)

Occasionally this method is applied using a metal and a concentrated acid. The only case of this you will encounter, though it is an important one, is

The Preparation of a Sample of Blue Vitriol (Crystalline Copper Sulphate) from Metallic Copper. Note especially that this preparation cannot be carried out like the two above, because dilute sulphuric acid will not act upon copper.

Into a beaker put some concentrated sulphuric acid and copper turnings (care!). Put the beaker on a tripod and gauze in the fume-cupboard and warm gently. After a time *effervescence* will begin, the gas evolved being sulphur dioxide, which must not be allowed to escape into the laboratory as it is injurious. The action will probably become vigorous, and the flame should then be removed. After effervescence has ceased there will be left a dark brown mass which may contain the following substances:

1. Solid copper sulphate as a **precipitate.**
2. Solid dark brown cuprous sulphide, formed in small amount, by a side reaction.
3. Excess copper.
4. Excess concentrated sulphuric acid.

Our problem is to prepare from this mixture a sample of pure blue vitriol. We cannot work in the presence of a large amount of concentrated sulphuric acid, so the first step must be to pour off as much liquid as possible. The liquid is simply a waste product. We are now left with a solid containing copper sulphate with impurities 2 and 3, as given above. They are both insoluble in water, so, to remove them, add a considerable quantity of water and heat gently to boiling. Filter, leaving the two impurities, copper and cuprous sulphide, on the filter-paper, and obtaining, as filtrate, blue copper sulphate solution. From this crystals can be obtained as previously described.

$$Cu + 2H_2SO_4 \rightarrow CuSO_4 + 2H_2O + SO_2$$
$$CuSO_4 + 5H_2O \rightarrow CuSO_4 . 5H_2O$$

This process of heating copper with concentrated sulphuric acid is the best laboratory method of making sulphur dioxide, and copper sulphate can be prepared from the residue left in the flask after carrying out this preparation (p. 313).

Nitrates of certain metals can be prepared by acting upon the metals with dilute or concentrated nitric acid and crystallising as described above. The nitrates, of common heavy metals, except lead nitrate, are, however, very soluble in water and deliquescent. This makes it a matter of greater difficulty to prepare their crystals.

$$\underset{\text{lead}}{3Pb} + 8HNO_3 \rightarrow \underset{\text{lead nitrate}}{3Pb(NO_3)_2} + 4H_2O + 2NO$$

$$\underset{\text{copper}}{3Cu} + 8HNO_3 \rightarrow \underset{\text{copper nitrate}}{3Cu(NO_3)_2} + 4H_2O + 2NO$$

Chlorides of heavy metals are generally prepared in the anhydrous state by heating the metal in a current of dry chlorine or hydrogen chloride (see p. 278).

The reason for this is that many of them crystallise with water of crystallisation, and, if an attempt is made to drive off this water by heating, they hydrolyse to basic salts (see p. 187).

Thus: $ZnCl_2 . H_2O \xrightarrow{\text{heat}} Zn(OH)Cl + HCl$

PREPARATION OF SALTS BY DOUBLE DECOMPOSITION

In a double decomposition reaction, we usually begin with two soluble compounds and use them to prepare one soluble and one insoluble compound (p. 129). Of these, the one which is wanted is usually the insoluble compound for it can be easily separated by filtering. That is, insoluble salts are prepared by double decomposition. For a more complete discussion of double decomposition see p. 129.

To prepare a Sample of Lead Sulphate. Here we must begin with a soluble lead salt to provide the lead ions, and a soluble sulphate to provide the sulphate ions of the lead sulphate. Suitable compounds will be lead nitrate and dilute sulphuric acid (a soluble sulphate).

One-third fill a beaker with lead nitrate solution. Heat it and add dilute sulphuric acid, stirring the mixture. There will be an immediate white precipitate of lead sulphate. Heat to boiling,[1] then filter. The lead sulphate is left on the filter-paper and the colourless filtrate contains dilute nitric acid, the other product of the double decomposition reaction. Wash the precipitate on the filter-paper several times with hot distilled water to remove soluble impurities. To be sure that the process is complete, test the washings for sulphate (p. 403) and continue till the test gives a negative result. Allow the precipitate to dry on the filter-paper or on a porous plate. It will become a white powder.

$$Pb(NO_3)_2 + H_2SO_4 \rightarrow PbSO_4 + 2HNO_3$$

lead nitrate hydrogen sulphate lead sulphate hydrogen nitrate

A solution of any soluble sulphate could have been used for this preparation; for example:

$$Pb(NO_3)_2 + Na_2SO_4 \rightarrow PbSO_4 + 2NaNO_3$$

lead nitrate sodium sulphate lead sulphate sodium nitrate

ionically: $Pb^{++} + SO_4^{--} \rightarrow PbSO_4 \downarrow$

The sodium nitrate, like the nitric acid above, would be removed in solution.

Other insoluble salts which can be prepared by double decomposition are:

Barium sulphate $BaCl_2 + H_2SO_4 \rightarrow BaSO_4 + 2HCl$
                      barium chloride

ionically: $Ba^{++} + SO_4^{--} \rightarrow BaSO_4 \downarrow$

Lead chloride[2] $Pb(NO_3)_2 + 2NaCl \rightarrow PbCl_2 + 2NaNO_3$

ionically: $Pb^{++} + 2Cl^- \rightarrow PbCl_2 \downarrow$

Calcium carbonate $CaCl_2 + Na_2CO_3 \rightarrow CaCO_3 + 2NaCl$
                      calcium chloride

ionically: $Ca^{++} + CO_3^{--} \rightarrow CaCO_3 \downarrow$

The carbonates of other heavy metals can be prepared like calcium carbonate but, in some cases, the method gives a basic carbonate.

---

[1] The chief reason for this is that a boiling solution filters more rapidly than a cold one.
[2] Lead chloride must be washed with *cold* distilled water. as it is appreciably soluble in hot water.

This does not matter much, however, because the method is chiefly used as an intermediate stage in preparing the oxide of a metal from one of its soluble salts (p. 197), and in this case it does not matter whether a true or a basic carbonate is precipitated.

In the cases of zinc carbonate, copper carbonate and lead carbonate, a purer product is obtained if sodium *bi*carbonate is used instead of sodium carbonate.

PREPARATION OF SALTS BY NEUTRALISATION

Neutralisation is an action between a *base* and an *acid* to produce a *salt* and *water* only (p. 183). The actual method of application of this process depends on whether the base in question is soluble in water, that is, is an alkali (p. 184) or not.

Preparation of a Salt from an Alkali (a Soluble Base).

Salts of *sodium, potassium* and *ammonium* can be prepared by this method from *caustic soda* (sodium hydroxide), *caustic potash* (potassium hydroxide) and *ammonia* (ammonium hydroxide) respectively, using the appropriate acid.

To prepare Sodium Sulphate from Caustic Soda. Into a conical flask, put 50 c.c. of bench caustic soda solution and add to it enough litmus solution to give a pale blue liquid. From a burette, add dilute sulphuric acid until the solution is purple in colour; that is, it contains no excess of either acid (which would make the litmus red), or alkali (which would make the litmus blue). The litmus is here the *indicator* (p. 104). The solution now contains sodium sulphate solution together with litmus. To remove the litmus, add a little animal charcoal on the end of a spatula, boil the mixture, and filter. The animal charcoal will be left on the filter-paper together with the litmus which it has absorbed, and a colourless solution of sodium sulphate will be left as filtrate. From this, crystals can be obtained as described above for zinc sulphate (p. 188).

$$2NaOH + H_2SO_4 \rightarrow Na_2SO_4 + 2H_2O$$
$$Na_2SO_4 + 10H_2O \rightarrow Na_2SO_4 . 10H_2O$$

To obtain sodium chloride or nitrate, use caustic soda solution with the appropriate acid.

$$NaOH + HCl \rightarrow NaCl + H_2O$$

sodium   dilute   sodium
hydroxide   hydro-   chloride
            chloric acid

$$NaOH + HNO_3 \rightarrow NaNO_3 + H_2O$$

dilute   sodium
nitric acid   nitrate

To obtain the common potassium salts, use caustic potash solution with the appropriate acid.

$$KOH + HCl \rightarrow KCl + H_2O$$
potassium
chloride

$$2KOH + H_2SO_4 \rightarrow K_2SO_4 + 2H_2O$$
potassium
sulphate

$$KOH + HNO_3 \rightarrow KNO_3 + H_2O$$
potassium
nitrate

Ammonium salts can be similarly prepared from ammonia.

$$NH_4OH + HCl \rightarrow NH_4Cl + H_2O$$
ammonium
chloride

$$2NH_4OH + H_2SO_4 \rightarrow (NH_4)_2SO_4 + 2H_2O$$
ammonium
sulphate

$$NH_4OH + HNO_3 \rightarrow NH_4NO_3 + H_2O$$
ammonium
nitrate

The above equations indicate the substances to be used (all in solution) in the preparation of the salt by the method described for sodium sulphate.

Preparation of a Salt from an Insoluble Base. In this case the base, being insoluble in water, is not an alkali, so the method given above cannot be applied.

To prepare Copper Sulphate Crystals from the Insoluble Base, Copper Oxide. Heat some dilute sulphuric acid in a beaker and add to it, a little at a time, some black copper oxide. Stir gently. A blue solution of copper sulphate will be formed.

$$\underset{\text{BASE}}{CuO} + \underset{\text{ACID}}{H_2SO_4} \rightarrow \underset{\text{SALT}}{CuSO_4} + \underset{\text{WATER}}{H_2O}$$

It is advisable not to leave an excess of acid (for reason see preparation of zinc sulphate from zinc), so continue the addition of the copper oxide until a permanent black precipitate of this material is left, showing that no more acid is available to act with it. Filter off the precipitate, leaving a clear blue filtrate, copper sulphate solution. From it, obtain crystals as described for zinc sulphate.

$$CuSO_4 + 5H_2O \rightarrow CuSO_4.5H_2O$$

Many salts of metals can be similarly prepared, using either the oxide or the hydroxide of the metal with the appropriate acid; for example,

Zinc sulphate $ZnO + H_2SO_4 \rightarrow ZnSO_4 + H_2O$
zinc
oxide

$Zn(OH)_2 + H_2SO_4 \rightarrow ZnSO_4 + 2H_2O$
zinc
hydroxide

Lead nitrate $PbO + 2HNO_3 \rightarrow Pb(NO_3)_2 + H_2O$
lead
oxide

$Pb(OH)_2 + 2HNO_3 \rightarrow Pb(NO_3)_2 + 2H_2O$
lead
hydroxide

PREPARATION OF SALTS BY THE ACTION OF AN ACID ON THE CARBONATE OF A METAL

The carbonate of any metal will react with the mineral acids to give the corresponding salt of the metal, water and carbon dioxide.

For example: $ZnCO_3 + H_2SO_4 \rightarrow ZnSO_4 + H_2O + CO_2$
zinc   zinc
carbonate   sulphate

$CaCO_3 + 2HCl \rightarrow CaCl_2 + H_2O + CO_2$
calcium   calcium
carbonate   chloride

$PbCO_3 + 2HNO_3 \rightarrow Pb(NO_3)_2 + H_2O + CO_2$
lead   lead nitrate
carbonate

The only limitation to this rule is that the action is unsatisfactory and incomplete if the carbonate is insoluble in water and, by its action on the acid, produces a salt which is also insoluble. In this case, the salt which is formed precipitates on the unchanged carbonate and stops the action. If, for example, dilute sulphuric acid is added to marble, there is rapid effervescence for a few seconds, but the action quickly stops.

$$CaCO_3 + H_2SO_4 \rightarrow CaSO_4 + H_2O + CO_2$$

The very slightly soluble calcium sulphate has precipitated on the marble, stopping the action. With this limitation, this method is of general application, for example:

Preparation of Lead Nitrate Crystals from Lead Carbonate. Half-fill a beaker with dilute nitric acid, warm it gently on a tripod and gauze and add lead carbonate at intervals. There will be effervescence with evolution of carbon dioxide. (Test: lime-water turned milky.) Continue the addition of the carbonate until a slight permanent precipitate shows that no acid is left, then filter to remove insoluble materials. The colourless solution contains lead nitrate, and crystals can be obtained from it as described for zinc sulphate (p. 188).

$$PbCO_3 + 2HNO_3 \rightarrow Pb(NO_3)_2 + H_2O + CO_2$$

Note. When an insoluble salt has to be prepared from a compound which is also insoluble in water, it is not advisable to try to convert one into the other by a single process.

For example: If it is required to convert *litharge* (insoluble in water) into *lead sulphate* (also insoluble in water), it is not advisable to attempt the change by the action of dilute sulphuric acid on the litharge. The reason is that the insoluble lead sulphate will precipitate, as fast as it is formed, round the particles of litharge, and it is very difficult to make sure that all the litharge has reacted.

In such cases, it is better to prepare first a soluble compound and then to precipitate the required insoluble salt by double decomposition. In the example, above, it is better to prepare first a solution of lead nitrate by dissolving the litharge in dilute nitric acid.

$$PbO + 2HNO_3 \rightarrow Pb(NO_3)_2 + H_2O$$

Then, after filtering off any undissolved material, the required ead sulphate can be precipitated by adding dilute sulphuric acid.

$$Pb(NO_3)_2 + H_2SO_4 \rightarrow PbSO_4 + 2HNO_3$$

By carrying out the conversion in two separate stages, we make sure that the process is complete and gives a pure product.

PREPARATION OF SALTS BY DIRECT COMBINATION OF TWO ELEMENTS

Certain binary salts can be prepared by direct combination of their two elements; for example

$$2Fe + 3Cl_2 \rightarrow 2FeCl_3 \text{ (see p. 278)}$$
ferric chloride

$$Fe + S \rightarrow FeS \text{ (see p. 7)}$$
ferrous sulphide

The method is of minor importance.

QUESTIONS

1. Describe fully, giving complete experimental details, how you would prepare the following. Consider in each case the solubility of the required compound and decide first which of the methods given

in the last chapter is the best for the given case. In some of them
it is advisable to use two steps (see Note, p. 195).

  (a) Copper sulphate crystals starting from malachite, basic copper
      carbonate, $CuCO_3 . Cu(OH)_2$.

  (b) Ferrous sulphate crystals starting from iron wire.

  (c) Nitre, potassium nitrate.

  (d) Calcium sulphate starting from marble, calcium carbonate.

  (e) Sal-ammoniac, ammonium chloride.

  (f) Lead chloride starting from lead carbonate.

  (g) Zinc sulphate crystals starting from zinc oxide.

  (h) Sodium chloride, common salt.

2. Describe fully, with complete experimental details, how you would
prepare (a) copper sulphate crystals from a mixture of charcoal
and black copper oxide. (b) zinc sulphate crystals from the commercial product, "zinc dust," which contains zinc and zinc oxide.
(c) a pure sample of barium sulphate and zinc carbonate, normal
or basic, from a mixture of zinc oxide and barium carbonate.

3. Describe one laboratory method of preparing specimens of each
of the following: (a) copper from copper sulphate, (b) solid sodium
hydrogen sulphate from sodium hydroxide, (c) potassium chlorate
from potassium hydroxide, (d) anhydrous ferric chloride from iron.
(B.)

4. Give four general methods of preparing acids, illustrating each
method by two examples.

    Describe experiments by which you could determine the basicity
of sulphuric acid. (L.)

5. Describe, giving experimental details, how you would prepare
crystalline specimens of (a) potassium nitrate starting from potassium hydroxide, (b) lead nitrate starting from red lead, (c) sodium
hydrogen sulphate starting from sodium hydroxide. (N.U.J.B.)

6. Starting from metallic zinc, describe carefully how you would
prepare reasonably pure specimens of (a) zinc sulphate, (b) zinc
carbonate.

    The zinc sulphate crystals are found to contain 43·9 per cent of
water of crystallisation. Calculate the number of molecules of water
in combination with one molecule of the anhydrous salt. (O.)

7. Explain clearly what is meant by a "normal" salt, an acid salt,
and a peroxide, giving two examples of each.

    Describe experiments by which you could prove that red lead
contains lead and oxygen, but no other elements. (L.)

8. Explain with examples what is meant by the basicity of an acid.
2 grams of oxalic acid which crystallises with two molecules of
water are heated with concentrated sulphuric acid. What volume
of gas is formed at 13° C. and 570 mm.? If this gas were allowed to
stand over potash, what volume of gas would remain at N.T.P.?
(L.)

9. How would you prepare (a) crystalline sodium carbonate starting
from sodium hydroxide, (b) lead sulphate starting from metallic
lead, (c) sodium hydroxide solution starting from sodium carbonate?
(N.U.J.B.)

CHAPTER XVII

OXIDES

THE BASIC OXIDES

(THESE oxides are the ones which correspond to the commonly occurring salts.)

K
Na } Oxides of these metals are soluble in water forming
Ca   alkalis.

Mg
Al
Zn } Oxides of these metals can be made from the metal
Fe   by the action of nitric
Pb   acid and then heat.
Cu

Oxides of these metals not reduced to metal by stream of hydrogen.

Hg
Ag } Oxides of these metals decompose when heated.
Au

Summary of preparation of the normal oxides of some common heavy metals from the metals or their soluble salts.

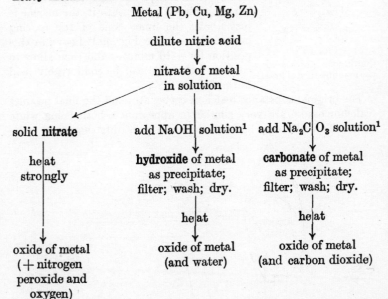

Metal (Pb, Cu, Mg, Zn)
|
dilute nitric acid
↓
nitrate of metal
in solution

solid **nitrate** — add NaOH solution[1] — add Na_2CO_3 solution[1]

heat strongly — **hydroxide** of metal as precipitate; filter; wash; dry. — **carbonate** of metal as precipitate; filter; wash; dry.

heat — heat

oxide of metal (+ nitrogen peroxide and oxygen) — oxide of metal (and water) — oxide of metal (and carbon dioxide)

[1] The hydroxide and carbonate may also be obtained by adding sodium hydroxide or sodium carbonate solution to a solution of any soluble salt of the metal.

Oxides of Sodium and Potassium, Na_2O and K_2O. These oxides are not much used in the laboratory or prepared in the usual course of experiment. They react vigorously with water to form sodium and potassium hydroxides.

$$Na_2O + H_2O \rightarrow 2NaOH$$

Calcium Oxide (lime, quicklime), CaO. It is made in industry by the action of strong heat upon limestone, calcium carbonate, the latter being placed in a kiln.

$$CaCO_3 \rightarrow CaO + CO_2$$

Very large quantities of lime are made in this way (Fig. 58). In

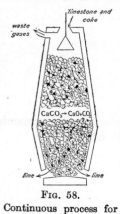

FIG. 58.
Continuous process for the manufacture of lime.

the laboratory, lime can be made by placing a piece of marble in a crucible and heating it strongly in a gas-heated muffle furnace. A high temperature is required and an hour or so is necessary to complete the action.

Class preparation of quick-lime. Make a loop in a stout iron wire large enough to hold a piece of marble about the size of a pea. Place the piece of marble in the wire and so arrange it on a tripod so that when a bunsen burner is placed underneath it, the marble is just above the inner cone of the roaring bunsen flame. (See Fig. 59.) Leave in this position for 5–10 minutes and then allow to cool until the solid can be comfortably held in the fingers.

The original substance (calcium carbonate) and the final product (calcium oxide) are very similar in appearance, both being white solids. The difference between them can be readily shown.

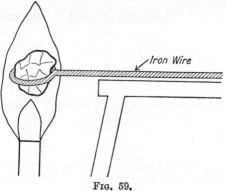

FIG. 59.
Calcining marble.

(a) *By the action of water.*

(i) On calcium carbonate—no action.

(ii) On lime. Add water a drop at a time to the piece of lime in a dish. Great heat is developed (there may be hissing as the water drops on to the lime), steam is formed and the lime cracks and puffs up and finally crumbles to a powder about three times as bulky. This is slaked lime.

$$CaO + H_2O \rightarrow Ca(OH)_2$$
slaked lime

Allow more water to fall on to the lime until there is no further action. If desired, at this stage, the mixture of slaked lime and solution can be filtered and the filtrate shown to be lime-water by expelling air from the lungs (containing carbon dioxide) through a glass tube into the solution.

(b) *By the action of dilute hydrochloric acid*

(i) On calcium carbonate. Effervescence is seen and the marble finally disappears. Carbon dioxide is evolved, which, if passed into lime-water, turns the latter turbid.

$$CaCO_3 + 2HCl \rightarrow CaCl_2 + H_2O + CO_2$$

(ii) On lime. No evolution of carbon dioxide. The lime will first give a similar action to (a) (ii) above (slaking) but will give finally a colourless solution of calcium chloride.

$$CaO + H_2O \rightarrow Ca(OH)_2$$
$$Ca(OH)_2 + 2HCl \rightarrow CaCl_2 + 2H_2O$$
basic   acid   salt   water
hydroxide

Properties of Lime. Lime is a white solid. It is very refractory; that is, it will not melt even when heated to a very high temperature. It merely becomes incandescent and gives out a powerful light. It was at one time used for this purpose (lime-light). It reacts vigorously with water (see above) to form slaked lime, which is a weak alkali. Its solution in water is called "lime-water". Since lime is basic in character and hygroscopic (that is, it absorbs water) it is used to dry ammonia gas. It is used in the building trade to make mortar, for manufacture of caustic soda (p. 208), and for a very great number of operations needing a cheap alkali.

Zinc Oxide, ZnO. This compound is a white powder (yellow when hot) made in industry by distilling zinc and burning the vapour at a jet.

$$2Zn + O_2 \rightarrow 2ZnO$$

It is made in the laboratory from zinc by dissolving the metal in dilute nitric acid, evaporating the zinc nitrate solution so formed to dryness and heating the residue strongly.

$$3Zn + 8HNO_3 \rightarrow 3Zn(NO_3)_2 + 4H_2O + 2NO$$
$$2Zn(NO_3)_2 \rightarrow 2ZnO + 4NO_2 + O_2$$

Zinc oxide is amphoteric (see p. 211).

Zinc oxide (and the oxides described above) cannot be converted into the metal by heating the oxides in a stream of hydrogen.

Zinc oxide, as "zinc white", is used as a base in the paint industry. Although its "covering power" is not so good as that of white lead paint it does not tarnish, as does a lead paint, on exposure to air which contains hydrogen sulphide. The reason is that zinc sulphide is white whereas lead sulphide is black. If there is any white paint in or near your laboratory, it will probably be a zinc paint. Otherwise the hydrogen sulphide fumes would rapidly turn it dark brown or black.

Ferric Oxide, Fe_2O_3. (Ferrous oxide is not important.) This compound is a red powder known as "jewellers' rouge". It is used for polishing precious stones, and as a pigment.

It is found in the impure state as hæmatite. Ferric oxide is made in the laboratory:

(*a*) By heating ferrous sulphate. (Note this action—it is a most unusual type.)

$$2FeSO_4 \rightarrow Fe_2O_3 + SO_2 + SO_3$$

sulphur   sulphur
dioxide   trioxide

(See p. 406.)

(*b*) By heating ferric hydroxide strongly.

$$2Fe(OH)_3 \rightarrow Fe_2O_3 + 3H_2O$$

Ferric oxide is also the product formed if ferrous hydroxide is heated strongly in the air. All ferrous compounds tend to become oxidised to ferric compounds by the oxygen of the atmosphere.

It has the usual properties of an oxide. It can be reduced to metallic iron by being heated in a stream of hydrogen or carbon monoxide.

$$Fe_2O_3 + 3H_2 \rightarrow 2Fe + 3H_2O$$
$$Fe_2O_3 + 3CO \rightarrow 2Fe + 3CO_2$$

Ferrosoferric Oxide, Fe_3O_4, magnetic oxide of iron. This compound may be prepared by passing steam over red hot iron (p. 217) or by burning iron in oxygen (p. 228).

It occurs naturally as magnetite and as such is a natural magnet or "lodestone".

On heating it in a stream of hydrogen it is reduced to iron (see p. 127).

$$Fe_3O_4 + 4H_2 \rightleftharpoons 3Fe + 4H_2O$$

Lead Oxide (litharge, lead monoxide, PbO). This is a yellow powder. It can be made in the laboratory by heating lead dioxide, red lead, lead nitrate, lead carbonate or lead hydroxide. (For details see compounds concerned.) It is best made from the metal by the action of nitric acid with subsequent evaporation, and heating of the lead nitrate. When prepared in the laboratory it usually ruins the test-tube in which it is prepared by fusing with the glass. It is, in fact, used to make lead glass—a glass of very high refractive index.

Although litharge can be considered a typical base, the only common acid in which it will readily dissolve is nitric acid. The reason why it does not react quantitatively with the others is a purely mechanical one.

Action of Litharge on Dilute Sulphuric or Hydrochloric Acids. Lead chloride and lead sulphate are not formed quantitatively. These two substances are almost insoluble in water and, as the action can only proceed on the outside of a particle of litharge, the lead chloride or sulphate forms as a layer on the outside. This layer of chloride or sulphate is not permeable to the acids and hence action stops before any appreciable amount of the salt has been formed. (For preparation, see these substances under "Chlorides" and "Sulphates".)

Litharge is easily reduced to grey metallic lead by heating it in a stream of hydrogen, coal-gas or carbon monoxide.

$$PbO + H_2 \rightarrow Pb + H_2O$$
$$PbO + CO \rightarrow Pb + CO_2$$

Litharge is also an amphoteric oxide dissolving in alkalis to form plumbites.

$$2NaOH + PbO \rightarrow Na_2PbO_2 + H_2O$$
$$\text{sodium}$$
$$\text{plumbite}$$

Black Copper Oxide, Cupric Oxide, CuO. This is made in the laboratory by several methods which are given with full experimental details on p. 29. Copper oxide is hygroscopic, absorbing moisture from the air.

It is a basic oxide and is readily attacked by acids to form cupric salts. For example, it will readily dissolve in dilute sulphuric acid to form a blue solution of copper sulphate.

$$CuO + H_2SO_4 \rightarrow CuSO_4 + H_2O$$

The copper sulphate can be obtained as crystals as described on p. 188.

Copper oxide is readily reduced to red metallic copper by heating it in a stream of hydrogen, coal-gas or carbon monoxide.

$$CuO + H_2 \rightarrow Cu + H_2O$$
$$CuO + CO \rightarrow Cu + CO_2$$

Like manganese dioxide, copper oxide will catalyse the action:

$$2KClO_3 \rightarrow 2KCl + 3O_2$$

Mercuric Oxide, a red powder, HgO, was used by Lavoisier in his famous work on combustion. He made it by heating mercury in the air for a long time at a temperature just below its boiling-point. He collected the red specks floating on the surface of the mercury (see p. 148).

$$2Hg + O_2 \rightarrow 2HgO$$

This oxide is interesting because it is one of the few basic oxides which yield oxygen on being strongly heated.

$$2HgO \rightarrow 2Hg + O_2$$
$$\text{mercury} \quad \text{oxygen}$$

THE HIGHER OXIDES

The higher oxides are oxides which contain more oxygen per molecule than the corresponding basic oxide. Thus, sodium is usually monovalent and its normal oxide is sodium oxide, Na_2O. Sodium peroxide, Na_2O_2, however, does exist.

Sodium Peroxide, Na_2O_2, is made by heating sodium in excess of oxygen.

$$2Na + O_2 \rightarrow Na_2O_2$$

It is a yellow powder and is a vigorous oxidising agent; it should never be allowed to come into contact with damp organic matter. With water it liberates oxygen (see p. 226). It is used in confined spaces (for example, in a submarine) where men are working, because it absorbs carbon dioxide, liberating oxygen at the same time:

$$2Na_2O_2 + 2CO_2 \rightarrow 2Na_2CO_3 + O_2$$

Sodium peroxide is a true peroxide, yielding hydrogen peroxide on treatment with acids (see p. 231).

Lead Dioxide, PbO_2. This oxide is a dark brown powder and can be made in the laboratory in the following manner:

Into a beaker put some dilute nitric acid and warm it. By means of a spatula, add red lead a little at a time. Care must be taken not to add too much red lead or it will contaminate the product. As the red lead reacts with the nitric acid, a brown powder is precipitated and lead nitrate is formed in solution. The mixture is filtered, the residue in the filter-paper is washed two or three times with hot distilled water and is allowed to dry on the filter-paper, from which it may then be shaken.

$$\underset{\text{red lead}}{Pb_3O_4} + 4HNO_3 \rightarrow \underset{\text{lead dioxide}}{PbO_2} + 2H_2O + \underset{\text{lead nitrate}}{2Pb(NO_3)_2}$$

The properties of lead dioxide are summed up by the following experiments:

(i) *Action of Heat.* Heat a little lead dioxide in a test-tube and hold a glowing splint in the mouth of the test-tube. The splint is rekindled, showing the presence of oxygen. Litharge remains as a yellow solid, often fused into the glass.

$$2PbO_2 \rightarrow 2PbO + O_2$$

(ii) *Action on Concentrated Hydrochloric Acid.* Warm a little lead dioxide with concentrated hydrochloric acid. A greenish-yellow gas which bleaches litmus is evolved (chlorine) and a white (often discoloured) solid, lead chloride, may be seen in the test-tube.

$$PbO_2 + 4HCl \rightarrow PbCl_2 + 2H_2O + Cl_2$$

(Compare manganese dioxide.)

It will be seen from the above that lead dioxide is an oxidising agent. If warm, it is converted by sulphur dioxide into lead sulphate (a white solid) and the mass glows as combination takes place.

$$PbO_2 + SO_2 \rightarrow PbSO_4$$

(iii) *Action of Hot Concentrated Sulphuric Acid.* Add lead dioxide to concentrated sulphuric acid in a test-tube and warm gently. Effervescence occurs, oxygen is evolved (test as in (i) above) and a white precipitate lead of sulphate is left.

$$2PbO_2 + 2H_2SO_4 \rightarrow 2PbSO_4 + 2H_2O + O_2$$

Red Lead, Pb$_3$O$_4$, triplumbic tetroxide. Red lead is prepared by heating lead oxide for some time in the presence of air at a temperature of 450° C.

$$6PbO + O_2 \rightarrow 2Pb_3O_4$$

This compound in many chemical properties acts as though it consists of lead monoxide and lead dioxide. For example, in the above experiment in preparing lead dioxide:

$$Pb_3O_4 + 4HNO_3 \rightarrow 2Pb(NO_3)_2 + 2H_2O + PbO_2$$

Compare $\underset{\text{base}}{\underbrace{2PbO}} + \underset{\text{acid}}{PbO_2 + 4HNO_3} \rightarrow \underset{\text{salt}}{2Pb(NO_3)_2} + \underset{\text{water}}{2H_2O} + \underbrace{PbO_2}$

$$\underbrace{\qquad\qquad\qquad\text{unchanged}\qquad\qquad\qquad}$$

Or, in the action of heat:

$$Pb_3O_4 \quad \rightarrow 3PbO + O$$

$$\overline{2PbO + PbO_2} \rightarrow 2PbO + PbO + O$$

or more correctly:

$$2Pb_3O_4 \rightarrow 6PbO + O_2$$

Hence the action of heat on any oxide of lead is to leave litharge.

Red lead reacts with concentrated hydrochloric acid or concentrated sulphuric acid when warmed to produce the same observed effects as lead dioxide (see above).

$$Pb_3O_4 + 8HCl \rightarrow 3PbCl_2 + 4H_2O + Cl_2$$
$$2Pb_3O_4 + 6H_2SO_4 \rightarrow 6PbSO_4 + 6H_2O + O_2$$

Red lead has been used for a long time as a pigment (the old name for red lead, "minium", gave the name "miniature" to that type of picture) and is used to-day, with oil, as a jointing material for gas and water pipes and in the manufacture of glass.

Manganese Dioxide, MnO_2. See Oxygen (p. 223), and Chlorine (p. 272) for the common laboratory uses of this substance. It is also used in the glass industry.

QUESTIONS ON THIS CHAPTER WILL BE FOUND ON PAGE 213

CHAPTER XVIII

HYDROXIDES

K
Na
Ca — The hydroxides of these metals are *soluble* in water and are alkalis. (Also ammonium hydroxide.) — Hydroxides of sodium and potassium not decomposed by heat.

Al
Zn
Fe
Pb — These metals form hydroxides which are insoluble in water. They are also amphoteric, excepting the two hydroxides of iron. — Decomposition into oxide and water when hydroxides of these metals are heated.

Cu — Hydroxide is insoluble in water.

Hg
Ag
Au — Hydroxides of these metals do not exist.

Metallic hydroxides can be considered[1] as substances formed by the replacement of one hydrogen atom per molecule of water by a metal or metallic group. Thus, if M is the symbol for a monovalent metal:

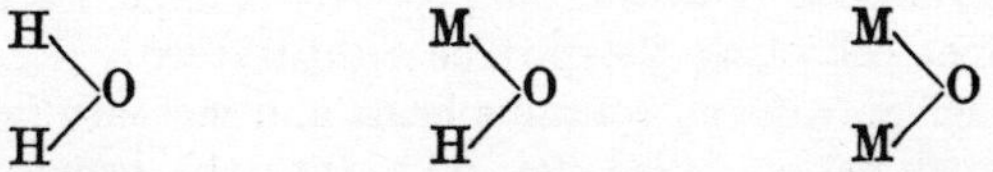

$$H_2O \qquad MOH \qquad M_2O$$

Hydrogen oxide   Metallic hydroxide   Metallic oxide

No hydrogen atoms displaced.   One hydrogen atom displaced by M.   Both hydrogen atoms displaced by M.

Example: NaOH   Na$_2$O

sodium hydroxide   sodium oxide

Note that the hydroxides are not salts since they are not formed by the replacement of hydrogen in an *acid*. They are a very important series of compounds. The soluble hydroxides (that is, the alkalis) are particularly important. They have numerous uses both in industry and in the laboratory.

[1] Only the first three can actually be made by the mere action of water on the metal.

Ammonium Hydroxide, NH_4OH, is not strictly speaking a metallic hydroxide since the radical (NH_4) is not a metal, nor has it been isolated. Ammonium hydroxide solution is made by dissolving ammonia gas in water (see Ammonia, p. 338, for fuller treatment).

$$NH_3 + H_2O \rightarrow NH_4OH$$
ammonIA   water   ammonIUM hydroxide

It will turn red litmus blue and precipitate metallic hydroxides from solutions of salts of the metal.

$$FeCl_3 + 3NH_4OH \rightarrow Fe(OH)_3 \downarrow + 3NH_4Cl$$

It forms salts by the neutralisation of acids, for example,

$$HNO_3 + NH_4OH \rightarrow NH_4NO_3 + H_2O$$
ammonium nitrate

Action of Heat. If ammonium hydroxide solution is heated, ammonia gas and steam are evolved.

$$NH_4OH \rightarrow NH_3 + H_2O$$

Potassium Hydroxide (Caustic potash, KOH) is made in a similar manner to that used for caustic soda. Its properties are almost identical. Note that caustic potash is much more soluble in alcohol than is caustic soda, and is used in industry to make soft soaps.

Since the properties are so nearly identical the cheaper sodium hydroxide is almost always used in preference.

Sodium Hydroxide (Caustic soda, NaOH) is made by the electrolysis of brine, collecting the products separately.

The Kellner-Solvay cell contains brine and mercury both flowing in the same direction. (See Fig. 60.) Into the brine dip carbon anodes whilst the flowing mercury is the cathode. Chlorine is liberated at the anodes and escapes by the pipe provided. Sodium is liberated at the cathode (see p. 120) and forms a dilute amalgam with the mercury. The amalgam passes into another cell where it is treated with water to obtain caustic soda and hydrogen.

at cathode

Na^+ discharges and amalgamates with mercury.

$$Na^+ + e = Na$$
$$Na + Hg = NaHg$$

The amalgam later reacts with water

$$2NaHg + 2H_2O = 2NaOH + H_2 + 2Hg$$

at anode

Cl^- discharges and the atoms combine in pairs to form molecules of chlorine gas.

$$Cl^- - e = Cl$$
$$Cl + Cl = Cl_2$$

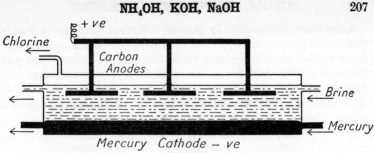

FIG. 60.

Illustration of Kellner-Solvay Cell. Fit up a burette with side tube as shown in Fig. 61. Adjust the taps of the two burettes so that mercury flows at approximately the same rate from each, and have a sufficient store of mercury in the upper burette for about 20 minutes flow. Connect the electrodes to a 12-volt battery (or equivalent supply of electricity) drop a piece of red litmus paper into water in the small beaker and arrange a piece of damp litmus paper so that gases from the anode come into contact with it. After a few minutes, the piece of litmus paper in contact with the anode gas is bleached (showing the presence of chlorine) and the litmus paper in the beaker has turned blue showing the presence of an alkali. To show the evolution of hydrogen from the amalgam, fill the narrow tube with mercury and run off the bulk of the mercury into water. A rapid evolution of hydrogen then takes place.

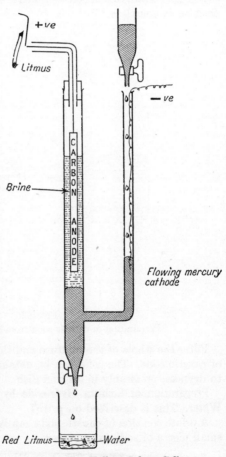

FIG. 61.—Kellner-Solvay Cell.

Laboratory Preparation by Gossage's Method. Half-fill a beaker with a 10% solution of sodium carbonate (the bench sodium carbonate solution will do) and warm the solution on a tripod and gauze (Fig. 62). Add slaked lime a little at a time by means of a spatula and stir. A white solid forms on the bottom of the beaker. This is mainly calcium carbonate together with some unattacked slaked lime.

$$Na_2CO_3 + Ca(OH)_2 \rightarrow CaCO_3 + 2NaOH$$

sodium   calcium   calcium   sodium
carbonate   hydroxide   carbonate   hydroxide

Filter off a portion of the contents of the beaker and, when the filtrate gives no effervescence with dilute hydrochloric acid, it is clear that no sodium carbonate remains in it and the double decomposition is complete.

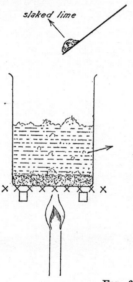

slaked lime

10 per cent solution of washing-soda crystals in water.

FIG. 62.

Preparation of caustic soda from sodium carbonate.

Filter the whole of the mixture and the liquid is a dilute solution of caustic soda. The solid can be obtained from it by evaporation to dryness, preferably in an iron dish.

Preparation of Sodium Hydroxide by the Action of Sodium on Water. This is described on p. 157.

A dilute solution of caustic soda can be obtained by placing very small pieces of sodium on water.

$$2Na + 2H_2O \rightarrow 2NaOH + H_2$$

Properties. Sodium hydroxide is a white solid. It is very deliquescent, has a soapy feel, and will corrode the skin. Care should be used in handling the solid and its solution.

Action on Exposure to Air. Leave a small piece of caustic soda on a watch-glass exposed to the atmosphere for a few days. There is formed a solution of caustic soda, showing the solid to be deliquescent. Finally, a white crystalline crust of sodium carbonate is formed by the action of the carbon dioxide of the atmosphere.

Action with Water. All deliquescent substances are very soluble in water. As caustic soda dissolves, a great amount of heat is liberated and the solution should always be made in a thin vessel, otherwise the glass may be cracked.

Action of Caustic Soda as an Alkali (that is, a soluble base). The solution is strongly alkaline to litmus, turning it blue. Caustic soda will react with acids to form salts (see p. 192), for example with hydrochloric acid:

$$NaOH + HCl \rightarrow NaCl + H_2O$$

sodium   dilute   sodium   water
hydroxide   hydro-   chloride
solution   chloric
          acid

Action of Gaseous Acidic Oxides on Alkalis. It can be stated as a general rule that if a gaseous acidic oxide is bubbled into any alkaline solution, the final product is the corresponding acid salt. (As a rule the normal salt is first formed but it is difficult to isolate in most cases.)

Thus when sulphur dioxide, hydrogen sulphide or carbon dioxide are bubbled for some time into caustic potash solution, caustic soda solution, lime-water or ammonium hydroxide, the product is the acid salt; for example:

$$CO_2 + NaOH \rightarrow NaHCO_3$$
sodium hydrogen
carbonate

$$H_2S + KOH \rightarrow KHS + H_2O$$
potassium
hydrogen
sulphide

$$2SO_2 + Ca(OH)_2 \rightarrow Ca(HSO_3)_2$$
calcium
hydrogen
sulphite

The normal salt can usually be made by the addition of the same weight of alkali as was taken at the commencement of the operation, for example:

$$H_2S + KOH \rightarrow KHS + H_2O$$
$$KHS + KOH \rightarrow K_2S + H_2O$$
potassium
sulphide

(See p. 310 for experimental details.)

Sodium Hydroxide as a Hydroxide-former. The majority of the metallic hydroxides are insoluble in water, and as we shall see in the remainder of this chapter, the usual method of making a hydroxide is to add caustic soda solution to the solution of a soluble salt of the metal, and isolate the product as described in Chapter XVI.

Action of Caustic Soda on Ammonium Salts. If any ammonium salt is boiled with caustic soda solution ammonia gas (turns red litmus blue) is liberated.

$$NH_4Cl + NaOH \rightarrow NaCl + H_2O + NH_3$$
ammonium   sodium   ammonia
chloride   chloride

Uses. Caustic soda is used extensively in the manufacture of hard soap and in paper-making.

Calcium Hydroxide, slaked lime, is a white solid not nearly so soluble in water as sodium or potassium hydroxide.

Preparation. It is prepared commercially and in the laboratory by the action of water on quicklime (which is obtained by the action of heat on limestone).

$$CaO + H_2O \rightarrow Ca(OH)_2$$
calcium
hydroxide

(See p. 199 for experimental details.)

Properties. Slaked lime is a white solid. Lime-water is formed when slaked lime is dissolved in water, but its solubility is only very small (about 0·14 gm. in 100 gm. water at 20° C.).

This solution is, however, definitely alkaline and will give the usual reactions of an alkali.

Action of Heat on Calcium Hydroxide. Strong heat will convert slaked lime into quicklime. In the laboratory the experiment is performed in a fire-clay furnace by the identical method used to convert calcium carbonate into quicklime (see p. 198).

$$Ca(OH)_2 \rightarrow CaO + H_2O$$

Action of Carbon Dioxide on Lime-water. Lime-water is used as a test for this gas owing to the fact that a white precipitate of chalk is formed on bubbling carbon dioxide into lime-water.

$$Ca(OH)_2 + CO_2 \rightarrow CaCO_3 + H_2O$$
calcium
carbonate

A milkiness is produced which is caused by small particles of solid chalk. Further passage of carbon dioxide produces calcium bicarbonate, which is soluble in water (see p. 163).

Uses. Slaked lime is used in the manufacture of mortar and bleaching powder and is also used by farmers to counteract acidity on the land.

Mortar is made by mixing lime, sand and water. The setting is due to the giving up of surplus moisture and for this reason new houses are always damp for some time. With the passage of years some of the slaked lime is converted into calcium carbonate by carbon dioxide from the air.

$$Ca(OH)_2 + CO_2 \rightarrow CaCO_3 + H_2O$$

Hence, an old mortar will give an effervescence with dilute acids, whereas a new mortar will not.

$$CaCO_3 + 2HCl \rightarrow CaCl_2 + H_2O + CO_2$$

Cement is made by strongly heating limestone and clay together. The cement is powdered and, after mixing with a suitable amount of water, sets to a mass of interlacing crystals of great strength. Some cements will set even under water. When mixed with gravel or brick rubble, cement forms *concrete*, and is used with water in the same way.

Zinc Hydroxide is a white powder. It is formed as a white precipitate when sodium hydroxide solution is carefully added to the solution of a soluble zinc salt (usually zinc sulphate).

$$ZnSO_4 + 2NaOH \rightarrow Zn(OH)_2 + Na_2SO_4$$
$$\text{zinc} \atop \text{hydroxide}$$

The white precipitate, if required, may be filtered off, washed with hot distilled water and dried on a porous plate.

Amphoteric Nature of Zinc Hydroxide. Care must be taken in the above experiment not to add excess sodium hydroxide solution, since zinc hydroxide is soluble in excess of caustic soda or potash solution, forming a zincate.

$$Zn(OH)_2 + 2NaOH \rightarrow Na_2ZnO_2 + 2H_2O$$
$$\text{sodium} \atop \text{zincate}$$

Here zinc hydroxide is acting with acidic properties because, with the alkali caustic soda, it forms the salt, sodium zincate, and water.

Like most metallic hydroxides, zinc hydroxide has basic properties also, and it reacts, for example, with dilute sulphuric acid to form the salt, zinc sulphate, and water.

$$\underset{\text{base}}{Zn(OH)_2} + \underset{\text{acid}}{H_2SO_4} \rightarrow \underset{\text{salt}}{ZnSO_4} + \underset{\text{water}}{2H_2O}$$

A metallic hydroxide which exhibits both basis and acidic properties is said to be *amphoteric*. The corresponding oxides are also amphoteric.

Action of Heat. Zinc hydroxide is readily converted into zinc oxide by the action of heat.

$$Zn(OH)_2 \rightarrow ZnO + H_2O$$
$$\text{zinc}$$
$$\text{oxide}$$
$$\text{(yellow hot,}$$
$$\text{white cold)}$$

Hydroxides of Iron

Iron forms two hydroxides, ferrous hydroxide and ferric hydroxide.

Ferrous Hydroxide is precipitated by the action of caustic soda solution on ferrous sulphate solution.

$$FeSO_4 + 2NaOH \rightarrow Fe(OH)_2 \downarrow + Na_2SO_4$$
$$\text{ferrous}$$
$$\text{hydroxide}$$

If air is excluded the substance is white, but under ordinary conditions it is seen as a dirty-green gelatinous precipitate. It is troublesome to isolate the solid, as it is so readily oxidised by the air. Make the precipitate in the way indicated above and allow it to stand or warm it. It will be seen to turn reddish-brown because it is oxidised by the oxygen of the atmosphere to reddish-brown ferric hydroxide.

$$4Fe(OH)_2 + O_2 + 2H_2O \rightarrow 4Fe(OH)_3$$

For the same reason, on heating ferrous hydroxide strongly, ferric oxide remains.

Ferric Hydroxide is precipitated as a reddish-brown gelatinous precipitate by adding an alkaline solution (for example, caustic soda solution) to a solution of ferric chloride.

$$FeCl_3 + 3NaOH \rightarrow Fe(OH)_3 + 3NaCl$$
$$\text{ferric}$$
$$\text{hydroxide}$$

To purify it, filter off, wash well with hot distilled water and allow it to dry.

On heating the hydroxide strongly, ferric oxide is obtained as a red powder.

$$2Fe(OH)_3 \rightarrow Fe_2O_3 + 3H_2O$$

Ferrous and ferric hydroxide dissolve in dilute acids with the formation of salts and water, thus indicating their basic nature.

Lead Hydroxide is formed as a white precipitate by adding caustic soda solution cautiously to lead nitrate solution.

$$Pb(NO_3)_2 + 2NaOH \rightarrow Pb(OH)_2 + 2NaNO_3$$
lead
hydroxide

It can be obtained as a white powder by filtering off, washing with hot distilled water, and allowing it to dry.

Like zinc hydroxide it is amphoteric and will dissolve in acids to form lead salts and in alkalis to form plumbites.

$$Pb(OH)_2 + 2HNO_3 \rightarrow Pb(NO_3)_2 + 2H_2O$$
$$2NaOH + Pb(OH)_2 \rightarrow Na_2PbO_2 + 2H_2O$$
sodium
plumbite

On strongly heating lead hydroxide, litharge remains as a yellow powder.

$$Pb(OH)_2 \rightarrow PbO + H_2O$$

Copper Hydroxide is formed as a blue gelatinous precipitate on adding caustic soda solution to cold copper sulphate solution. The substance can be obtained as a blue powder by filtering off the precipitate, washing it several times with cold distilled water and allowing it to dry.

$$CuSO_4 + 2NaOH \rightarrow Cu(OH)_2 + Na_2SO_4$$
copper
hydroxide

It is soluble in dilute acids forming solutions of copper salts. For example,

$$Cu(OH)_2 + H_2SO_4 \rightarrow CuSO_4 + 2H_2O$$

On warming the hydroxide it readily loses water and forms black copper oxide (see p. 29).

$$Cu(OH)_2 \rightarrow CuO + H_2O$$

Copper hydroxide dissolves in ammonia to form a deep blue solution. This blue solution will dissolve cellulose (for example, a filter-paper) and this solution of cellulose has been used to make artificial silk by forcing the solution through tiny holes into an acid solution. The fibres so formed are spun into threads.

QUESTIONS

1. Describe a method for the preparation of sodium hydroxide from sodium chloride.
   Give an account of the reaction of sodium hydroxide with (a) carbon dioxide, (b) zinc, (c) a solution of zinc sulphate.
   Give the equations in each case. (C.)

H

2. Sulphur dioxide is called an acidic oxide and copper oxide a basic oxide. What is meant by these terms? Give two other examples of each of these classes of oxides and describe how you would test an oxide in order to assign it to one of these classes. (O. and C.)

3. What chemical properties distinguish metals as a class? Describe in detail three methods by which a metal may be converted into its oxide. In each case name the metal which you would use. (L.)

4. How would you obtain from calcium carbonate pure specimens of (a) calcium oxide, (b) calcium hydroxide? Describe the properties of an aqueous solution of calcium hydroxide, explaining what changes occur when carbon dioxide is passed through the solution. (O. and C.)

5. Name five gases which can be absorbed by caustic soda. Explain the reactions which take place on absorption, and in each case give one test by which you could recognise the product. (L.)

6. How may lead monoxide and lead peroxide be obtained, starting from metallic lead?

Describe how you would show by experiment that their composition is in agreement with the Law of Multiple Proportions. (L.)

7. What is the chemical nature of galena and white lead? Starting with red lead (Pb_3O_4), how would you prepare a specimen of each of the following: (a) metallic lead, (b) lead monoxide, (c) lead dioxide? (N.U.J.B.)

8. Explain the meaning of the terms base, basic oxide, hydroxide. Classify the following substances: lime, ammonia, caustic soda. Give reasons for your classification. (O. and C.)

9. Define base, hydroxide, alkali, giving two examples of each with formulæ. Indicate briefly how you would prepare (a) sodium hydroxide, using sodium carbonate, (b) ferric hydroxide, using ferric chloride. (N.U.J.B.)

10. What do you understand by (a) a base, (b) an alkali?

Draw a labelled diagram to show how sodium hydroxide is prepared electrolytically. (The diagram should show the nature of the electrolyte and all products, the names, signs and materials of the electrodes, and any other details essential to the process.)

State concisely what you would observe when a stick of sodium hydroxide is left exposed to the air for a long time. (Equations are not required in this question.) (N.U.J.B.)

11. What are the four chief classes of oxides? Give one example of each class.

How do oxides of metals differ chemically from those of non-metals?

State briefly how you would prepare from suitable oxides (a) a solution of copper sulphate, (b) a dilute solution of hydrogen peroxide.

What happens when manganese dioxide is added to a solution of hydrogen peroxide? (N.U.J.B.)

CHAPTER XIX

HYDROGEN

K
Na
Ca
Mg
Al
Zn
Fe
Pb
(H)
Cu
Hg
Ag
Au

} Dilute sulphuric and hydrochloric acids attack these metals with the liberation of hydrogen.

Hydrogen was first recognised by Cavendish (1766). It was called "inflammable air", and the name hydrogen (*i.e.*, water producer) was given to it by Lavoisier.

Occurrence. Uncombined hydrogen does not occur in nature to any appreciable extent, but the element occurs in vast quantities in a combined state in such compounds as water, acids, and many organic substances.

Industrial Preparation of Hydrogen. Hydrogen has acquired much greater importance in recent years because of new uses given below. There are now two chief methods of manufacture—from water-gas and by electrolysis.

(1) *From water-gas.* Steam is passed through a mass of coke kept at minimum temperature of 1000° C. A mixture of equal volumes of hydrogen and carbon monoxide is formed, known as "water-gas".

$$C + H_2O \rightleftharpoons CO + H_2$$

This water-gas is passed, together with excess of steam, over a catalyst, mainly ferric oxide, at 450° C. The products are hydrogen and carbon dioxide.

$$CO + H_2 + H_2O \rightleftharpoons CO_2 + 2H_2$$

Carbon dioxide is dissolved out by water under 30 atmos. pressure

$$H_2O + CO_2 \rightleftharpoons H_2CO_3$$

Any remaining traces of carbon monoxide are absorbed under pressure, by cuprous formate in ammonia.

(2) *By electrolysis.* Hydrogen is obtained as a by-product in the electrolytic manufacture of caustic soda from common salt (p. 206).

Where electrical power is cheap, hydrogen can be made by electrolysis of water containing sulphuric acid. The laboratory version of this method is fully discussed on p. 120.

Uses of Hydrogen.

(1) *For filling balloons and airships.* It is the lightest gas known but has the great disadvantage of inflammability.

(2) *In the "hardening" of oils to make margarine.* Oils, e.g. olive oil or whale-oil, are heated to 180° C. and finely divided nickel is added as catalyst. They are then treated with hydrogen at about 5 atmos. pressure. The oil combines with hydrogen and is converted to a *fat*, which is solid at ordinary temperature and is used in the manufacture of margarine. In this way, a liquid oil, unacceptable in our diet, is "hardened" to an acceptable solid fat and used as a butter-substitute.

(3) *In the conversion of coal to synthetic "petrol".* A paste of coal-dust and oil, containing iron oxide and alkali as catalyst, is sprayed into hydrogen at 200 atmos. pressure and 450° C. The products are hydrocarbon gases and a liquid oil. On distillation, this oil yields a fraction suitable for petrol. This new process is potentially very valuable to Great Britain, which has plenty of coal but little oil.

(4) *In the manufacture of ammonia.* This is Haber's Process, described on p. 340.

Preparation of Hydrogen by the action of dilute Acids on Metals.

Note: Hydrogen explodes violently with air if a spark or flame reaches the mixture. For safety, always collect a *sample* of hydrogen and test as described on p. 58 *before* lighting a jet or collecting the gas in bulk.

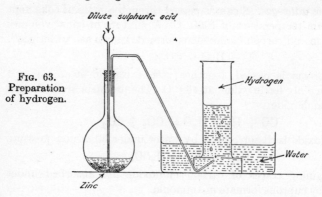

FIG. 63.
Preparation
of hydrogen.

Into a flat-bottomed flask or bottle, put some pieces of zinc and add dilute sulphuric acid by means of a thistle funnel. There is effervescence, and a gas is given off which is collected over water, as shown in Fig. 63. Zinc sulphate, which is formed, dissolves in the water to form zinc sulphate solution.

$$Zn + H_2SO_4 \rightarrow ZnSO_4 + H_2$$
zinc   dilute   zinc   hydrogen
     sulphuric   sulphate
      acid

Hydrogen from Water. Action of Steam on Heated Iron.
This method is very suitable for obtaining hydrogen in quantity.

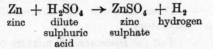

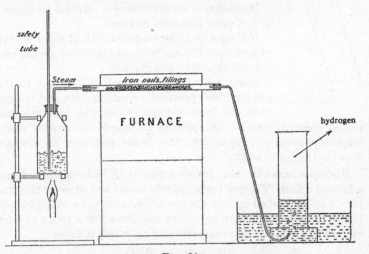

FIG. 64.
Preparation of hydrogen in quantity from steam.

The apparatus consists of a long iron tube loosely filled with iron filings and nails which are heated to redness by a furnace (Fig. 64). Steam is generated by boiling water in a can, and the steam passes over the heated iron, forming hydrogen, which is collected over water. Any excess steam condenses as it comes into contact with the cold water. The iron is converted into triferric tetroxide (black oxide of iron).

$$3Fe + 4H_2O \rightarrow Fe_3O_4 + 4H_2$$
iron   steam   triferric   hydrogen
          tetroxide

This reaction is reversible (see p. 127).

Hydrogen from Alkalies. Warm caustic soda (or potash) solution will react with zinc, aluminium or silicon to liberate hydrogen and leave a solution of sodium (or potassium) zincate, aluminate or silicate.

$$Zn + 2NaOH \rightarrow Na_2ZnO_2 + H_2$$
$$2Al + 2NaOH + 2H_2O \rightarrow 2NaAlO_2 + 3H_2$$
$$Si + 2NaOH + H_2O \rightarrow Na_2SiO_3 + 2H_2$$

FIG. 65.

These methods are not usually used in the laboratory.

Test for Hydrogen. **A mixture of hydrogen and air explodes when a flame is applied.**

PROPERTIES OF HYDROGEN

Hydrogen is an invisible gas, neutral to litmus, and, if pure, possesses no smell.

Hydrogen is Lighter than Air. Hold a gas-jar full of hydrogen (B) under a gas-jar full of air (A) and take off the cover (see Fig. 65).

Count ten. Now apply a lighted splint to the gas-jar which previously contained air, and the gas in it will burn or explode, showing hydrogen has passed upwards into it. On applying a flame to the gas-jar which originally contained hydrogen, the flame produces no change, showing the gas to be air.

Hydrogen burns in Air. Invert a gas-jar of hydrogen and apply a lighted splint. The gas burns quietly round the edges of the gas-jar. A splint pushed up into the gas will be seen to be extinguished. Hence hydrogen will burn in air but will not allow a splint to burn in it. The product of the combustion of hydrogen is water.

$$2H_2 + O_2 \rightarrow 2H_2O$$

Hydrogen explodes if mixed with Air and a Flame is applied. (The usual test for hydrogen.) When collecting the hydrogen over water, bubble the gas into a gas-jar containing about two-thirds its volume of air, passing in hydrogen until the water is all displaced. Apply a flame to the mixture and there is an explosion.

$$2H_2 + O_2 \rightarrow 2H_2O$$

Hydrogen is a Reducing Agent. Hydrogen readily reduces the oxides of copper, lead or iron to the metal when they are heated in a stream of the gas, *i.e.,* (See p. 58.)

$$CuO + H_2 \rightarrow Cu + H_2O$$

Nascent Hydrogen. At the moment of liberation from an acid hydrogen is a much more vigorous reducing agent, and is called nascent hydrogen. Thus ordinary gaseous hydrogen has no effect on ferric chloride solution, but if the hydrogen is liberated in the solution by the action of zinc on hydrochloric acid the solution is readily reduced to ferrous chloride. (See p. 386.)

By courtesy of Metropolitan-Vickers Co., Ltd.

PLATE V.

Atomic hydrogen welding.

The heat liberated when atoms of hydrogen combine to form molecules is utilised in this apparatus to produce very high temperatures.

Action of Hydrogen on the Halogens. Hydrogen combines with chlorine to form hydrogen chloride,

$$H_2 + Cl_2 \rightarrow 2HCl$$

with bromine, less readily, to form hydrogen bromide

$$H_2 + Br_2 \rightarrow 2HBr$$

with iodine, less readily still. (See Halogens.)

Diffusion. Invert a gas-jar of hydrogen over a gas-jar of air (*i.e.* the hydrogen is the *uppermost* of the two). Remove the

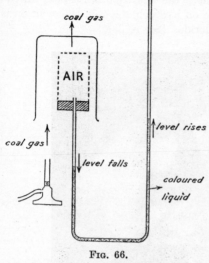

FIG. 66.
Coal-gas diffuses more rapidly than air.

plates and leave for *ten minutes*. Plunge a lighted taper into each gas-jar separately and in *both* cases there is an explosion, showing hydrogen to be present in quantity in both of the gas-jars. Hence some of the hydrogen must have descended from the upper gas-jar to the lower. This seems contrary to the result of the experiment above which shows the gas to be lighter than air.

This process of filling the whole of a vessel in which a gas is placed is termed diffusion. Hydrogen diffuses (*i.e.* spreads throughout the vessel in which it is placed) more rapidly than any other gas. This can be shown by the simple apparatus depicted in Fig. 66.

To Show the Rapidity with which Hydrogen Diffuses. A porous pot has a rubber stopper which fits tightly in its mouth and is connected to a bent glass tube containing coloured water (Fig. 66).

A beaker surrounds the pot and coal-gas is passed into the beaker by placing an unlit bunsen burner under it and turning on the gas tap. On doing so, the level of water in the limb directly below the pot begins to fall because the coal-gas (which contains about half its volume of hydrogen) diffuses through the tiny pores of the pot more quickly than the air diffuses out of the pot. This causes an excess pressure of gas in the pot making the level fall. When the level returns to normal, as it will do in a few moments, the beaker containing the coal-gas is removed. Now the reverse happens and the level of the water in the shorter tube rises. This is because the coal-gas (now inside the pot) diffuses out more rapidly than the air can diffuse in, and causes a lowering of the pressure inside the pot, and hence the level rises.

Graham found that the rate of diffusion of a gas was inversely proportional to the square root of its density.

For example,

$$\text{Density of hydrogen} = 1 \text{ (relative to hydrogen)}$$
$$\text{Density of oxygen} = 16 \text{ (relative to hydrogen)}$$

$\therefore$ Rate of diffusion of hydrogen $\propto \dfrac{1}{\sqrt{1}}$

$$= \dfrac{k}{\sqrt{1}}$$

where k is a constant

$$\text{Rate of diffusion of oxygen} \ \propto \frac{1}{\sqrt{16}}$$

$$= \frac{k}{\sqrt{16}}$$

$$\therefore \ \frac{\text{Rate of diffusion of hydrogen}}{\text{Rate of diffusion of oxygen}} = \frac{k}{\sqrt{1}} \div \frac{k}{\sqrt{16}}$$

$$= \frac{k}{\sqrt{1}} \times \frac{\sqrt{16}}{k} = \frac{4}{1}$$

Hence hydrogen diffuses four times as rapidly as oxygen.

This may be applied as a method of finding the molecular weight of a gas by finding the vapour density from its rate of diffusion.

All gases diffuse. That is, they attempt to distribute themselves uniformly throughout the vessel in which they are placed.

The Burning of Hydrogen in Air to Form Water. This is the *synthesis* of water, *i.e.*, the building-up of water from its elements.

Fit up the apparatus as shown in Fig. 67.

Hydrogen is generated by the action of dilute hydrochloric acid on zinc.

$$Zn + 2HCl \rightarrow ZnCl_2 + H_2$$

The gas then passes through a U-tube containing calcium chloride in order to dry the gas, the hydrogen is burnt at a jet, and the vapours are cooled by coming into contact with a can kept cool by water.

When the apparatus has been set up (use rubber stoppers or very well-fitting bark corks), place a test-tube over the jet and collect a test-tube full of hydrogen by displacement of air. When this test-tube full of gas burns quietly on the application of a flame to it, light the jet and allow the flame to burn so that it just does not touch the cooled can.

Moisture will condense on the can and will drop off into a dish which is placed below to receive the liquid.

The liquid can be shown to be water by the tests described below:

1. *Action on Anhydrous Copper Sulphate.*

Allow a drop of the liquid to fall on to anhydrous

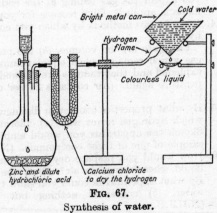

Bright metal can ⟶

Cold water

Hydrogen flame

Colourless liquid

Zinc and dilute hydrochloric acid

Calcium chloride to dry the hydrogen

FIG. 67.

Synthesis of water.

H*

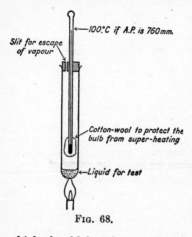

← 100° C if A.P. is 760 mm.

Slit for escape of vapour

Cotton-wool to protect the bulb from super-heating

←Liquid for test

FIG. 68.

copper sulphate. A blue patch on the white solid (with hissing and development of heat) proves water is present, but does NOT prove the liquid to be pure water.

$$CuSO_4 + 5H_2O = CuSO_4.5H_2O.$$
blue vitriol

2. *Boiling-point.* (See Fig. 68.)

If the atmospheric pressure is 760 mm., the thermometer should register 100° C.

These two tests together prove the liquid to be pure water. An additional, but less convenient test, is to find the freezing-point, which should be 0° C. at 760 mm. pressure.

$$2H_2 + O_2 = 2H_2O.$$
from
air

QUESTIONS

1. What weight of sulphuric acid would be necessary to react with zinc to provide sufficient hydrogen to fill 6 gas-jars, each containing 400 c.c. at 15° C. and 750 mm.?

2. Hydrogen is a reducing agent. Illustrate this statement by reference to the action of the gas with (a) oxygen, (b) chlorine, (c) copper oxide.

3. If a mixture of hydrogen and oxygen is passed slowly through a long porous tube the gas issuing at the other end does not explode when a flame is applied. Explain this. If the same experiment was performed with a mixture of carbon monoxide and air, would you expect the gas issuing at the end to explode or burn when a flame is applied? Give reasons for your answer.

4. Describe *two* methods by which you could prepare reasonably pure hydrogen.

Calculate (a) the volume, (b) the percentage composition of the gas which remains when equal volumes of air and hydrogen are exploded and the products are allowed to cool down to room temperature again. (Air contains 21 per cent of oxygen by volume.) (O.)

5. By what properties could you distinguish between the compounds which hydrogen forms with (a) chlorine, (b) sulphur, (c) nitrogen? Sketch the apparatus you would employ to prepare and collect a sample of one of these compounds. (N.U.J.B.)

6. How would you prepare dry hydrogen, and show that it forms a liquid when burned in air? Draw the apparatus you would use. By what experiments could you show that the liquid (a) contained water, (b) contained nothing but water? Give full details. (N.U.J.B.)

CHAPTER XX

OXYGEN

K
Na
Ca
Mg
Zn
Fe
Pb
Cu
} When heated in air these metals oxidise with a readiness indicated by the order shown; that is, potassium most easily, copper least readily.

Hg
Ag
Au
} These metals do not oxidise easily; their oxides *yield* oxygen on heating.

Oxygen was first discovered by Scheele in 1772, but Priestley discovered it independently two years later by heating oxide of mercury. He called it "dephlogisticated air", but Lavoisier called it oxygen (acid-producer) because he obtained acids by heating several non-metals in oxygen and dissolving the oxides in water.

Occurrence. Uncombined oxygen exists in the air, forming 21% by volume (or 23% by weight). The earth's crust consists of almost half of its weight of oxygen in a combined state in the form

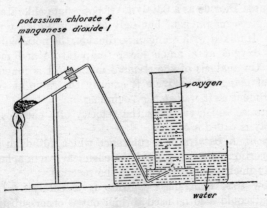

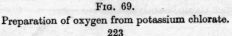

FIG. 69.
Preparation of oxygen from potassium chlorate.

223

of water, silicates, many metallic and non-metallic oxides, and in the form of salts.

Laboratory Preparation of Oxygen from Potassium Chlorate. Crush some potassium chlorate crystals (20 gm.) in a mortar and grind with them about one-quarter of their weight (5 gm.) of manganese dioxide. Place the mixture in a hard-glass tube and fit up the apparatus as shown (Fig. 69). Heat the mixture and a gas will readily be given off which can be collected over water.

Since oxygen has about the same density as air, it cannot be collected by displacement of air. If required dry it can be dried by calcium chloride and collected over mercury. Potassium chloride is left in the tube.

$$2KClO_3 \rightarrow 2KCl + 3O_2$$
$$\text{potassium} \quad \text{potassium} \quad \text{oxygen}$$
$$\text{chlorate} \quad \text{chloride}$$

Test for Oxygen.

It rekindles a glowing splint of wood. This distinguishes it from all gases except nitrous oxide, N_2O. It is distinguished from this gas:—

 (*a*) by having no smell (nitrous oxide has a sweet, sickly smell).

 (*b*) with nitric oxide, oxygen produces brown fumes of nitrogen peroxide.

$$2NO + O_2 \rightarrow 2NO_2$$
$$\text{nitric} \quad \text{nitrogen}$$
$$\text{oxide} \quad \text{peroxide}$$

Nitrous oxide has no effect on nitric oxide.

Manganese Dioxide as a Catalyst. If potassium chlorate is heated alone, it gives off oxygen, but only at a fairly high temperature (400° C.). If mixed with manganese dioxide, the potassium chlorate gives off oxygen at a much lower temperature and much more steadily. On analysis of the residual mixture, it is found that the amount of manganese dioxide is exactly the same at the end of the experiment as it was at the beginning.

A substance which can alter the velocity of a chemical reaction in this way is called a *catalyst*.

Definition. **A Catalyst is a substance which, although present in small proportions, alters the speed of a chemical reaction, but remains chemically unchanged at the end of the reaction.**

To Show that Manganese Dioxide is a Catalyst. This same experiment could also be used to find out if other substances, for example copper oxide, catalyse this reaction.

Fit up the apparatus as shown in Fig. 70 and put some potassium chlorate in the flask and manganese dioxide in a tube attached to the flask by a flexible tube. Heat the potassium chlorate until oxygen just begins to be evolved (the gentle stream of bubbles at first is merely due to expansion) and then take away the flame. No gas will now be evolved but, if a little manganese dioxide is

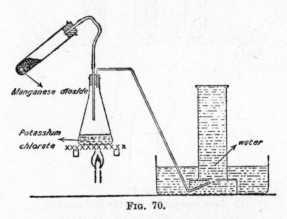

FIG. 70.

Showing manganese dioxide is a catalyst.

shaken from the boiling-tube into the flask, evolution of oxygen again commences. This shows that the manganese dioxide is a catalyst.

Class Experiment to Show Manganese Dioxide is a Catalyst. Mix a little manganese dioxide with about four times its bulk of potassium chlorate and place in an ignition tube. Into each of two other tubes put an approximately equal bulk of manganese dioxide and potassium chlorate respectively. Surround each with sand on a sand tray so that they are close together and vertical. (See Fig. 71.) Commence to heat and test at intervals for oxygen by lowering a glowing splint into each test-tube. After about one minute oxygen is freely evolved from the mixture with no signs of gas from either of the other tubes.

In order to be quite certain that the oxygen was coming from the chlorate and not merely from the manganese dioxide, it would be necessary to show that the weight of manganese dioxide was the same after the experiment as before it. This could be done by dissolving the chlorate and chloride of potassium in water and recovering the manganese dioxide by filtering, washing with water, and drying in a steam oven. It would be found that there was no

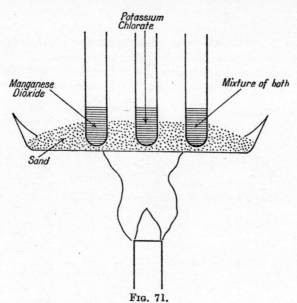

FIG. 71.
To show manganese dioxide is a catalyst.

appreciable loss of weight. For further discussion of catalysis, see p. 127.

Oxygen is also evolved by the action of heat on most peroxides, nearly all nitrates (although it may be evolved together with nitrogen peroxide) and on some few oxides. (See pp. 405, 406.)

A convenient method of obtaining oxygen is by dropping water from a tap funnel on to sodium peroxide in a flask. The oxygen evolved can be collected over water.

$$2Na_2O_2 + 2H_2O \rightarrow 4NaOH + O_2$$
$$\text{sodium} \quad \text{oxygen}$$
$$\text{hydroxide}$$

This reaction takes place in the cold and is therefore very convenient, but sodium peroxide is rather a dangerous substance to handle. The following reaction (which also takes place in the cold) has been found to be very satisfactory. Potassium permanganate is placed in a flask and excess of dilute sulphuric acid added. Hydrogen peroxide is run in as required from a tap-funnel and the evolution of oxygen can be steadily maintained. When the permanganate is all used up it is completely decolourised. This saves a wastage of materials.

$$5H_2O_2 + 2KMnO_4 + 3H_2SO_4 \rightarrow K_2SO_4 + 2MnSO_4 + 8H_2O + 5O_2$$

PROPERTIES OF OXYGEN

Oxygen is a colourless, odourless, neutral gas, is almost insoluble in water and has approximately the same density as that of air. It is an exceptionally active element, combining vigorously with many metals and non-metals, forming basic and acidic oxides respectively:

METALS + OXYGEN → METALLIC OXIDES most of which are

BASIC

in character

NON-METALS + OXYGEN → NON-METALLIC OXIDES most of

which are

ACIDIC

in character.

Action of Oxygen with Non-metals to Form Acidic Oxides. *Phosphorus.* Place a small piece of yellow phosphorus in a deflagrating spoon, warm it until it begins to burn, and then plunge it into a gas-jar of oxygen (Fig. 72) into which you have previously poured a little blue litmus solution. The phosphorus burns with a dazzling flame, emitting white clouds of oxides of phosphorus which dissolve in the water to form acids of phosphorus, which turn the litmus red.

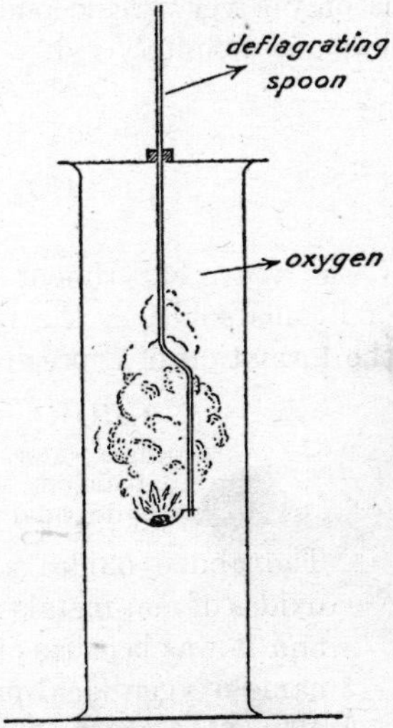

$$P_4 + 5O_2 \rightarrow P_4O_{10}$$
phosphoric
oxide

$$P_4 + 3O_2 \rightarrow P_4O_6$$
phosphorous
oxide

FIG. 72.

Phosphorus burning in oxygen.

On solution in water:

$$6H_2O + P_4O_{10} \rightarrow 4H_3PO_4$$
phosphoric
acid

$$6H_2O + P_4O_6 \rightarrow 4H_3PO_3$$
phosphorous
acid

Sulphur. In a similar manner lower a piece of burning sulphur into a gas-jar of oxygen containing blue litmus solution. Misty fumes of sulphur dioxide are given off as the sulphur burns more brightly with its characteristic blue flame, and this gas dissolves in the water to form sulphurous acid, which turns the litmus red.

$$S + O_2 \rightarrow SO_2$$
sulphur oxygen sulphur
dioxide

$$SO_2 + H_2O \rightarrow H_2SO_3$$
sulphurous
acid

Carbon. Perform the same experiment with wood charcoal (carbon). The charcoal burns and emits a shower of sparks, combining vigorously with the oxygen to form a colourless gas, carbon dioxide, which dissolves in the water to form a carbonic acid. This is only a very weak acid and the litmus is turned claret-coloured but not definitely red.

$$C + O_2 \rightarrow CO_2$$
carbon dioxide

$$CO_2 + H_2O \rightarrow H_2CO_3$$
carbonic acid

If the above experiment is performed with lime-water in the place of litmus solution, the lime-water will become turbid because of the formation of a precipitate of chalk.

$$Ca(OH)_2 + CO_2 \rightarrow CaCO_3 + H_2O$$
lime-water   chalk
(calcium   (calcium
hydroxide)   carbonate)

The above oxides are examples of *anhydrides* (that is, oxides of non-metals which react with water to form acids), and it was because of these that Lavoisier gave the gas the name oxygen (acid-producer).

Action of Oxygen with Metals to form Bases. *Magnesium.* Lower a piece of burning magnesium ribbon by means of tongs into a gas-jar of oxygen. It burns with a more dazzling flame and forms a white ash, magnesium oxide.

$$2Mg + O_2 \rightarrow 2MgO$$
magnesium
oxide

If dilute hydrochloric acid is added to the white ash, the ash readily dissolves to form magnesium chloride.

$$MgO + 2HCl \rightarrow MgCl_2 + H_2O$$
BASE   ACID   SALT   WATER

Iron. Attach a piece of iron wire to the end of a deflagrating spoon and dip the end of the wire in sulphur (to start the action). Warm the wire in the bunsen flame until the sulphur begins to burn and then plunge it quickly into a gas-jar of oxygen which contains a little water. The iron wire burns, giving off a shower of sparks, and finally a molten bead of oxide drops into the water.

$$3Fe + 2O_2 \rightarrow Fe_3O_4$$
triferric
tetroxide

Industrial Preparation. Since oxygen exists to such a large extent in air, it is natural for attempts to be made to obtain it from this source. It is not easy to do this, since nitrogen is an inert element and cannot be made to combine with anything and thus leave the oxygen pure. By far the best process for obtaining oxygen industrially is from liquid air.

Liquid Air. Air can be liquefied by compressing it to 200 atmospheres pressure, cooling it, and allowing the gas to escape from a small jet. This cools the air (just as the opposite, that is, compressing a gas, warms it—a fact you will often have noticed when pumping up your bicycle tyres), and the cooled air is allowed to flow away by passing round the tubes containing the compressed air. This cools the incoming air further and these successive coolings are finally sufficient to liquefy the air. On evaporation of this liquid, nitrogen is first evolved, leaving a liquid very rich in oxygen. The oxygen is sold for commercial use, not as liquid oxygen, but as oxygen compressed at about 100 atmospheres pressure in strong steel cylinders.

Uses. (1) As an aid to breathing where the natural supply of oxygen is insufficient, for example, in high altitude flying or climbing, and also when anæsthetics are administered to a patient.

(2) In the oxyacetylene flame, which can be used for welding steel and also for cutting even very thick armour plate. The oxyacetylene flame is very hot indeed and raises the steel to a very high temperature. Then by reducing the supply of acetylene and by directing a jet of oxygen, the steel can be made to burn away in any desired direction. This process is used extensively in engineering.

QUESTIONS

1. Under what conditions does oxygen react with the following substances: (a) phosphorus, (b) sulphur, (c) magnesium, (d) copper? Name the products and mention any manner in which you could classify them.
2. How would you employ pure nitric oxide (contained in a vessel under pressure) to estimate the volume of oxygen in a sample of air enclosed over water in a graduated tube?
3. Describe the preparation and properties of oxygen. If you had two vessels, one containing air and the other oxygen, how would you distinguish them by simple tests? (O. and C.)

4. Describe an accurate method of finding the percentage of oxygen in the air.

How do you account for the percentage being so nearly constant when there are many causes which remove oxygen from the air? (L.)

5. Manganese dioxide is said to catalyse the decomposition of potassium chlorate; what does this statement mean? Describe experiments you would carry out to prove that the statement is true. (O. and C.)

6. Describe one method for the quantitative estimation of oxygen in the air. State the precautions which are necessary to obtain an accurate result. Calculate the density of air (in terms of hydrogen) on the assumption that air is a mixture of four volumes of nitrogen and one volume of oxygen. (H = 1; N = 14; O = 16.) (N.U.J.B.)

7. Outline the usual laboratory preparation of oxygen. How is it collected? (Details of apparatus are not required.) How is oxygen obtained from the air?

Describe an *accurate* method for measuring the percentage by volume of oxygen in the air. (Methods involving the use of a belljar should not be given.)

State briefly how oxygen may be converted into ozone. (N.U.J.B.)

8. Describe *two* experiments which you could perform in the laboratory in illustration of Lavoisier's historic method of obtaining oxygen from the air. What evidence is there that the gases of the atmosphere are not chemically combined with each other? (L.)

9. Describe the usual preparation and collection of oxygen in the laboratory. State how oxygen may be converted into (a) an acidic oxide, (b) an alkaline oxide, (c) an insoluble basic oxide, (d) an allotropic form. Give also a sketch illustrating (d). (L.)

CHAPTER XXI

HYDROGEN PEROXIDE AND OZONE

HYDROGEN PEROXIDE

THE commoner oxide of hydrogen is water, H_2O. It forms, in addition, another oxide, hydrogen peroxide, H_2O_2. This compound is a colourless liquid and has been known for more than a century. Its purification is difficult and it was not until 1894 that it was obtained in a pure state.

Preparation of Hydrogen Peroxide, H_2O_2. Hydrogen peroxide may be prepared by acting upon the peroxides of certain metals with acids. The materials usually used are barium peroxide and dilute sulphuric acid, because the barium sulphate produced is insoluble and can be filtered off.

$$BaO_2 + H_2SO_4 \rightarrow BaSO_4 \downarrow + H_2O_2$$

To 200 c.c. of water add 20 c.c. of concentrated sulphuric acid. Place the beaker containing the dilute acid in a freezing-mixture of ice and salt and allow it to cool. Gradually add to it a quantity of previously moistened hydrated barium peroxide until the mixture only just reacts acid. Then allow the mixture to settle and filter it. Add to the filtrate a few drops of baryta water (barium hydroxide solution) until it is accurately neutral, and the resulting aqueous solution of hydrogen peroxide is ready for use.

The above method of making hydrogen peroxide gives a pure solution, but the yield is small unless great care is taken with the experiment.

For the reactions of hydrogen peroxide make a solution as follows:—

Dilute about 5 c.c. of syrupy phosphoric acid with its own volume of water. Cool under the tap and add in small portions at a time two or three saltspoonfuls of barium peroxide. Filter the solution and use it for the reactions described below.

$$3BaO_2 + 2H_3PO_4 \rightarrow Ba_3(PO_4)_2 \downarrow + 3H_2O_2$$

Note. If the solution is acidic it will contain some barium ions but these do not interfere with the tests.

231

PROPERTIES OF HYDROGEN PEROXIDE

The pure compound is a syrupy liquid. It is usually used in dilute solution in water.

Action of Heat on Hydrogen Peroxide. Warm hydrogen peroxide solution in a test-tube. Effervescence occurs. The gas given off is *oxygen*. The gas will not rekindle a glowing splint because of the presence of steam.

$$2H_2O_2 \rightarrow 2H_2O + O_2$$

It will be readily understood from the above action that hydrogen peroxide acts as an oxidising agent.

Action of Hydrogen Peroxide on Lead Sulphide. Precipitate lead sulphide by passing hydrogen sulphide into a solution of lead nitrate in a boiling-tube. Allow the precipitate to settle, pour off the liquid and add to the black lead sulphide some hydrogen peroxide solution. Leave it to stand for some time, shaking occasionally. The precipitate gradually turns white, because it is slowly converted to lead sulphate.

$$PbS + 4H_2O_2 \rightarrow PbSO_4 + 4H_2O$$

Hydrogen peroxide is here acting as an oxidising agent, oxidising lead sulphide to lead sulphate, and being itself reduced to water.

This reaction is used in restoring pictures. Hydrogen sulphide in the air reacts with the white lead paint (lead carbonate) of the picture to produce lead sulphide, which is brown and makes the picture dingy. Washing with hydrogen peroxide restores the white colour.

Action of Hydrogen Peroxide on Acidified Potassium Iodide Solution. Acidify a solution of potassium iodide with dilute sulphuric acid. Add hydrogen peroxide. A brown colouration is caused by the production of free iodine.

$$2KI + H_2SO_4 + H_2O_2 \rightarrow K_2SO_4 + I_2 + 2H_2O$$

Here again, hydrogen peroxide is an oxidising agent, oxidising potassium iodide to iodine, and being reduced to water.

Its powerful oxidising action makes hydrogen peroxide useful as a bleaching agent. It oxidises many dyes to colourless substances, without damaging the fabric carrying the dye. It bleaches hair to the well-known "peroxide blonde" colour, and is also used for bleaching the more delicate materials, such as silk or feathers. It is also employed for cleansing wounds.

Action of Hydrogen Peroxide on Lead Dioxide. Suspend some lead dioxide in dilute nitric acid. Add hydrogen peroxide. Vigorous effervescence occurs with evolution of oxygen (rekindles a glowing splint) and a clear colourless solution remains.

In this reaction, the hydrogen peroxide is reduced to water and the lead dioxide to litharge. Each loses one atom of oxygen per molecule and the two atoms of oxygen combine to give an oxygen molecule, O_2

$$PbO_2 + H_2O_2 \rightarrow PbO + H_2O + O_2$$

The litharge then reacts with the nitric acid to leave a solution of lead nitrate.

$$PbO + 2HNO_3 \rightarrow Pb(NO_3)_2 + H_2O$$

Reactions of this type are called *"deoxidising actions"*.

Other examples are:

$$2KMnO_4 + 5H_2O_2 + 3H_2SO_4 \rightarrow K_2SO_4 + 2MnSO_4 + 8H_2O + 5O_2$$
potassium
permanganate

$$O_3 + H_2O_2 \rightarrow 2O_2 + H_2O$$
ozone

(Very slow unless alkalis present.)

Hydrogen peroxide is decomposed catalytically by many substances, *e.g.*, manganese dioxide, finely powdered gold and platinum.

$$2H_2O_2 \rightarrow 2H_2O + O_2$$

Add a pinch of manganese dioxide to a test-tube containing about 5 c.c. of hydrogen peroxide. There is a rapid evolution of oxygen from the hydrogen peroxide which is catalytically decomposed.

Sale of Hydrogen Peroxide. Hydrogen peroxide is sold in "10 volume", "20 volume" and (rarely) "100 volume" solutions. This means that 1 c.c. of the solutions will yield, on heating, 10 c.c., 20 c.c., or 100 c.c. of oxygen respectively, measured at ordinary temperature and pressure. Hydrogen peroxide decomposes slowly at ordinary temperature and so gradually deteriorates when kept in stock.

OZONE, O_3

Ozone can be prepared from oxygen by the use of the silent electrical discharge. The apparatus is shown in Fig. 73.

Dry oxygen is passed through the space between the glass tubes. Each tube is coated with tin-foil (T), which is connected to the terminals of an induction coil. No actual sparking takes place between the layers of tin-foil, nor does the oxygen come into contact with them, but a state of electrical strain exists. The issuing gas may contain up to 5% of ozone. This ozonised oxygen should not be allowed to come into contact with rubber, which is attacked by ozone.

Other forms of apparatus may be used for making ozonised

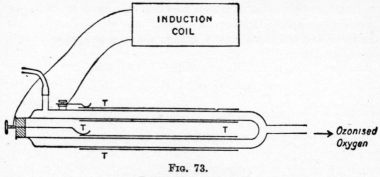

FIG. 73.
Preparation of ozone.

oxygen. Their principle is the same as above, but dilute sulphuric acid takes the place of the layers of tin-foil.

Tests for Ozone. It possesses a smell which resembles that of very dilute chlorine. (It is noticeable near an electrical machine in operation.)

Ozone oxidises mercury and makes the mercury "tail", *i.e.*, leave a trail of mercury stuck to glass as the mercury flows across it. Quite small traces of ozone can be detected in this way.

PROPERTIES OF OZONE

Ozone is a gas at ordinary temperature and pressure. It is obtained pure by liquefaction and is then a dark blue, explosive liquid, boiling at about −110° C. under ordinary pressures.

Ozone as an Oxidising Agent. Ozone is a vigorous oxiliser. Its oxidising actions all depend on its yielding one atom of oxygen per molecule for oxidation, leaving behind an ordinary oxygen molecule.

$$O_3 \rightarrow O_2 + (O)$$

It oxidises lead sulphide to lead sulphate.

$$PbS + 4O_3 \rightarrow PbSO_4 + 4O_2$$

black
lead
sulphide

white
lead
sulphate

and hydrogen sulphide to sulphuric acid.

$$H_2S + 4O_3 \rightarrow H_2SO_4 + 4O_2$$

It also liberates iodine from potassium iodide.

$$2KI + H_2O + O_3 \rightarrow I_2 + O_2 + 2KOH$$

(iodine;
brown
colouration)

This powerful oxidising action of ozone makes it useful for ventilating places to which fresh air has little access. It attacks the organic compounds which are responsible for the "stuffy" smell. Some of the London tube railways are ventilated in this way, metallic ozonisers of the type described above being used to supply ozonised air. The gas becomes poisonous at concentrations exceeding about 1 in 50,000 of air, by volume.

QUESTIONS

1. How is ozonised oxygen prepared in the laboratory? Describe THREE experiments to show how it differs from oxygen. If 100 c.c. of pure ozone were heated and then reduced to the original temperature and pressure, what would be the volume of the resulting gas? (N.U.J.B.)

2. How would you prepare a weak solution of hydrogen peroxide? What is the action of hydrogen peroxide solution on (a) ozone, (b) lead sulphide, (c) acidified potassium iodide solution?
   What is meant by a "10 volume" solution of hydrogen peroxide? (N.U.J.B.)

3. How is ozonised oxygen obtained?
   In what respects does this gas differ from ordinary oxygen? How has it been shown (a) that ozone is composed of oxygen atoms only, (b) that its molecular weight is greater than that of oxygen? (O. and C.)

4. (a) How would you prepare a dilute solution of hydrogen peroxide? How does hydrogen peroxide react with (i) ozone, (ii) acidified potassium iodide solution?
   (b) What volume of oxygen, measured at 136·5° C. and 760 mm. pressure, could be obtained by boiling 100 gm. of a solution containing 17% by weight of hydrogen peroxide? (N.U.J.B.)

5. Describe the properties of ozone.
   On partly ozonising 100 c.c. of oxygen a decrease of volume of 10 c.c. resulted. What volume of ozone had been produced? The resulting gas was treated with excess of a solution of potassium iodide when the following reaction took place:

$$O_3 + 2KI + H_2O \rightarrow 2KOH + I_2 + O_2$$

   Calculate (a) what volume of gas would remain, (b) what weight of iodine would be liberated, assuming the volumes to have been measured at N.T.P. (C.)

6. How can oxygen be converted into its allotropic form? Compare the properties of oxygen with those of its allotropic form. (O. and C.)

CHAPTER XXII

CARBON AND THE OXIDES OF CARBON, FLAME

CARBON

Occurrence. Pure carbon is found in the form of diamond (India, South Africa) and impure carbon as graphite (Ceylon). Carbon is a constituent of numerous naturally occurring substances such as coal, mineral oils, carbonates, organic matter of all kinds and occurs in the air to a small but very important extent ($\cdot 03$–$\cdot 04\%$ by volume) as carbon dioxide (see p. 148).

Carbon exists in the following allotropic modifications:

Diamond. The diamond is in the form of octahedral crystals of density $3 \cdot 5$ which have, when cut and polished, an amazing lustre which makes them valuable as jewellery. It is also the hardest substance known and has a commercial value for the manufacture of glass cutters and rock borers.

Graphite. Graphite exists as black, slippery, hexagonal crystals. It is found naturally as plumbago and is manufactured artificially by heating coke to a very high temperature in the electric furnace (Acheson process).

It is used extensively in the manufacture of lead pencils (which contain a long thin cylinder of graphite and clay) and also as "black lead" as a protective coating for iron articles. It is used as a lubricant, particularly for small bearings (for example, those in dynamos and vacuum cleaner motors) which require little, but regular, lubrication.

Amorphous carbon (which is really made up of similar crystals of graphite) exists in many forms:

Animal Charcoal is made by heating animal refuse and bones with a limited supply of air. It also contains much calcium phosphate. It has the property of absorbing colouring matter (for example litmus) and has a use in industry in removing the colouring matter from brown sugar.

Wood charcoal is made by heating wood with a limited supply of air. It is a light porous variety, and is a remarkably good absorbent for gases (1 c.c. of wood charcoal will absorb nearly 100 c.c. of ammonia gas at $0°$ C.).

Lampblack is made by burning oils (for example turpentine) with

236

a limited supply of air, and it is used for making printers' ink and boot-blacking.

Sugar charcoal is a very pure form of carbon, and is made by removing the elements of water from sugar.

Coke, gas carbon and soot are other forms of impure amorphous carbon.

PROPERTIES OF CARBON

Carbon is not a very reactive substance chemically. All forms of carbon can be made to burn in excess of oxygen to form carbon dioxide, although the temperature at which they commence to burn varies. As the carbon burns a great amount of heat is liberated.

$$C + O_2 \rightarrow CO_2$$

Sulphur will also combine with carbon at a high temperature to form carbon disulphide.

$$C + 2S \rightarrow CS_2$$
carbon
disulphide

Owing to the fact that carbon combines readily with oxygen, it acts as a reducing agent and is used in industrial practice in obtaining iron and zinc from their ores. (See p. 380, and p. 383.)

Reducing Property of Carbon. Scrape a small hole in a charcoal block and place in the hole a mixture of litharge and anhydrous sodium carbonate. (The carbonate melts and forms a protective coating, preventing the metal from being oxidised.) Turn the luminous bunsen flame low, direct a jet of flame by means of a mouth blowpipe on to the mixture and heat it for a few moments (Fig. 73). Allow to cool and, on ejecting the substance from the hole, you will find a small grey globule of metallic lead which can be cut with a knife and which will mark paper.

$$PbO + C \rightarrow PbO + CO$$
litharge carbon   lead carbon monoxide
which will burn to
carbon dioxide

Carbon is insoluble in all common solvents, a fact which all motor car owners know to their cost. Petrol consists of hydrocarbons similar to methane, CH_4. In the cylinders these hydrocarbons are oxidised by the oxygen of the air. If the supply of air is insufficient a deposit of carbon is left inside the cylinders as a hard black solid. This would, in time, choke up the engine and hence the carbon has to be removed. Since carbon is not soluble in any common solvent, this has to be done by dismantling the engine and removing the carbon mechanically.

Coal-gas. Coal is an impure form of carbon and, as such, is used as a domestic source of heat. Its use is, however, uneconomic, as a considerable amount of the heat of the combustion goes up the chimney and also many valuable products are lost. Further, much

FIG. 74.
Reduction of litharge to lead.

of the carbon escapes as soot, polluting the air in the larger industrial areas. Coal-gas is much cleaner, its combustion can be made much more complete, and hence it is used to a considerable extent industrially and in almost every home.

Coal-gas is made by the destructive distillation of coal from a retort. (Destructive distillation means that the products cannot be converted into coal again by allowing them to cool together.) The retorts are heated by means of producer-gas. The products are:

Coal-gas, which consists of hydrogen 50%, methane 30%, carbon monoxide 8%, and smaller quantities of other gases.

Coal-tar, a dark brown or black liquid from which many valuable chemicals can be obtained.

Ammoniacal liquor, a liquid rich in ammonia from which the fertiliser, ammonium sulphate, can be made.

Coke, a purer form of carbon which can be used as a fuel, for making producer- and water-gas, in the smelting of ores to obtain metals, and for many other purposes.

The coke is left in the retorts and the coal-tar and ammoniacal

By courtesy of Messrs. Millar and Harris.

PLATE VI.
The coke-ovens at Haworth Colliery.

liquor separate out as the coal-gas cools. The coal-gas still contains certain gases (ammonia, sulphur dioxide, hydrogen sulphide) which, if allowed to remain in the gas, would have injurious effects. For instance, if the hydrogen sulphide were left in, all the silver articles in the rooms where gas was used would be turned black in time by any unburnt gas, and sulphur dioxide would be formed in the room when the hydrogen sulphide was burnt.

$$2H_2S + 3O_2 \rightarrow 2H_2O + 2SO_2$$

This would become sulphuric acid by the action of moisture and oxygen of the air, and this acid would corrode objects of all kinds.

The various parts of the coal-gas plant and the functions of each are summarised below. (See Fig. 75.)

Retort. Vertical retorts give more uniform heating. Gas carbon is left as a hard crust on the inside.

Hydraulic main (*H*) runs the length of the retorts and collects the materials which first condense—coal-tar and water.

Tar well contains the tar from which many products can be obtained, benzene, aniline, phenol, naphthalene and others.

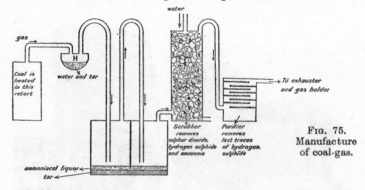

FIG. 75.
Manufacture
of coal-gas.

Condensers cool the gas, and water, tar and ammonia collect as a brown liquid.

Scrubbers. The gas is washed with water to remove most of the ammonia and sulphur dioxide and some of the sulphuretted hydrogen.

Purifiers contain bog ore (hydrated ferric oxide) and this removes the last traces of sulphuretted hydrogen.

$$2Fe_2O_3 + 6H_2S \rightarrow 2Fe_2S_3 + 6H_2O$$

   basic   acid   salt   water
   oxide   gas

Smokeless Fuels. The objections (p. 238) to the burning of "raw" coal have led to the investigation of smokeless fuels. Coal-gas is, of course, smokeless and so is coke. But coke is hard to ignite and burns badly in the ordinary domestic grate.

Low temperature carbonisation of coal has been tried. Coal is distilled in retorts as in making coal-gas, but the temperature of distillation is much reduced (under 750° C. instead of about 1000° C.). Some coal-gas, oil and tar are produced. The solid residue is a fuel which ignites and burns much more readily than coke *and is smokeless.* So far, however, this solid fuel is too expensive compared with "raw" coal.

PRODUCER-GAS AND WATER-GAS

These gases are usually made together because the making of producer-gas evolves heat, and the making of water-gas absorbs heat.

Producer-gas is made by blowing air through a large mass of coke, combustion of which has already been started (Fig. 76). On entering the furnace air causes the coke to burn to carbon dioxide.

$$C + O_2 \rightarrow CO_2$$

Higher in the furnace, however, the supply of oxygen is used up, the hot coke reduces the carbon dioxide to carbon monoxide, and this gas passes on with the nitrogen of the air.

$$CO_2 + C \rightarrow 2CO$$

Producer-gas consists of about one third of its volume of carbon monoxide and two-thirds of its volume of nitrogen.

Water-gas. In Fig. 76 pro-ducer-gas is being made, since pipes A_1 and A_2 are open. After about seven minutes these pipes are closed and pipes B_1 and B_2 are opened. Steam now passes over the white hot coke for about four minutes. The coke decomposes the steam, forming a gas which consists of approximately equal volumes of carbon monoxide and hydrogen.

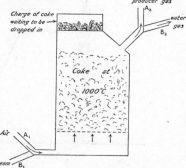

Fig. 76.

Furnace for making alternately Producer - gas (pipes A_1 A_2 open) and Water-gas (pipes B_1 B_2 open).

$$H_2O + C \rightarrow CO + H_2$$

1 volume   1 volume
of carbon   of hydro-
monoxide   gen

The temperature, however, quickly falls and so pipes B_1 B_2 are closed and A_1 A_2 are opened, permitting air to be blown in again to raise the temperature once more.

These gases are used to heat the retorts which distil the coal, and water-gas is sometimes used to "boost up" the supply of gas to a town at certain periods of the day when demand for gas is greatest.

CARBON DIOXIDE

This gas was first observed by Van Helmont towards the end of the sixteenth century, but Black (1728–99) first showed that the gas could be prepared by the action of dilute acids on calcium carbonate. It occurs in the air on the earth's surface to the extent of about 0·03% of its volume; it issues from rocks in volcanic regions, and occurs in mines as "choke damp". Certain mineral springs contain the gas and it is always present in natural drinking water because of its solubility in water. Its biological importance is dealt with on p. 148.

Preparation of Carbon Dioxide. It is usually made in the laboratory by the action of dilute hydrochloric acid on marble.

Place several pieces of marble in a flask (or bottle), as shown in Fig. 77, and pour some dilute hydrochloric acid down the thistle funnel on to the marble. There is effervescence and a colourless gas is liberated which is collected over water[1] or by displacement

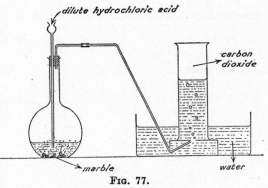

FIG. 77.
Preparation of carbon dioxide.

of air, the gas being heavier than air. Calcium chloride solution is left in the flask.

$$CaCO_3 + 2HCl \rightarrow CaCl_2 + H_2O + CO_2$$

calcium   dilute   calcium   water   carbon
carbonate   hydro-   chloride   dioxide
        chloric
        acid

If the gas is required pure and dry it can be passed through potassium bicarbonate solution in a wash bottle (to remove suspended hydrochloric acid), dried by passing it through a calcium chloride U-tube and collected by displacement of air (the gas being heavier than air) or over mercury.

Collect several gas-jars of the gas, and perform the following experiments:

Effect of Carbon Dioxide on a Lighted Splint. Plunge a lighted splint into a gas-jar of the gas. It is extinguished. Carbon dioxide does not support combustion.

Action of Carbon Dioxide on Lime-water. Pour lime-water into a gas-jar full of carbon dioxide. **The lime-water goes milky.** If the mixture is allowed to stand, you

[1] There is some loss due to the solubility of the gas in water. Water, at ordinary temperature and pressure, absorbs its own volume of carbon dioxide.

will see white solid particles separate out. These are particles of chalk. The milkiness is due to a suspension of the insoluble substance, chalk, in water.

$$Ca(OH)_2 + CO_2 \rightarrow CaCO_3 + H_2O$$

calcium   carbon   calcium   water
hydroxide   dioxide   carbonate
solution   (chalk)
(lime-water)

The above test serves to distinguish carbon dioxide from any other gas.

Effect of Carbon Dioxide on a Lighted Candle. Lower a candle on a deflagrating spoon into a gas-jar of air. The candle can be extinguished by "pouring" carbon dioxide into the gas-jar in which the candle is burning (Fig. 78). This shows carbon dioxide to be heavier than air (density 22 relative to hydrogen).

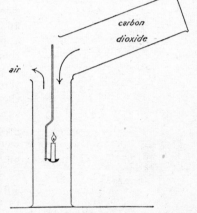

Effect of burning Magnesium on Carbon Dioxide. Lower a piece of burning magnesium into carbon dioxide in a gas-jar. It continues to burn for a short time with a spluttering flame, and black specks of carbon can be seen on the sides of the gas-jar. The magnesium burns to magnesium oxide.

FIG. 78.

Pouring carbon dioxide on to a candle.

$$2Mg + CO_2 \rightarrow 2MgO + C$$

This clearly shows carbon dioxide to contain carbon and oxygen.

Solution of the Gas in Water. Invert a gas-jar of carbon dioxide in a trough of cold water and shake the gas-jar. The water rises slowly, showing that the gas is soluble. Put a glass plate over the mouth of the jar and remove it. To the liquid in it, add blue litmus solution and shake. The solution becomes claret-coloured but not red. This is because carbon dioxide reacts with water to produce *carbonic acid*, which is, however, too weak to turn litmus solution red.

$$H_2O + CO_2 \rightarrow H_2CO_3$$

water   carbon   carbonic
       dioxide   acid

Carbon dioxide is an acidic oxide.

Action of Carbon Dioxide with Caustic Soda Solution. Repeat the above experiment, using caustic soda solution instead of water. The rapid rise of the solution shows that the gas is quickly absorbed. The acidic carbon dioxide reacts with the alkaline solution producing sodium carbonate.

$$CO_2 + 2NaOH \rightarrow Na_2CO_3 + H_2O$$
$$\text{caustic} \qquad \text{sodium}$$
$$\text{soda} \qquad \text{carbonate}$$

This reaction is discussed more fully, later (p. 258).

Determination of the Percentage Yield of Carbon Dioxide from Marble. Weigh a small dry test-tube, introduce a small piece of marble and weigh again. Set up the apparatus as shown in Fig. 79. (A very *small* piece of marble must be added to the acid just before the apparatus is assembled, to saturate the acid with carbon dioxide and displace the air in the flask.) Weigh the whole apparatus, then loosen the cork to allow the small tube to slip, and agitate the flask gently so that the acid comes into contact with the marble. There is an effervescence and *damp* carbon dioxide is given off. The moisture which the gas would normally carry off into the atmosphere is removed by the calcium chloride tube. Hence the loss in weight of the whole apparatus is due to evolution of carbon dioxide. When action has ceased weigh the whole apparatus.

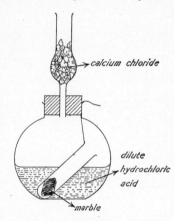

Fig. 79.
Percentage yield of carbon dioxide from marble.

$$CaCO_3 + 2HCl \rightarrow CaCl_2 + H_2O + CO_2$$

Work out the results as in the following case:

Results.

Weight of small tube empty	= 4·52 gm.
„ „ „ and marble	= 6·35 gm.
∴ weight of marble	= 1·83 gm.
Weight of whole apparatus before experiment	= 49·20 gm.
„ „ „ after „	= 48·39 gm.
∴ weight of carbon dioxide evolved	= 0·81 gm.

1·83 gm. of marble yielded   0·81 gm. of carbon dioxide.

1 gm.   ,,   ,,   ,, $\dfrac{0·81}{1·83}$ gm.   ,,   ,,

100 gm.   ,,   ,,   ,, $\dfrac{0·81 \times 100}{1·83}$ gm.   ,,   ,,

$$= 44·3\%$$

Uses of Carbon Dioxide. Solutions of the gas in water have a pleasant taste (the taste of soda water), and hence the gas is used in the manufacture of the effervescing drinks called "mineral waters". The effervescence is caused by dissolving the gas in water at a pressure of several atmospheres; when the pressure is released (by opening the bottle) the gas is liberated.

Its use in the solid form is increasing. Carbon dioxide can be made into a white solid (carbon dioxide snow) by allowing liquid carbon dioxide to evaporate, the temperature falling to $-78°$ C. as the solid forms. This solid evaporates when heated, leaving no residue, and it is, therefore, used as a refrigerating agent for perishable goods.

Owing to its non-inflammable nature carbon dioxide is used for extinguishing fires. The usual fire extinguisher contains a solution of sodium carbonate which can be made to come into contact with dilute sulphuric acid by striking a knob. The carbon dioxide liberated forces a stream of effervescing liquid on to the fire, and the carbon dioxide prevents the air from getting to the burning material and so helps to put out the fire.

CARBON MONOXIDE

Carbon monoxide is a poisonous, colourless gas with practically no smell. It is present in coal-gas and other gaseous fuels. It is formed by the partial combustion of carbon, and poisoning by the exhaust fumes of a motor-car in an enclosed space, for example a garage, is due to the presence of carbon monoxide. The blood of a person poisoned by the gas is a characteristic cherry-red colour. An atmosphere containing as little as 0·5% carbon monoxide may cause death if breathed for some time, and an atmosphere containing 0·1% is injurious.

Preparation from Oxalic Acid. Fit up the apparatus as shown in Fig .80. Place some oxalic acid crystals ($H_2C_2O_4 . 2H_2O$) in the strong flat-bottomed flask and pour concentrated sulphuric acid down the thistle funnel. Warm the mixture gently (always have the greatest respect for hot concentrated sulphuric acid). The white crystals dissolve, effervescence is observed, and a mixture of carbon

I

monoxide and carbon dioxide gases is evolved. By passing the mixture through a strong solution of caustic potash the carbon dioxide is absorbed, and the carbon monoxide passes on and is collected over water in which it is insoluble.

$$2KOH + CO_2 \rightarrow K_2CO_3 + H_2O$$

Chemistry of the Action. Oxalic acid has the formula $H_2C_2O_4$ and the hot concentrated sulphuric acid removes **the elements of water** from the molecule of oxalic acid, leaving a mixture of equal volumes

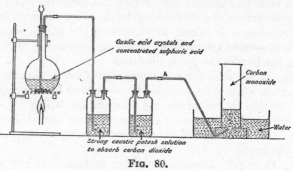

Fig. 80.
Preparation of carbon monoxide.

of carbon monoxide and carbon dioxide. It is because the carbon dioxide is there in quantity, and not merely as a small trace of impurity, that it is necessary to pass the gas through two wash-bottles containing potassium hydroxide solution.

$$\underset{\substack{\text{oxalic}\\ \text{acid}}}{H_2C_2O_4} - \underset{\substack{\text{water}\\ \text{(removed}\\ \text{by acid)}}}{H_2O} \rightarrow \underset{\substack{\text{carbon}\\ \text{monoxide}}}{CO} + \underset{\substack{\text{carbon}\\ \text{dioxide}}}{CO_2}$$

Preparation from Formic Acid. Fit up the apparatus shown in Fig. 81. Place one or two teaspoonfuls of sodium formate in the

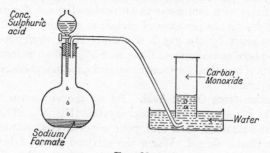

Fig. 81.
Preparation of carbon monoxide.

flat-bottomed flask and allow concentrated sulphuric acid to run in from the tap funnel. The reaction takes place in the cold, effervescence is observed and carbon monoxide is collected over water in which it is insoluble.

Chemistry of the Action. Sodium formate is converted into formic acid from which the elements of water are immediately removed by the concentrated sulphuric acid:—

$$HCOONa + H_2SO_4 \rightarrow HCOOH + NaHSO_4$$
$$\underset{\substack{\text{removed} \\ \text{by acid}}}{HCOOH - H_2O} \rightarrow CO$$

The above actions take place simultaneously and can be represented by the equation:—

$$HCOONa + H_2SO_4 \rightarrow NaHSO_4 + CO + H_2O$$

Test. Carbon monoxide burns in air with a blue flame, forming carbon dioxide (the latter will turn lime-water milky, forming a precipitate of chalk.)

Collect a gas-jar of the gas and perform the following experiment: *Action of Lime-water.* Take away the glass plate, quickly pour in a little lime-water and shake. **There should be no turbidity.** (It is very difficult to get rid of all the carbon dioxide present. If necessary, shake first with caustic potash solution.) Apply a light to the gas and it will burn with a blue flame, and on shaking, the lime-water will go turbid.

$$\underset{\substack{\text{carbon} \\ \text{monoxide}}}{2CO} + \underset{\substack{\text{oxygen} \\ \text{(air)}}}{O_2} \rightarrow \underset{\substack{\text{carbon} \\ \text{dioxide}}}{2CO_2}$$

Reducing Properties of Carbon Monoxide. Take a hard glass tube containing a porcelain boat full of litharge and attach it to the apparatus (Fig. 80) at A, or at a similar point in apparatus (Fig. 81). After allowing a few moments for the hard glass tube to be filled with the gas, light the jet and heat the litharge. A glow will spread through the litharge and, on allowing the apparatus to cool, grey metallic lead will be observed. The carbon monoxide has reduced the litharge to lead, being itself oxidised to carbon dioxide.

$$\underset{\substack{\text{lead} \\ \text{monoxide}}}{PbO} + \underset{\substack{\text{carbon} \\ \text{monoxide}}}{CO} \rightarrow \underset{\text{lead}}{Pb} + \underset{\substack{\text{carbon} \\ \text{dioxide}}}{CO_2}$$

The gas will similarly reduce copper oxide and ferric oxide to the metal.

$$CuO + CO \rightarrow Cu + CO_2$$
$$Fe_2O_3 + 3CO \rightarrow 2Fe + 3CO_2$$

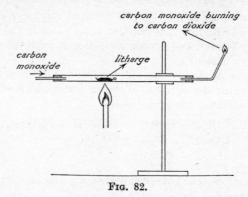

FIG. 82.

Reduction of litharge to lead by carbon monoxide.

Preparation of Carbon Monoxide from Carbon Dioxide. Carbon monoxide may be prepared by passing a stream of carbon dioxide through an iron tube containing pieces of carbon heated to red

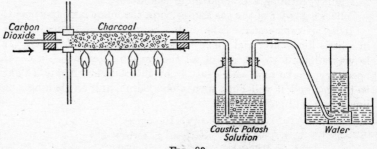

FIG. 83.

Preparation of carbon monoxide by passing carbon dioxide over red-hot carbon.

heat (Fig. 83). Any carbon dioxide present is then absorbed by caustic potash solution and the gas collected over water.

$$\underset{\text{carbon}}{\text{C}} + \underset{\substack{\text{carbon} \\ \text{dioxide}}}{\text{CO}_2} \rightarrow \underset{\substack{\text{carbon} \\ \text{monoxide}}}{2\text{CO}}$$

Reactions in a Coal-fire. The reactions in a deep, brightly glowing coal-fire are similar to that by which carbon monoxide is produced in the last experiment. They are sufficiently explained in Fig. 84.

FLAME

Definition. Flame is a region of combining gases accompanied by light and heat.

At A plenty of air available. Carbon burns to carbon dioxide.

$$C + O_2 \to CO_2$$

At B ascending carbon dioxide is reduced by red-hot carbon to carbon monoxide.

$$CO_2 + C \to 2CO$$

At C the hot carbon monoxide burns in the air (to form carbon dioxide) with a flickering blue flame.

$$2CO + O_2 \to 2CO_2$$

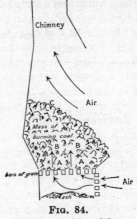

FIG. 84.
The household coal fire.

Examples of flame with which you are familiar are the burning in air of such materials as hydrogen, coal gas, wood or coal. In the latter case, wood or coal when heated give out gases which will burn in air and since the wood or coal are supplying these combustible gases, the flame is closely associated with the solid matter. In every flame, there is produced by the chemical reaction so much heat that the system is raised to incandescence. We know, on the other hand, many cases where gases combine slowly with little rise of temperature and no flame. An example of this type of reaction is the combination of hydrogen and chlorine when left in contact with each other in diffused daylight.

The terms "combustible material" and "supporter of combustion" are interchangeable. When considering a bunsen flame in air, we usually refer to the gas coming from the burner as the "combustible material" and the air as the "supporter of combustion". This is mainly because we live in an atmosphere of air (which contains oxygen, a very reactive gas) which surrounds any burning material. If, by accident, this atmosphere of ours were to consist of coal gas, it would be possible to produce the flame of a bunsen burner by pumping air down the pipe usually connected to the gas-works. To illustrate this, set up the apparatus shown in Fig. 85,

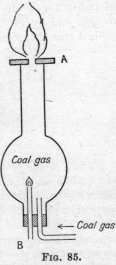

FIG. 85.
Air burning in coal gas.

which consists of a lamp chimney with a square of asbestos (containing a round hole) resting on the top of the chimney. The cork at the base is fitted with a glass tube for a gas inlet and a mica or metal tube at B. The gas is turned on, and the aperture at A is closed momentarily whilst the gas issuing from B is ignited. The aperture at A is now opened and the gas is lighted. On inspection, it will be seen that there is now a flame at the top of the mica tube which consists of air burning in an atmosphere of coal gas.

Structure of flame. The structure of a flame varies according to the chemical composition of the gas which is burning. The general conical shape is brought about by several factors, the more important of which are the effects of convection and the necessity for further supplies of gas to search for air with which to burn. The gas burning immediately on issue from the burner, uses up the air in that region and the gas following has to seek its supply of air from more distant sources. At the same time the convection currents set up confine this search to an upward direction. The blue zone seen at the base of a bunsen or candle flame (see Fig. 87) is caused by the upward stream of air impinging on the base of the issuing cone of gas. The inner zone near the burner contains unburnt gas, since the outside of the flame has obviously the best opportunity to come in contact with the air, and the inside of the flame, the least.

We will consider the structure of some well-known flames:—

(a) *The flame of hydrogen burning in air.* This flame is, as we should expect, a simple one. Two zones only are produced, a zone of unburnt gas surrounded by a zone in which combination of oxygen and hydrogen takes place. The flame is almost invisible in dust-free air. (See Fig. 86.)

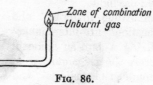

FIG. 86.
Hydrogen flame.

(b) *The candle flame.* Candle wax consists of hydrocarbons, both the carbon and the hydrogen being combustible materials. It is assumed that both elements do not burn completely to form water and carbon dioxide except at the very outside of the flame where there is plenty of air. In the bright yellow zone there is incomplete combustion and particles of carbon raised to a white heat are present in it to give the flame most of its luminosity, whereas the outside zone where combustion becomes complete is only faintly visible. The zone round the wick consists of unburnt gas, and the blue zone at the base is a zone of rapid burning caused by the upward rush of air due to convection first meeting the combustible gases. (See Fig. 87.)

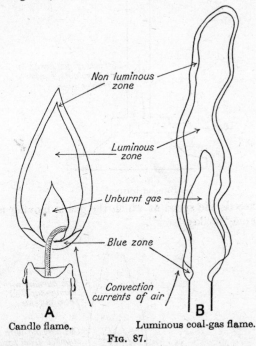

Non luminous zone

Luminous zone

Unburnt gas

Blue zone

Convection currents of air

A **B**
Candle flame. Luminous coal-gas flame.
FIG. 87.

The luminous bunsen flame (air holes closed) gives a parallel with the candle flame, the gases in the coal gas being methane (a hydrocarbon), hydrogen and carbon monoxide.

(c) *The bunsen flame.* The flame of a burning hydrocarbon or the luminous bunsen flame is not a very hot flame and deposits soot on a cold article held in it. Bunsen devised a simple burner (Fig. 88) to ensure more complete combustion by introducing a supply of air entering with the gas, so that this supply of air together with the external supply is sufficient to produce complete combustion. Hence the flame with the air holes open is more compact, much hotter and non-luminous. The structure of this flame is shown in Fig. 89, and it will be seen that the luminous zone has been replaced by a zone in which the coal gas burns with the internal supply of air. There is a limit to the amount of air which can be supplied by the holes at the base, for if sufficient is introduced to cause almost complete combustion, the rate of burning of the

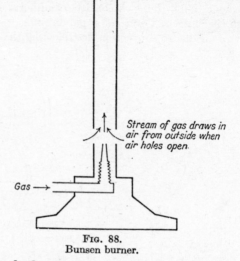

Stream of gas draws in air from outside when air holes open.

Gas →

FIG. 88.
Bunsen burner.

mixture exceeds the speed at which the gas is moving up the tube and the flame "strikes back".

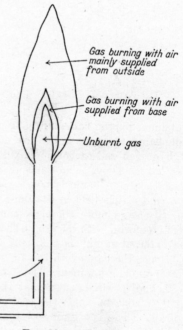

Gas burning with air mainly supplied from outside

Gas burning with air supplied from base

Unburnt gas

FIG. 89.
Non-luminous bunsen flame.

Experiments to illustrate the structure of flame. The existence of a zone of unburnt gas and zones of varying temperatures may be shown by exploring the flame in the following way: hold a piece of paper or cardboard horizontally in the flame and remove it just

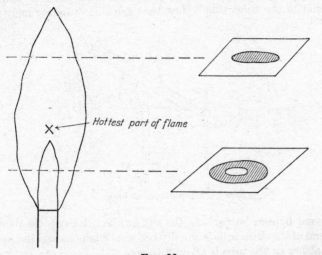

FIG. 90.

Exploring temperature of flame.

before burning would occur. (Fig. 90.) The inner zone will be found to cause no burning of the paper, whilst the hot parts of the flame will turn the paper brown. Alternatively, copper gauze may be held in the flame by means of tongs.

The causes of luminosity of flame. The luminosity of a flame is affected by alteration of temperature and pressure of the burning gases and also by the presence or absence of solid particles.

The presence of solid particles in a flame increases luminosity. Sprinkle a few iron filings into the non-luminous bunsen flame. Sparks are formed as each particle is raised to a white heat. Similarly, platinum foil or a porcelain rod become white hot and emit light when heated to a high temperature in the non-luminous bunsen flame. This principle is used in the incandescent mantle where small particles of thorium and cerium oxides are suspended in a non-luminous bunsen flame.

Hold a cold evaporating dish by means of tongs for a minute in the luminous bunsen flame. On removal, the dish will be found to be blackened by carbon. No such effect is observed if the experiment is repeated using the non-luminous flame. The presence of the

I*.

particles of carbon is thought to be responsible for the luminosity of this type of flame.

The effect of temperature on luminosity. Set up the apparatus of Fig. 91 with a silica tube extension fitting over a bunsen burner tube. Open the air holes and obtain the non-luminous flame at the end of the silica tube. Now heat the silica tube strongly with

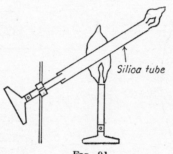

Silica tube

FIG. 91.
Effect of temperature on luminosity.

a second bunsen burner. As the silica tube is heated, the flame at the end of the silica tube gradually becomes luminous and luminosity diminishes as the tube is allowed to cool.

Effect of increase of pressure. Increase of pressure of the gases taking part in the combustion increases the luminosity of the flame.

Explosions. Explosions result from very rapid, exothermic chemical reactions. Consider a mixture of hydrogen, two volumes, and oxygen, one volume. If the mixture is sparked, the gases are heated to very high temperature near the spark. They combine and liberate heat.

$$H_2 + \tfrac{1}{2}O_2 \rightarrow H_2O + 68,400 \text{ cals.}$$

This heat raises the temperature of neighbouring gas, which combines liberating more heat, and so on with great rapidity. The mass of gas is raised to incandescence in a fraction of a second and the consequent great expansion produces a pressure wave in the air. The whole effect is called an explosion.

QUESTIONS ON THIS CHAPTER WILL BE FOUND ON PAGE 263.

CHAPTER XXIII

CARBONATES

K	Carbonates	Carbonates of these metals	Any carbonate
Na	soluble.	not decomposed by heat.	with any acid
Ca			liberates car-
Mg	Carbonates	Carbonates of these metals	bon dioxide.
Al	of these	decomposed into oxide of	
Zn	metals	the metal by heat.	
Fe	insoluble		
Pb	in water.		
Cu			

Ammonium carbonate is also soluble in water.

The above table summarises briefly the important properties of the common carbonates.

Test for any Carbonate. Put some of the suspected carbonate in a test-tube and add dilute nitric acid. If a carbonate is present there will be effervescence and the gas which comes off will turn lime-water milky; for example,

$$PbCO_3 + 2HNO_3 \rightarrow Pb(NO_3)_2 + H_2O + CO_2$$
$$\text{lead} \qquad\qquad\qquad\qquad\qquad \text{carbon}$$
$$\text{carbonate} \qquad\qquad\qquad\qquad\qquad \text{dioxide}$$

Ammonium Carbonate, $(NH_4)_2CO_3$. This compound is prepared as a sublimate, by heating ammonium sulphate with limestone.

$$(NH_4)_2SO_4 + CaCO_3 \rightarrow (NH_4)_2CO_3 + CaSO_4$$

It is used as a constituent of "smelling salts" and as a chemical reagent.

Potassium Carbonate. Potassium carbonate is very similar to sodium carbonate. (See below.) It cannot, however, be made by the Solvay process because the bicarbonate of potassium is too soluble. It is made by the Leblanc process and in other ways.

Potassium carbonate differs chiefly from sodium carbonate in that it is very deliquescent, and is anhydrous.

It is used to make soft soap, hard glass and potassium salts generally.

SODIUM CARBONATE, Na_2CO_3, Soda Ash

Sodium carbonate is obtained in both the anhydrous and crystalline states ($Na_2CO_3 . 10H_2O$, washing soda) by the Solvay process.

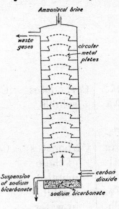

FIG. 92.

Solvay tower.

Solvay Process. Brine is saturated with ammonia gas in a tower and the ammoniacal brine is made to run down towers up which carbon dioxide is forced. The towers consist of a series of compartments and the liquid and gas meet at a large number of small holes in metal plates separating the compartments. This increases the area of reaction and enables the process to proceed more quickly. The final product of the reaction is sodium bicarbonate, which is not very soluble in water. This, therefore, separates out, forming a white sludge at the base of the tower (Fig. 92).

$$NH_4OH + NaCl + CO_2 \rightarrow NaHCO_3 + NH_4Cl$$

ammonium   sodium   carbon   sodium   ammonium
hydroxide   chloride   dioxide   bicarbonate   chloride

The sodium bicarbonate is filtered off and is placed in pans and heated, when it is converted into sodium carbonate, and the carbon dioxide evolved used again.

$$2NaHCO_3 \rightarrow Na_2CO_3 + H_2O + CO_2$$

sodium
carbonate

The substance formed is anhydrous sodium carbonate, and much sodium carbonate is used as such to-day. If the crystalline variety is required the anhydrous solid is dissolved in a quantity of hot water such that crystallisation takes place on cooling. The crystals are removed and allowed to dry.

$$Na_2CO_3 + 10H_2O \rightarrow Na_2CO_3 . 10H_2O$$

Economics of the Solvay Process. This process is an excellent example of modern methods in which waste (and consequently cost) is kept down to a minimum. The raw materials are brine and limestone. On heating the latter, it forms quicklime and carbon dioxide.

$$CaCO_3 \rightarrow CaO + CO_2$$

used for
Solvay tower

(A further supply of carbon dioxide is obtained by the heating of the bicarbonate.)

It will be noticed that the only substance produced in the Solvay tower besides the sodium bicarbonate is ammonium chloride. This

By courtesy of Imperial Chemical Industries Ltd.

PLATE VII.

Imperial Chemical Industries. (Works at Billingham.)

substance, together with the lime left after heating the limestone, generates the only missing reagent, namely, ammonia.

$$2NH_4Cl + CaO \rightarrow CaCl_2 + 2NH_3 + H_2O$$

The weakness of the Solvay process is that no use is made of the chlorine of the sodium chloride. It is lost in the form of calcium chloride (see last equation).

Leblanc Process. This process was used for many years, being the first process for the commercial manufacture of sodium carbonate. It was devised to compete for a prize of 100,000 francs offered by Napoleon for a process for the manufacture of sodium carbonate from sodium chloride. It won the prize for Nicolas Leblanc.

The process consisted of first heating rock salt with concentrated sulphuric acid in large iron pans. The reaction proceeds in two stages.

$$NaCl + H_2SO_4 \rightarrow NaHSO_4 + HCl$$

sodium hydrogen sulphate   hydrogen chloride

$$NaHSO_4 + NaCl \rightarrow Na_2SO_4 + HCl$$

sodium sulphate "salt cake"   hydrogen chloride

The "salt cake" was then mixed with limestone and coke, and heated in a revolving reverberatory furnace, when the following reaction took place

$$Na_2SO_4 + 4C + CaCO_3 \rightarrow Na_2CO_3 + CaS + 4CO$$

sodium carbonate   calcium sulphide   carbon monoxide

The mixture (black ash) was lixiviated with water and the solution was evaporated down and allowed to crystallise. The crystals of washing soda were allowed to dry on a porous floor.

$$Na_2CO_3 + 10H_2O \rightarrow Na_2CO_3 . 10H_2O$$

washing soda crystals

The process, which is now obsolete, was kept going for many years, simply because of valuable by-products, especially hydrochloric acid, which could be obtained from it.

Laboratory Preparation of Sodium Carbonate. (a) By the action of heat on sodium bicarbonate (see p. 262).

(b) *From caustic soda solution.*

Fit up the apparatus as shown (Fig. 93). Pass carbon dioxide (free from hydrochloric acid) into a moderately concentrated solution of caustic soda for some time until finally a white solid (sodium bicarbonate) appears on the bottom of the boiling-tube,

$$2NaOH + CO_2 \rightarrow Na_2CO_3 + H_2O \quad \text{(1st stage)}$$

$$Na_2CO_3 + H_2O + CO_2 \rightarrow 2NaHCO_3 \quad \text{(2nd stage)}$$

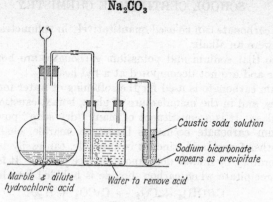

Caustic soda solution

Sodium bicarbonate appears as precipitate

Marble & dilute hydrochloric acid

Water to remove acid

Fig. 93.

Preparation of sodium bicarbonate.

Filter this off, wash the solid residue two or three times with a little cold water, and then transfer the solid to a dish and heat. Finally sodium carbonate will be obtained as a fine white powder.

$$2NaHCO_3 \rightarrow Na_2CO_3 + H_2O + CO_2$$

Carbon dioxide is evolved during the reaction.

Properties and Uses of Washing Soda. Washing soda is sodium carbonate decahydrate $Na_2CO_3 . 10H_2O$, large translucent crystals.

Efflorescence. On exposure to air the crystals lose weight and become coated with a fine white powder which renders them opaque. Each molecule of washing soda has given up to the atmosphere 9 molecules of water of crystallisation.

$$Na_2CO_3.10H_2O \rightarrow Na_2CO_3.H_2O + 9H_2O$$
$$\text{sodium carbonate} \qquad \text{sodium carbonate}$$
$$\text{decahydrate} \qquad \text{mono-hydrate}$$

Such an action, that is, the giving up of water of crystallisation to the atmosphere, is termed efflorescence.

The crystals are readily soluble in water.

Anhydrous sodium carbonate can be made by heating the hydrated sodium carbonate. It is a fine white powder and does not dissolve as readily in water as do the crystals.

Solutions of sodium carbonate in water are alkaline to litmus. This is due to the feebly acid properties of carbonic acid. This acid is expelled by almost every other acid, and hence, sodium carbonate acts like sodium hydroxide, although the former is a salt and the latter an alkali.

$$Na_2CO_3 + 2HCl \rightarrow 2NaCl + H_2O + CO_2$$

Sodium carbonate can be used quantitatively in volumetric analysis, as if it were an alkali.

Notice that sodium and potassium carbonates are both soluble in water and are not decomposed at a red heat.

Sodium carbonate is used for the softening of water for domestic purposes, and in the manufacture of glass, borax, caustic soda and water glass. It is a constituent of many "dry soap" powders.

Calcium carbonate occurs as limestone, marble, chalk, and in many other forms, and, since it is insoluble, can easily be made in the laboratory by double decomposition (see p. 129). It is seen as a white precipitate when carbon dioxide is bubbled into lime-water.

$$Ca(OH)_2 + CO_2 \rightarrow CaCO_3 + H_2O$$
$$\text{calcium}$$
$$\text{carbonate}$$
$$\text{(chalk)}$$

The chalk can be obtained by filtering off the precipitate, washing it a few times with hot water and allowing it to dry.

It is attacked by dilute hydrochloric and nitric acids with the evolution of carbon dioxide, for example:—

$$CaCO_3 + 2HCl \rightarrow CaCl_2 + H_2O + CO_2$$

With dilute sulphuric acid, however, the action slows down and finally stops, particularly if the calcium carbonate is in lump form, for example, marble. The reason is that calcium sulphate, being only sparingly soluble, forms a protective layer on the outside preventing the sulphuric acid from acting upon the solid within.

Although practically insoluble in pure water, calcium carbonate is dissolved by water which contains dissolved carbon dioxide, because it forms soluble calcium bicarbonate.

$$CaCO_3 + H_2O + CO_2 \rightarrow Ca(HCO_3)_2$$
$$\text{calcium}$$
$$\text{bicarbonate}$$

(See pp. 164, 166 for treatment of calcium carbonate under "hardness of water" and "stalagmites and stalactites".)

Action of heat on calcium carbonate (see p. 198).

Zinc carbonate is formed as a white precipitate when sodium bicarbonate solution is added to a solution of zinc sulphate in water.

$$ZnSO_4 + 2NaHCO_3 \rightarrow ZnCO_3 + Na_2SO_4 + H_2O + CO_2$$

(If sodium carbonate is used, *basic* carbonate of zinc is formed.)

The white precipitate is filtered off, washed with hot distilled water and allowed to dry.

Zinc carbonate is attacked by dilute acids liberating carbon dioxide, for example:—

$$ZnCO_3 + 2HCl \rightarrow ZnCl_2 + H_2O + CO_2$$

On heating a little zinc carbonate in a test-tube, carbon dioxide is given off and zinc oxide (yellow when hot, white when cold) remains in the test-tube.

$$ZnCO_3 \rightarrow ZnO + CO_2$$
zinc
oxide

Zinc carbonate is used medicinally.

Lead carbonate. Lead carbonate is made in the laboratory by adding sodium bicarbonate solution to a solution of lead nitrate in water.

$$Pb(NO_3)_2 + 2NaHCO_3 \rightarrow PbCO_3 + 2NaNO_3 + H_2O + CO_2$$

It is seen as a white precipitate.

White lead, basic lead carbonate, $Pb(OH)_2. 2PbCO_3$, is used extensively as a paint when mixed with oils. It is made by subjecting strips of lead to the action of acetic acid, water-vapour, carbon dioxide and air. It is poisonous and blackens rapidly in industrial areas where hydrogen sulphide occurs.

N.B. Lead carbonate is not readily acted upon by either dilute hydrochloric or sulphuric acids. A layer of insoluble chloride or sulphate formed round the carbonate protects it from further action. Dilute nitric acid attacks it to liberate carbon dioxide in accordance with the general action of acids on carbonates:

$$PbCO_3 + 2HNO_3 \rightarrow Pb(NO_3)_2 + H_2O + CO_2$$

Copper carbonate, $CuCO_3$, is made by double decomposition and it is usually obtained as a basic salt, having the formula $CuCO_3$. $Cu(OH)_2$. This is a bright green powder which liberates carbon dioxide on being heated, and black copper oxide is left.

$$CuCO_3 \rightarrow CuO + CO_2$$

It dissolves in dilute acids with the liberation of carbon dioxide, for example:

$$CuCO_3 + H_2SO_4 \rightarrow CuSO_4 + H_2O + CO_2$$
copper
sulphate
solution

THE BICARBONATES

We are only concerned with the bicarbonates of sodium and calcium, all the others being unstable or unimportant.

Sodium bicarbonate, $NaHCO_3$, "baking soda", is manufactured by the Solvay process and it can be isolated in the dry state before sodium carbonate is made from it by heating.

Laboratory Preparation of Sodium Bicarbonate. Sodium bicarbonate is made in the laboratory by bubbling carbon dioxide for some time through a strong solution in water, of either sodium hydroxide or sodium carbonate (see Fig. 93, p. 259). In the latter case the reaction takes place much more quickly:

$$CO_2 + Na_2CO_3 + H_2O \rightarrow 2NaHCO_3$$
sodium
carbonate

With caustic soda

$$2NaOH + CO_2 \rightarrow Na_2CO_3 + H_2O$$
sodium
hydroxide

then

$$Na_2CO_3 + H_2O + CO_2 \rightarrow 2NaHCO_3$$

In both cases the sodium bicarbonate is deposited as a white powder and this is filtered off, washed two or three times with a little cold distilled water, and allowed to dry.

With dilute acids, sodium bicarbonate liberates carbon dioxide, for example:

$$NaHCO_3 + HCl \rightarrow NaCl + H_2O + CO_2$$
$$2NaHCO_3 + H_2SO_4 \rightarrow Na_2SO_4 + 2H_2O + 2CO_2$$

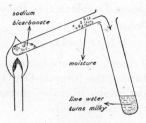

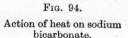

Action of Heat on Sodium Bicarbonate. Place a small amount of sodium bicarbonate in a dry test-tube and heat gently with the lip of the tube projecting into a boiling-tube containing lime-water (see Fig. 94). A gas is given off which turns the lime-water milky and is, therefore, carbon dioxide. Water is seen to condense on the cooler parts of the tube.

FIG. 94.
Action of heat on sodium bicarbonate.

$$2NaHCO_3 \rightarrow Na_2CO_3 + H_2O + CO_2$$
sodium   sodium   water   carbon
bicarbonate   carbonate   dioxide

The white residue is sodium carbonate. This test distinguishes sodium bicarbonate from sodium carbonate, which is unaffected by heat.

Sodium bicarbonate is used in the manufacture of baking powders. Under the action of heat it decomposes, as above, and gives off carbon dioxide which causes the cake to "rise" and so be light. This is why it is commonly called "baking soda". Baking powders also contain rice powder as a diluent, and tartaric acid (or a similar compound) to react with the sodium carbonate, which would otherwise be left when the bicarbonate decomposes.

Calcium Bicarbonate. See Hardness of Water, p. 162.

Its method of preparation and its reactions are similar to those of sodium bicarbonate.

Calcium bicarbonate cannot, however, be isolated as a solid, since it decomposes too easily, and all its reactions are carried out in solution.

QUESTIONS ON CARBON, CARBONATES AND OXIDES OF CARBON, FLAME

1. Graphite is called an "allotropic form" of carbon. What do you understand by this statement? Give *one* other example of allotropy. How would you prove by a quantitative experiment that the statement is correct in the case of graphite and pure charcoal? (N.U.J.B.)

2. What is the action of (a) carbon dioxide, (b) steam, upon red-hot carbon? and what is the practical importance of these reactions? (O. and C.)

3. What are the general methods employed for the preparation of metallic carbonates?
    5 gm. of a mixture of anhydrous sodium carbonate and sodium bicarbonate were heated until there was no further loss in weight. The resulting solid weighed 3·84 gm. Find the percentage weight of the normal carbonate in the mixture. (Na = 23; C = 12.) (L.)

4. How does calcium carbonate occur in nature? Describe qualitative and quantitative experiments which you would do in order to determine the composition of this substance. (L.)

5. Describe the preparation of a pure dry specimen of carbon monoxide.
    From carbon monoxide how would you prepare and collect a pure specimen of carbon dioxide? (C.)

6. Describe how you would find by experiment the weight of carbon dioxide that can be obtained from 1 gm. of calcium carbonate.
    How would you prove that the gas obtained from calcium carbonate is identical with that produced when carbon is burnt? (O. and C.)

7. Describe the preparation and collection of carbon monoxide and compare its properties with those of carbon dioxide. What would be the result, in the case of each oxide, of passing it (a) over heated copper oxide, (b) over red-hot charcoal, (c) into cold, dilute caustic soda solution? (B.)

8. When oxalic acid is heated with concentrated sulphuric acid a mixture of the two oxides of carbon is evolved.
    Give a detailed account of how you would:
    (a) Prepare a specimen of pure carbon dioxide from this mixture.
    (b) Find the percentage by volume of each gas in the mixture.
        (O.)

9. Describe carefully an apparatus by which you could collect for examination the products of the action of steam on red-hot carbon.
    Describe how you would identify each of the products of the reaction.
    Of what importance is the reaction in industry? (C.)

10. How is carbon monoxide prepared? Describe the chief properties of this compound. What volume will be found after the explosion of a mixture of one volume of carbon monoxide and ten volumes of air? (You may assume air to contain one-fifth by volume of oxygen.) (O. and C.)

11. Describe how you would prepare sodium hydroxide from sodium carbonate.
    State clearly how you could:
    (a) Distinguish sodium carbonate from sodium bicarbonate;
    (b) Prepare sodium bicarbonate from sodium carbonate. (O.)

12. Write a short essay on "Flames", with special reference to those of hydrogen and coal-gas (luminous and non-luminous). (O.)

13. Describe, using diagrams, the structure of the flame of a bunsen burner. How do you account for the differences in the flame when the air holes of the bunsen burner are closed? Indicate experiments which might be carried out in support of your answer. (L.)

14. What views were formerly held as to the nature of combustion, and what led to their overthrow? Who first gave the true explanation of combustion?
    State clearly all that you believe to be taking place in the burning of a candle. (L.)

15. Starting with solid sodium hydroxide, describe how you would prepare in the dry solid state (a) sodium carbonate, (b) sodium bicarbonate. Give *two* tests by means of which you could distinguish between these compounds. Describe and explain what happens when crystals of washing soda are exposed to the air. (L.)

16. Explain fully any *four* of the following:—(a) Why a bunsen burner "strikes back", (b) the comparatively low percentage of carbon dioxide in the air, (c) the difference in the bleaching action of chlorine and sulphur dioxide, (d) why sodium sulphate dissolved in water increases its conductivity, (e) how the flame of a candle differs from the flame of hydrogen. (L.)

17. What is flame? By means of *three* labelled sketches *only* compare the structures of (a) a hydrogen flame, (b) a luminous bunsen flame, (c) a candle flame. How would you demonstrate the presence of unburnt gas in a candle flame, and that this unburnt gas can be used as a reducing agent? (L.)

18. Powdered marble is strongly heated in the open air until no further change occurs. Explain what happens and give *three* tests proving that the resultant residue is different from the powdered marble. Give short accounts of *two* important uses of the residue. Why does a precipitate form when temporarily hard water is boiled? How does the impurity enter the water in the first place? (L.)

CHAPTER XXIV

SILICON

SILICON is the second most abundant element in the earth's crust, the most abundant of all being oxygen. Silicon is found in the following forms:

1. *As Metallic Silicates.* Igneous rocks, such as granite and basalt, consist largely of mixtures of silicates, those of magnesium, aluminium, potassium and iron being most common. China clay, kaolin, is a hydrated silicate of aluminium; ordinary clay is a mixture of particles of quartz, mica and other substances bound together by a sticky material which is a hydrated silicate of aluminium of approximate formula $Al_2Si_2O_7 . 2H_2O$.

2. *As Silica (Silicon Dioxide)*, SiO_2. The purest form of silica is rock crystal or transparent quartz. Sand usually consists of silica, with various impurities, and opal, hornstone and jasper are forms of this oxide. It also exists in a less pure form as flint.

The porous material "kieselguhr", is a form of silica made up of the fossil shells of small plants called diatoms. It is used to absorb the explosive, nitroglycerine, forming the product called "dynamite", which is safer to transport and handle than the explosive itself.

SILICON

The element may be prepared in the amorphous state by heating magnesium powder with silica, SiO_2.

$$SiO_2 + 2Mg \rightarrow 2MgO + Si$$

The reaction is very violent.

Silicon from silica. Mix one saltspoonful of magnesium powder with three times its bulk of amorphous silica and place the mixture in a test-tube. Clamp the tube with the mouth pointing upwards and in a safe direction, place a bunsen burner underneath the tube to heat it strongly and retire to a distance of two yards or more. After a few moments the reaction occurs with a flash of light. Allow to cool and break the test-tube in a mortar and pick out the pieces of brown amorphous silicon.

$$2Mg + SiO_2 \rightarrow 2MgO + Si$$

Reactions of silicon. Place a small piece of silicon, obtained in the above experiment, on a tripod stand and direct the flame of a bunsen burner on to it from above. It will react, sometimes by burning, to form a white solid, silica.

$$Si + O_2 \rightarrow SiO_2$$

Put the rest of the silicon into a test-tube, add caustic soda solution and warm. There is an evolution of hydrogen and finally the silicon dissolves.

$$2NaOH + Si + H_2O \rightarrow Na_2SiO_3 + 2H_2$$

Amorphous silicon combines with chlorine at low red heat and also decomposes steam.

$$Si + 2Cl_2 \rightarrow SiCl_4$$
$$Si + 2H_2O \rightarrow SiO_2 + 2H_2$$

Silicon is used in the manufacture of certain types of steel and bronze.

SILICON DIOXIDE, SILICA, SiO_2

Silica from sodium silicate. (Water-glass.) Add concentrated hydrochloric acid to a solution of sodium silicate and warm if necessary. White hydrated silica (silicic acid) will come down as a gelatinous precipitate.

$$Na_2SiO_3 + 2HCl \rightarrow 2NaCl + SiO_2.H_2O$$

Show that the precipitate is readily soluble in dilute caustic soda solution.

$$2NaOH + SiO_2 \rightarrow Na_2SiO_3 + H_2O$$

Uses. In its naturally occurring form, sand, silica finds great use as a constituent of mortar and cement, for the manufacture of glass (see below) and for filtration of water in bulk.

Fused silica is used for the manufacture of certain types of laboratory apparatus. Its coefficient of expansion is very low (about one-fiftieth of that of glass) and consequently the strains set up in it by irregular contraction under sudden reduction of temperature are small and insufficient to break it. A red-hot silica tube or crucible can be plunged into cold water without damage. Fused quartz threads are used in the construction of physical apparatus. They can be made so thin as to be invisible to the naked eye and yet strong enough to support a weight of 2 gm. Their tenuity and elasticity make them invaluable for light, delicate suspensions. The difficulty in working fused silica is that the very high temperature of at least 1,500° C. is required.

Properties of Silica. Silica is only slightly soluble in water, and is generally resistant to chemical action. Being the oxide of a non-metal, however, it acts as an acidic oxide. It is attacked by alkalis and, when heated, by metallic oxides, forming *silicates*.

$$SiO_2 + 2NaOH \rightarrow Na_2SiO_3 + H_2O$$
sodium
silicate

$$SiO_2 + PbO \rightarrow PbSiO_3$$
lead
silicate

Sodium silicate from silica. Wash some of the white gelatinous precipitate of hydrated silica obtained above and ignite it in a crucible. The product is amorphous silica and is no longer easily soluble in caustic soda solution even if hot and concentrated. That silica is an acidic oxide can, however, be shown as follows:—Put a small piece of solid caustic soda about half an inch long into a crucible, add a saltspoonful of amorphous silica and heat the mass strongly for about ten minutes. Take great care when doing this, that none of the molten mass is spilled or comes into contact with the flesh. Allow the melt to cool, fill the crucible two-thirds full of water and warm. The solution obtained is sodium silicate and from it gelatinous silica can be obtained by the action of hydrochloric acid.

Silica is non-volatile and can, at high temperatures, displace volatile acidic oxides from combination. They pass off as vapour, leaving a silicate, *e.g.*,

$$Na_2SO_4 + SiO_2 \rightarrow Na_2SiO_3 + SO_3$$

Silicates. Silicates are salts of the silicic acids. The chemistry of these acids is complex, and little is known for certain about them.

The gelatinous substance precipitated by acidifying a hot solution of "water-glass" has the empirical formula, H_2SiO_3, and is called meta-silicic acid, and an acid of approximate formula H_4SiO_4, ortho-silicic acid, is obtained by the action of water on silicon tetrachloride.

$$Na_2SiO_3 + 2HCl \rightarrow H_2SiO_3 + 2NaCl$$
$$SiCl_4 + 4H_2O \rightarrow H_4SiO_4 + 4HCl$$

The salts of these acids are called silicates. The meta-silicates are the most important.

Sodium Silicate, "Water-glass", Na_2SiO_3. Sodium silicate is prepared by heating two parts by weight of silica with one part of sodium carbonate.

$$Na_2CO_3 + SiO_2 \rightarrow Na_2SiO_3 + CO_2$$

The product is a glassy solid. It is heated with water (under pressure) to dissolve it, and is sold in tins in the form of a concentrated solution, similar in consistency to "golden syrup", but colourless. This is called "water-glass".

Water-glass is chiefly used for preserving eggs. The shell of an egg consists largely of calcium carbonate. This, when the egg is immersed in a suitable solution of "water-glass", reacts with the sodium silicate to produce a precipitate of calcium silicate which seals the pores of the shell, excluding bacteria and so preserving the egg from putrefaction.

$$CaCO_3 + Na_2SiO_3 \rightarrow CaSiO_3 + Na_2CO_3$$

"Silica-Garden." An interesting chemical phenomenon, called a "silica-garden", can be shown in the following way. Dilute some water-glass until it has a density of 1·1 gm. per c.c. (test with a hydrometer), then filter it and put the liquid into a tall, rather narrow vessel. Drop into it crystals of manganese chloride, cobalt nitrate, ferrous sulphate and copper sulphate. From these crystals there will shoot fantastic coloured growths. Those from the cobalt salt usually appear within a few seconds and grow rapidly. They are dark blue. Growths from the other crystals appear more slowly. Those from the manganese salt are pale pink, from copper sulphate light blue, and from the ferrous salt green. The growths are tubes of the silicates of the metals.

Glass. The substance to which the term "glass" is usually applied consists of a mixture of two or more silicates. Common soft glass, of which bottles and laboratory apparatus are made, is prepared by heating together silica in the form of sand, sodium carbonate or sodium sulphate, and chalk or limestone (calcium carbonate). (Some broken glass and a little coke are usually added.) The glass so prepared consists of a mixture of sodium silicate and calcium silicate.

$$Na_2CO_3 + SiO_2 \rightarrow Na_2SiO_3 + CO_2$$

or   or

$$Na_2SO_4 \qquad\qquad SO_3$$
$$CaCO_3 + SiO_2 \rightarrow CaSiO_3 + CO_2$$

If potassium carbonate is used instead of sodium carbonate, a "hard" glass, that is, a glass needing a higher temperature to melt it, will be produced, and will consist of a mixture of calcium silicate and potassium silicate.

Glass containing lead silicate has a brilliant appearance, and is made by adding to the ordinary glass mixture some red lead, Pb_3O_4, or litharge, PbO. Such a glass ("flint glass") has a high refractive index and is used for prisms and lenses, but it is soft and should be wiped only with silk, to avoid scratching the surface.

Coloured glass is obtained by addition of metallic oxides, for

Left:

A hand blown Mercury Arc Rectifier bulb made by Chance Bros., Smethwick.

Below:

Blowing a flask for use in analysis.

Both by courtesy of New York Times Photos

PLATE VIII.

example, cobalt produces blue glass, chromium produces green glass. Opalescent glass may be produced by addition of calcium phosphate.

Physical Nature of Glass. Glass is not really a solid. This is shown by the fact that, when heated, it does not suddenly pass from the solid to the liquid state at a definite temperature, but softens slowly as the temperature rises and gradually becomes liquid. A true solid would melt suddenly over a small temperature-range. Glass is a super-cooled liquid. By this we mean that its molecules have not taken up a definite formation to produce crystals, but are arranged at random as they were in liquid glass.

The softening of glass before it melts is a very valuable property. It enables a skilled worker or a machine to blow it into various shapes—bottles, flasks, beakers—by using suitable moulds. While soft, glass can also be moulded and joined to produce elaborate scientific apparatus. Large sheets of glass are produced by rolling out a mass of hot glass on a long, flat table or by blowing a hollow cylinder, which is afterwards cut longitudinally, heated, and flattened while soft. Glass-tubing is made by first blowing a mass of glass into a thick-walled cylinder, and then drawing the cylinder out between two workers walking in opposite directions, one manipulating the blow-iron. The "unbreakable glass" used for motor-car wind-screens is made by cementing a sheet of glass on to each side of a sheet of celluloid. The cement prevents splinters from flying off.

Articles made of glass usually have to be annealed, that is, heated to a suitable temperature and then allowed to cool very slowly and uniformly so that no stresses are set up which might break the glass. The annealing of considerable masses of glass may require several weeks, or even months, as in the case of the glass for the mirror of the 200-in. telescope erected at the Mount Wilson observatory in the U.S.A. Working with glass is a very ancient art. It was practised by the Egyptians at least 2,300 years ago, while some of the finest specimens of glassware are the work of Venetian craftsmen of the Middle Ages.

QUESTIONS

1. What is the chemical nature of glass? How is it made? Why is glass stated to be a super-cooled liquid?
2. Silica is an acid-forming oxide. Justify this statement by reference to the chemical properties of silica.
3. In what forms does silica occur in nature? How may the element silicon be obtained from silica?
4. What is silica? Starting with the naturally occurring substance describe how you would obtain (a) water-glass, (b) a solution of silicic acid, and (c) pure silica. (L.)

CHAPTER XXV

CHLORINE

THE four non-metals, fluorine, chlorine, bromine and iodine, make up a family of related elements, the chemical properties of which form an interesting study. The first of the series is the very active element fluorine, which is so active that it evaded efforts to isolate it for many years, because it combined with almost every element or substance with which it came into contact—even the glass of the apparatus in which the reaction took place! Of fluorine we need say but little since it is so difficult to isolate that its properties could have no practical application in the school laboratory, and of the others we shall see that bromine is almost an "arithmetical mean" between chlorine and iodine. *Chlorine* was first isolated by Scheele in 1774.

Scheele was a Swedish apothecary who carried out, during the short time which he lived (he died when only 44 years of age), a vast number of illuminating experiments, performed in an old shed attached to his house. It was whilst he was investigating the properties of pyrolusite (impure manganese dioxide) that he heated it with concentrated hydrochloric acid in a retort and collected the chlorine gas which came off into a pig's bladder.

It is usually made by the oxidation of concentrated hydrochloric acid. The oxidation can be brought about by many oxidising agents, for example, lead dioxide, manganese dioxide, red lead or potassium permanganate.

$$O + \begin{matrix} H Cl \\ H Cl \end{matrix} \rightarrow H_2O + Cl_2$$

| oxygen from oxidising agent | concentrated hydrochloric acid | water | chlorine |

Preparation of Chlorine from Concentrated Hydrochloric Acid by Oxidation with Manganese Dioxide. Fit up the apparatus as shown in Fig. 95. Put some manganese dioxide into the flask, pour concentrated hydrochloric acid down the funnel and shake well before connecting up the flask with the rest of the apparatus. (Note. The use of a gas ring and gauze keeps the flask low and makes the apparatus more stable.)

271

Heat the mixture in the flask and effervescence is observed. A greenish-yellow gas is evolved which, together with a certain amount of hydrogen chloride (misty fumes), passes over into the first bottle

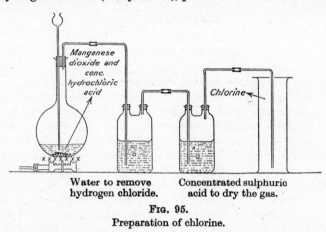

Water to remove   Concentrated sulphuric
hydrogen chloride.   acid to dry the gas.

FIG. 95.
Preparation of chlorine.

which contains water. This removes the hydrochloric acid gas (which is very soluble in water), and the concentrated sulphuric acid in the second bottle dries the gas which is collected by upward displacement of air, the gas being heavier than air.

$$MnO_2 + 4HCl \rightarrow MnCl_2 + 2H_2O + Cl_2$$

manganese   concentrated   manganese   water   chlorine
dioxide   hydrochloric   chloride
             acid

The above experiment should be carried out in a fume-chamber, as should any preparation of chlorine in which it is collected by displacement of air.

Preparation of Chlorine from Concentrated Hydrochloric Acid by Oxidation with Potassium Permanganate. [If the chlorine is required pure and dry, insert wash bottles containing (a) water, and (b) concentrated sulphuric acid in Fig. 96 and collect by displacement of air.]

$$2KMnO_4 + 16HCl \rightarrow 2KCl + 2MnCl_2 + 8H_2O + 5Cl_2$$

potassium   concentrated   potassium   manganese   water   chlorine
permanganate   hydrochloric   chloride   chloride
                 acid

This is a very convenient laboratory method because it takes place in the cold, and if the gas is collected over brine the experiment need not be conducted in a fume-chamber.

Solid potassium permanganate is placed in a flask and concentrated hydrochloric acid is dropped on to it from a tap-funnel

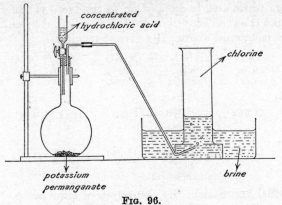

concentrated hydrochloric acid

chlorine

potassium permanganate

brine

FIG. 96.
Preparation of chlorine.

(Fig. 96). As each drop of acid reaches the permanganate there is evolved at once the corresponding quantity of chlorine. The apparatus is filled with the greenish-yellow fumes of the gas. Several gas-jars of the gas should be collected and the experiments described later performed to illustrate its properties.

Preparation of Chlorine from Common Salt

Chemistry of the Action. Concentrated sulphuric acid acts upon the common salt to form hydrogen chloride, which is then oxidised to chlorine by manganese dioxide.

The apparatus is identical with Fig. 95, and the experiment is performed in a similar manner except that an intimate mixture of common salt and manganese dioxide is placed in the flask and concentrated sulphuric acid added. In this experiment the presence of hydrogen chloride as an impurity is more obvious. It is removed by passing the gases through water, and the chlorine is dried by means of concentrated sulphuric acid and collected by displacement of air, as shown in Fig. 95

$$2NaCl + MnO_2 + 2H_2SO_4 \rightarrow Na_2SO_4 + MnSO_4$$

common salt (sodium chloride)   manganese dioxide   concentrated sulphuric acid   sodium sulphate   manganese sulphate

$$+ 2H_2O + Cl_2$$

water chlorine

Preparation of Chlorine from Bleaching Powder.

In this case the chlorine is not prepared by the oxidation of concentrated hydrochloric acid. The apparatus used is identical with that above (Fig. 96), bleaching powder is placed in the flask and a dilute acid, *e.g.*, nitric acid is dropped on to the powder. Effervescence occurs and the greenish-yellow gas can be collected by either of the methods mentioned above. Heat is not required.

$$CaOCl_2 + 2HNO_3 \rightarrow Ca(NO_3)_2 + H_2O + Cl_2$$

bleaching   dilute   calcium   water   chlorine
powder   nitric acid   nitrate

Similarly:

$$CaOCl_2 + 2HCl \rightarrow CaCl_2 + H_2O + Cl_2$$

dilute
hydrochloric acid

$$CaOCl_2 + H_2SO_4 \rightarrow CaSO_4 + H_2O + Cl_2$$

dilute
sulphuric acid

Industrial Preparation. By electrolysis of brine (see p. 123).

Test for Chlorine. **Chlorine is a greenish-yellow gas which rapidly bleaches damp litmus paper.**

PROPERTIES OF CHLORINE

Chlorine is a greenish-yellow gas with a choking, unpleasant, irritating smell. It is very poisonous if inhaled to even a small extent (1 part of chlorine in 50,000 of air may be injurious). It was used extensively during the War of 1914—18 and, being about $2\frac{1}{2}$ times as dense as air, it would roll along the ground when propelled by a very gentle wind without a great deal of it escaping upwards.

It bleaches damp litmus and is a very reactive gas indeed. The following experiments illustrate its properties and they are classified according to the various ways in which the gas can act.

Chlorine as a Bleaching Agent. Pour a little litmus solution into a gas-jar of the gas. The litmus immediately turns colourless. Chlorine will bleach the colour from most dyes and will remove writing ink (but not printer's ink, which consists mainly of carbon, which chlorine does not attack).

Bleaching Action. The chlorine combines with the water, forming hypochlorous acid.

$$Cl_2 + H_2O \rightarrow HClO + HCl$$

chlorine   water   hypochlorous   hydrochloric
acid   acid

This hypochlorous acid is a very reactive compound and readily gives up its oxygen to the dye, to form a colourless compound.

$$dye + HClO \rightarrow HCl + (dye + O)$$

coloured   colourless

Notice that hydrochloric acid is produced whenever chlorine bleaches, and hence an article must be thoroughly washed after bleaching or it will be attacked by the free acid.

In industry the article to be bleached is dipped into a tank containing a solution of bleaching powder, then into very dilute sulphuric acid, and then carefully treated to remove excess chlorine and acid.

Dry Chlorine will not Bleach. Pour about 20 c.c. of concentrated sulphuric acid into a gas-jar of the gas as soon as it is collected. After a time put a piece of dry coloured cloth into the gas-jar. At the same time put a piece of damp coloured cloth into a gas-jar of chlorine; the latter is immediately bleached, whereas the former remains unattacked. (If the chlorine and cloth are perfectly dry, the cloth remains unbleached indefinitely.)

From the equation above, it is seen that water is necessary for the formation of hypochlorous acid, the compound which liberates the oxygen and which performs the bleaching. Hence, if no water is present no bleaching can occur.

Chlorine as an Element which combines readily with Hydrogen to form Hydrogen Chloride.

(Bleaching can also be considered under this heading.)

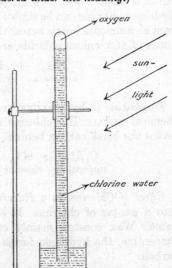

Exposure of Chlorine Water to Sunlight. Pass chlorine gas into water in a beaker for some time until the water becomes quite yellowish-green in colour. Fill a long tube with this chlorine water, invert it in a beaker containing some of the water and expose to bright sunlight (Fig. 97). After some time, a gas collects in the tube and on applying a glowing splint, the latter is rekindled, showing the gas to be oxygen.

$$2Cl_2 + 2H_2O \rightarrow 4HCl + O_2$$

FIG. 97.
Exposure of chlorine water to sunlight.

The chlorine has combined with the hydrogen of the water to form hydrogen chloride and oxygen is liberated.

The above reaction probably occurs in two stages, as indicated by the equations:

$$H_2O \quad + \quad Cl_2 \quad \rightarrow \quad HClO \quad + \quad HCl \text{ (instantaneous)}$$
water   chlorine   hypochlorous   hydrochloric
acid   acid

$$2HClO \rightarrow 2HCl + O_2 \text{ (slow)}$$
oxygen

The burning of Hydrogen in Chlorine. Lower a jet of burning hydrogen (great care before lighting, see p. 58) into a gas-jar full of chlorine. The hydrogen continues to burn with a white flame and clouds of steamy fumes of hydrogen chloride are seen, whilst the yellowish-green colour of the chlorine gradually disappears.

$$H_2 \quad + \quad Cl_2 \quad \rightarrow \quad 2HCl$$
hydrogen   chlorine   hydrogen
chloride

The readiness with which hydrogen and chlorine combine together is so great that, if a tube containing equal volumes of chlorine and hydrogen is exposed to sunlight, it explodes.

Action of Chlorine and Warm Turpentine. Warm a little turpentine in a dish, dip into it a filter-paper, and then drop this into a gas-jar of chlorine. There is a red flash accompanied by a violent action whilst a black cloud of solid particles of carbon is also formed. Hydrogen chloride can be shown to be present by blowing the fumes from an ammonia bottle across the top of the jar, when dense white fumes of ammonium chloride are observed.

$$NH_3 \quad + \quad HCl \quad \rightarrow \quad NH_4Cl$$
ammonia   hydrogen   ammonium
chloride   chloride

Turpentine (a hydrocarbon) consists of hydrogen and carbon in chemical union. The chlorine combines with the hydrogen and leaves the black carbon behind.

$$C_{10}H_{16} \quad + \quad 8Cl_2 \quad \rightarrow \quad 10C \quad + \quad 16HCl$$
turpentine   chlorine   carbon   hydrogen
chloride

Effect of Chlorine on a Burning Taper. Lower a burning taper into a gas-jar of chlorine. It burns with a small, red and sooty flame. Wax consists mainly of hydrocarbons and, as with the turpentine, the hydrogen forms hydrogen chloride and leaves the carbon.

Action of Chlorine on Sulphuretted Hydrogen. Invert a gas-jar of sulphuretted hydrogen over a gas-jar of chlorine and remove the plates. You will observe a yellow precipitate of sulphur, and hydrogen chloride will be formed.

$$H_2S \quad + \quad Cl_2 \quad \rightarrow \quad 2HCl \quad + \quad S$$
sulphuretted   chlorine   hydrogen   sulphur
hydrogen   chloride

The above experiment can also be shown in solution by bubbling sulphuretted hydrogen through chlorine water.

Chlorine as a Chloride Former. Chlorine is a very reactive element and will combine with most other elements to form chlorides. In many cases chlorine will combine with elements spontaneously, *i.e.*, without applying a flame or in any way inducing the reaction to take place.

Action of Chlorine on Phosphorus (a Non-metal). Lower a piece of dry yellow phosphorus into a gas-jar of chlorine. It burns spontaneously, giving off white fumes of chlorides of phosphorus.

$$P_4 + 6Cl_2 \rightarrow 4PCl_3$$
phosphorus
trichloride

$$P_4 + 10Cl_2 \rightarrow 4PCl_5$$
phosphorus
pentachloride

In the following cases the reactants are all metals.

Action of Chlorine on Sodium. Lower a piece of burning sodium on a deflagrating spoon into a gas-jar of chlorine. It continues to burn, giving off white clouds of sodium chloride.

$$\underset{\text{sodium}}{2Na} + \underset{\text{chlorine}}{Cl_2} \rightarrow \underset{\substack{\text{sodium} \\ \text{chloride}}}{2NaCl}$$

Action of Chlorine on Copper. Drop a piece of Dutch metal (a very thin sheet of an alloy of copper and zinc, mainly copper) into a gas-jar of chlorine. It burns spontaneously with a green flame to form copper chloride and a little zinc chloride.

$$Cu + Cl_2 \rightarrow \underset{\substack{\text{copper} \\ \text{chloride}}}{CuCl_2}$$

$$Zn + Cl_2 \rightarrow \underset{\substack{\text{zinc} \\ \text{chloride}}}{ZnCl_2}$$

Action of Chlorine on Iron. Place a coil of iron wire in the hard glass tube in the apparatus shown in Fig. 98 and pass a stream of pure dry chlorine over it. On heating the wire by means of a burner, the wire glows and the reaction continues without application of the flame, black crystals of ferric chloride collecting in the small flask, which acts as a condenser.

$$\underset{\text{iron}}{2Fe} + \underset{\text{chlorine}}{3Cl_2} \rightarrow \underset{\substack{\text{ferric} \\ \text{chloride}}}{2FeCl_3}$$

Note that the *ferric* salt is formed—an indication that chlorine is an oxidising agent.

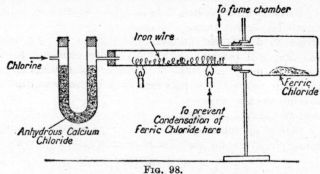

FIG. 98.

Preparation of anhydrous ferric chloride.

The black crystals of anhydrous ferric chloride should be removed and placed in a desiccator, as they are very deliquescent.

Chlorine as an Oxidising Agent

Formation of Ferric Chloride by the above Experiment. An oxidising agent favours the formation of the salt corresponding to the higher valency of the metal. Compare the action of dilute hydrochloric acid on iron where the reducing agent hydrogen, formed during the reaction, favours the formation of the lower chloride, ferrous chloride.

Action on Ferrous Chloride Solution. Bubble a stream of chlorine through a solution of ferrous chloride (which is pale green in colour). The colour changes to yellow, and on adding a little caustic soda solution there is obtained a reddish-brown precipitate of ferric hydroxide, showing that the ferrous chloride has been oxidised to ferric chloride.

$$\underset{\substack{\text{ferrous} \\ \text{chloride}}}{2FeCl_2} + \underset{\text{chlorine}}{Cl_2} \rightarrow \underset{\substack{\text{ferric} \\ \text{chloride}}}{2FeCl_3}$$

Oxidation of Sulphurous Acid to Sulphuric Acid. On bubbling chlorine into a solution of sulphurous acid in water for a few minutes, dilute sulphuric acid is obtained.

$$2H_2O + SO_2 + Cl_2 \rightarrow H_2SO_4 + 2HCl$$

The presence of the sulphuric acid can be shown by testing with dilute hydrochloric acid and barium chloride before and after the experiment. There is obtained after the experiment a white precipitate of barium sulphate. [*N.B.* The sulphurous acid solution must be fresh, otherwise it will contain a certain amount of sulphuric acid due to atmospheric oxidation.]

The Displacing Action of Chlorine. Chlorine can displace bromine and iodine from bromides and iodides.

Displacement of Bromine. Bubble chlorine into a solution of potassium bromide in water. The clear solution immediately turns red (due to formation of bromine water) and finally a drop of a red liquid (bromine) is observed at the bottom of the boiling-tube.

$$2KBr + Cl_2 \rightarrow 2KCl + Br_2$$

| potassium bromide | | potassium chloride | bromine |

Displacement of Iodine. The above experiment is repeated with potassium iodide solution. The clear solution turns to the characteristic dark brown "iodine" colour and finally a black solid (iodine) is deposited. On warming the solution the characteristic violet vapour of iodine is seen.

$$2KI + Cl_2 \rightarrow 2KCl + I_2$$

| potassium iodide | | potassium chloride | iodine |

Action of Chlorine on the Alkalis

On the Cold Dilute Aqueous Solution. Chlorine is absorbed by a solution in water of caustic potash or caustic soda, forming a solution of the hypochlorite and chloride of the metal.

$$Cl_2 + 2NaOH \rightarrow NaClO + NaCl + H_2O$$

| sodium hydroxide | sodium hypochlorite | sodium chloride | |

$$Cl_2 + 2KOH \rightarrow KClO + KCl + H_2O$$

| potassium hydroxide | potassium hypo- chlorite | | |

On the Hot Concentrated Aqueous Solution. If chlorine is passed into a hot concentrated solution of caustic potash for some time there is formed a mixture of potassium chloride and potassium chlorate, and the latter can be obtained by crystallising the mixture when crystals of potassium chlorate separate first. (These can be purified by recrystallisation.)

$$6KOH + 3Cl_2 \rightarrow KClO_3 + 5KCl + 3H_2O$$

| potassium hydroxide | potassium chlorate | potassium chloride | |

A similar action is observed if hot concentrated caustic soda solution or milk of lime is substituted for the caustic potash solution.

Notice that in the above actions the alkalis are dissolved or suspended in water.

BLEACHING POWDER

If chlorine is passed for a considerable time over **solid slaked lime** the product is bleaching powder, which is very suitable for use as a source of chlorine, and, being a solid, is much more easily transported than gaseous or liquid chlorine.

Laboratory preparation. Take a gas-jar full of chlorine and shake a teaspoonful of freshly prepared slaked lime into it. The colour of the chlorine disappears immediately. The product may be used to absorb the chlorine from several more gas-jars before absorption is complete.

$$Ca(OH)_2 + Cl_2 \rightarrow CaOCl_2 . H_2O$$

calcium   chlorine   bleaching
hydroxide   powder

Manufacture. Slaked lime is moved forward by Archimedian screws through a series of pipes against a counter current of chlorine until the requisite weight of chlorine has been absorbed. The solid is removed and packed.

It contains about 36% of available chlorine, *i.e.*, chlorine which can be removed by dilute acids and even by the carbonic acid of the atmosphere. Hence bleaching powder usually smells of chlorine and deteriorates if in contact with air. It has an extensive use in dye works, laundries and even in the home.

$$CaOCl_2 + CO_2 \rightarrow CaCO_3 + Cl_2$$

bleaching   carbon   chlorine
powder   dioxide

Industrial Uses of Chlorine. Apart from its bleaching properties, chlorine even in great dilution is a germicide and disinfectant. It is employed in public swimming baths where the same water is being continually circulated. The water is kept comparatively free from bacteria by the addition of a little chlorine. Drinking water during the Great War was sterilised by the addition of a little bleaching powder, and although the water was much less palatable it was far less harmful.

For industrial purposes it is made

(i) by electrolysis of common salt solution (see p. 123);

(ii) by the catalytic oxidation of hydrochloric acid by air. A mixture of the two at a temperature of about 450° is passed over bricks impregnated with solutions of cupric salts.

$$\overset{(CuCl_2)}{4HCl + O_2 \rightarrow 2H_2O + Cl_2}$$

air

(Deacon's process).

QUESTIONS ON THIS CHAPTER WILL BE FOUND ON PAGE 298.

CHAPTER XXVI

HYDROGEN CHLORIDE AND THE CHLORIDES

HYDROGEN CHLORIDE

THE gas is usually called hydrogen chloride, or hydrochloric acid gas, whereas the solution of the gas in water (which when saturated contains about 36% by weight of the gas) is termed hydrochloric acid.

Preparation. Common salt is placed in a flask fitted with a thistle funnel and delivery-tube, and concentrated sulphuric acid is added (Fig. 99). There is effervescence, and misty fumes are observed.

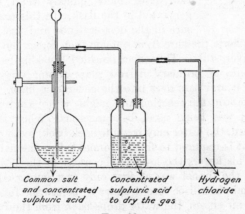

Common salt and concentrated sulphuric acid   Concentrated sulphuric acid to dry the gas   Hydrogen chloride

FIG. 99.

Preparation of hydrogen chloride.

The gas is passed through a wash-bottle containing concentrated sulphuric acid to dry it, and collected as shown by upward displacement of air, the gas being heavier than air.

$$\underset{\substack{\text{concentrated}\\\text{sulphuric}\\\text{acid}}}{H_2SO_4} + \underset{\substack{\text{sodium}\\\text{chloride}}}{NaCl} \rightarrow \underset{\substack{\text{sodium}\\\text{hydrogen}\\\text{sulphate}}}{NaHSO_4} + \underset{\substack{\text{hydrogen}\\\text{chloride}}}{HCl}$$

The reaction proceeds in the cold, although a further yield of the gas is obtained in the industrial process by heating to a red heat.

281

$$NaCl + NaHSO_4 \rightarrow Na_2SO_4 + HCl$$

sodium   sodium   sodium   hydrogen
chloride   hydrogen   sulphate   chloride
              sulphate

(The above indicates clearly the acid nature of sodium hydrogen sulphate.)

A solution of the gas in water can be made by means of the funnel arrangement as in Fig. 100. This solution is hydrochloric acid. If the gas is passed into water until no more gas is absorbed, the product is concentrated hydrochloric acid and contains about 36% by weight of hydrogen chloride.

FIG. 100.

Method of dissolving a very soluble gas in water.

This device of passing a gas into water by means of an inverted funnel is essential when the gas is very soluble in water. If the gas is sufficiently soluble, it may be absorbed in the water more quickly than it is being generated in the flask. In this case, the pressure in the delivery-tube and flask is reduced and atmospheric pressure from outside then forces the water back up the delivery-tube. This effect is called "sucking-back". If the tube is made of ordinary narrow glass tubing, the water will quickly fill it and pass over into the generating flask. This would in any case stop the reaction and might, if hot concentrated sulphuric acid was being used, be dangerous. When the inverted funnel is used, the water may begin to suck back, but a considerable volume of it is required to fill the funnel before the narrow tube is reached. This lowers the level of the water in the beaker, and, if the rim of the funnel was at first only just immersed, it will be exposed, and air will be forced under it, before the funnel is filled. As soon as air enters, the water drops back from the funnel to the beaker and the process begins again. Notice that, to be effective, the funnel must be arranged with its rim only just immersed. An additional advantage is that the funnel offers a large water surface for absorption of the gas.

Test for the Gas. It is a clear gas (although when mixed with air it appears misty), **acid to litmus, and causes a white precipitate of silver chloride in a drop of a solution of silver nitrate and nitric acid held on a glass rod in the gas.**

$$HCl + AgNO_3 \rightarrow AgCl \downarrow + HNO_3$$

Properties. It has a choking, irritating smell, and is an acid gas, which is very soluble in water. These latter two properties are neatly shown by means of *the "fountain experiment"*. See p. 336. The experiment is performed in a similar manner to that employed for ammonia gas. Blue litmus can, however, be placed in the trough and this turns red on entering the flask, showing the gas to be acidic.

Hydrochloric acid is the solution of the gas in water. It has the usual properties of an acid.

(i) *Action on Metals.* Zinc, magnesium and iron dissolve in the solution and give off hydrogen, leaving in solution the chloride of the metal, *e.g.*,

$$Zn + 2HCl \rightarrow ZnCl_2 + H_2$$
$$\text{dilute} \quad \quad \text{zinc}$$
$$\text{hydrochloric} \quad \text{chloride}$$
$$\text{acid}$$

Neither dilute nor concentrated hydrochloric acid acts on copper.

(ii) *Action of Oxidising Agents.* Chlorine is the product of oxidation of hydrochloric acid and most oxidising agents will liberate chlorine from it (see p. 271).

(iii) *Action of Heat.* If a strong hydrochloric acid solution is heated, hydrogen chloride escapes into the air. If a very weak solution is heated, water is driven off to make the solution stronger. In both cases a mixture is finally obtained containing 20·24% of hydrochloric acid, which distils over unchanged. This is termed a "constant boiling mixture".

Manufacture of Hydrogen Chloride. Until recently, hydrogen chloride was manufactured exclusively by heating common salt with concentrated sulphuric acid. This was the first stage of the Leblanc process (p. 258).

$$2NaCl + H_2SO_4 \rightarrow 2HCl + Na_2SO_4$$

The gas was absorbed in water to form hydrochloric acid.

Recently, improved methods of manufacture of hydrogen have made it possible to produce hydrogen chloride in quantity by direct combination of hydrogen with chlorine, which is obtained by electrolysis of brine.

$$H_2 + Cl_2 \rightarrow 2HCl$$

This method is likely to increase in importance.

CHLORIDES

Metallic Chlorides. *Preparation.* All metals are attacked by chlorine to form chlorides. The methods of preparation are summarised below.

The chlorides of these metals are made by the action of:

the alkali (or oxide) or carbonate on dilute hydrochloric acid.	**K** **Na** **Ca^1**	These metals are attacked by dilute hydrochloric acid.
the metal, oxide, or carbonate on dilute hydrochloric acid.	**Mg^1** **Zn^1** **Fe^1**	
by double decomposition.	**Pb**	(ferrous)
the oxide or carbonate on dilute hydrochloric acid.	**Cu**	These metals not attacked by dilute hydrochloric acid.
by double decomposition.	**Ag**	

All attacked by chlorine to form a chloride.

N.B. Ferric [1] chloride is made by the action of chlorine on the metal.

Ammonium chloride, NH$_4$Cl, Sal-ammoniac. This compound has many uses, two of the chief being as a constituent of the Leclanché electric battery, and as a flux in soldering. It is usually prepared by boiling ammonium sulphate solution with common salt.

$$(NH_4)_2SO_4 + 2NaCl \rightleftharpoons 2NH_4Cl + Na_2SO_4$$

On cooling, sodium sulphate crystallises first and may be removed by filtration, after which ammonium chloride may be obtained from the filtrate as a white solid. It sublimes on being heated. For the action of heat on ammonium chloride see p. 341.

Potassium chloride occurs as carnallite (KCl . MgCl$_2$. 6H$_2$O). Potassium chloride can be prepared in the laboratory by the neutralisation of potassium hydroxide solution with dilute hydrochloric acid.

$$\underset{\substack{\text{potassium} \\ \text{hydroxide}}}{KOH} + \underset{\substack{\text{dilute} \\ \text{hydrochloric} \\ \text{acid}}}{HCl} \rightarrow \underset{\substack{\text{potassium} \\ \text{chloride}}}{KCl} + \underset{\text{water}}{H_2O}$$

It forms white cubic crystals similar to those of sodium chloride. It imparts a *lilac* colour to the non-luminous bunsen flame. It is not deliquescent.

Sodium chloride occurs as rock salt, and is pumped out of the ground as brine. It is prepared by similar methods to those used for potassium chloride and forms white cubic crystals. It imparts

[1] The chlorides of these metals are very deliquescent. The above is a list of common metals in the order of the electrochemical series.

a golden yellow colour to the bunsen flame. Pure common salt is not deliquescent (the dampness of ordinary salt is due to impurities, *e.g.*, magnesium chloride which is deliquescent).

Sodium chloride is a most important chemical. The total world output of it is 20,000,000 tons per year, of which about two-thirds is used in connection with food. The remainder is used in chemical manufacture. As a sodium compound, common salt is converted

PLATE IX.
Crystals obtained by allowing a drop of salt solution
to dry up magnified 72 times.

into caustic soda, washing-soda, baking-soda, "salt-cake" (sodium sulphate) and other less important sodium compounds. It is used for "salting-out" soap during its manufacture.

As a chloride, common salt is used in the large-scale production of hydrochloric acid and chlorine, which is very important as a bleaching agent and in the manufacture of bleaching-powder and fine chemicals.

The chemical industry of South Lancashire is dependent on the salt of Cheshire as well as the coal of the Lancashire coal-field.

Calcium chloride is very deliquescent and can be used as a drying agent for most gases (but not for ammonia, with which it forms a compound). The anhydrous salt is prepared by heating a strong solution until the solid formed fuses. The solution is most easily

K*

prepared by adding marble or limestone to dilute hydrochloric acid until a little of the marble remains. The mixture is then filtered.

$$CaCO_3 + 2HCl \rightarrow CaCl_2 + H_2O + CO_2$$

Anhydrous ferric chloride is made by the action of iron on chlorine by the method described on p. 277.

The anhydrous salt cannot be made by the evaporation of the solution because the chloride is attacked by water when a strong solution is evaporated. This type of action is termed *hydrolysis*.

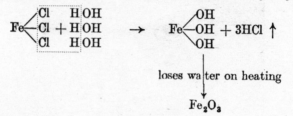

On heating the solution in air the final product is ferric oxide.

This action is the reverse of neutralisation.

Ferric chloride is a black solid in the anhydrous state, but forms a dark brown solution if strong, and a yellow solution if dilute. It can be reduced by reducing agents (*e.g.*, zinc and dilute hydrochloric acid) to ferrous chloride.

$$FeCl_3 + H \rightarrow FeCl_2 + HCl$$

With alkaline solutions, it gives (as do all ferric salts dissolved in water) a reddish-brown gelatinous precipitate of ferric hydroxide.

$$FeCl_3 + 3NaOH \rightarrow Fe(OH)_3 + 3NaCl$$
$$\text{ferric} \qquad \text{sodium} \qquad \text{ferric} \qquad \text{sodium}$$
$$\text{chloride} \qquad \text{hydroxide} \qquad \text{hydroxide} \qquad \text{chloride}$$

ionically: $Fe^{+++} + 3OH^- \rightarrow Fe(OH)_3 \downarrow$

Ferrous chloride. Anhydrous ferrous chloride, a white solid, is made by heating iron wire strongly in a stream of dry hydrogen chloride.

$$Fe + 2HCl \rightarrow FeCl_2 + H_2$$
$$\text{iron} \quad \text{hydrogen} \quad \text{ferrous} \quad \text{hydrogen}$$
$$\text{chloride} \quad \text{chloride}$$

It forms a pale green solution which gives, with alkaline solutions, a dirty green precipitate of ferrous hydroxide (as will any ferrous salt dissolved in water).

$$FeCl_2 + 2NaOH \rightarrow 2NaCl + Fe(OH)_2$$
$$\text{ferrous} \qquad\qquad\qquad \text{ferrous}$$
$$\text{chloride} \qquad\qquad\qquad \text{hydroxide}$$

ionically: $Fe^{++} + 2OH^- \rightarrow Fe(OH)_2 \downarrow$

Lead chloride is a white insoluble substance made by the inter-action of a solution of ANY soluble lead salt with a solution of ANY soluble chloride.

Into a beaker put some dilute hydrochloric acid and add lead nitrate solution. There is a white precipitate.

$$Pb(NO_3)_2 + 2HCl \rightarrow PbCl_2 + 2HNO_3$$
$$\text{lead nitrate} \qquad\qquad \text{lead chloride}$$

ionically: $Pb^{++} + 2Cl^- \rightarrow PbCl_2 \downarrow$

Filter off the white precipitate, wash it two or three times with a little *cold* distilled water and put it on a porous plate to dry.

Lead chloride is almost insoluble in cold water yet fairly soluble in hot water. (It is the only common substance which shows this peculiar behaviour.)

Silver chloride is a white insoluble compound made by adding a solution of ANY soluble silver salt to a solution of ANY soluble chloride.

$$AgNO_3 + NaCl \rightarrow AgCl \downarrow + NaNO_3$$
$$\text{silver} \quad \text{sodium} \quad \text{silver} \quad \text{sodium}$$
$$\text{nitrate} \quad \text{chloride} \quad \text{chloride} \quad \text{nitrate}$$

ionically: $Ag^+ + Cl^- \rightarrow AgCl \downarrow$

The white solid is filtered off, washed two or three times with hot distilled water and dried on a porous plate. (The whole action should be performed in the absence of light since silver chloride turns violet on exposure to light.)

Silver chloride is insoluble in dilute nitric acid but soluble in ammonia.

Properties of Chlorides

(1) *Action with concentrated sulphuric acid.* On being treated with concentrated sulphuric acid, a chloride evolves hydrogen chloride, *e.g.*,

$$NaCl + H_2SO_4 \rightarrow NaHSO_4 + HCl$$
$$\text{sodium} \quad \text{concentrated} \quad \text{sodium} \quad \text{hydrogen}$$
$$\text{chloride} \quad \text{sulphuric} \quad \text{hydrogen} \quad \text{chloride}$$
$$\text{acid} \quad \text{sulphate}$$

(2) Chlorides are more volatile than most salts.

The chlorides are on the whole a volatile class of compounds. This makes them suitable for use in the "flame-test" in which certain metals can be detected by the colour their vapour imparts to the bunsen flame. To perform the flame-test, the substance

under consideration is moistened with concentrated hydrochloric
acid and a porcelain rod or platinum wire is dipped into the mixture
and applied to the non-luminous bunsen flame.

Metal Chloride.	*Colour.*
Sodium . . .	Persistent golden yellow (invisible through blue glass).
Potassium. . .	Lilac flame (visible through blue glass).
Barium . . .	Green flashes.
Copper . . .	Green (blue zone).
Calcium . . .	Red.

(3) *Hydrolysis of Chlorides.* Several chlorides are readily
hydrolysed by water, *e.g.*, magnesium, zinc and iron chlorides. If
solutions of the chlorides are evaporated a basic salt or the oxide
of the metal remains.

(4) *Action of Concentrated Sulphuric Acid on mixture of Chloride
and Oxidising Agent.* Mix together a little common salt and manganese dioxide (many other oxidising agents would be suitable).
Put this into a test-tube, add a few drops of concentrated sulphuric
acid, and warm. A green gas, chlorine, is evolved.

$$2NaCl + 2H_2SO_4 + MnO_2 \rightarrow MnSO_4 + Na_2SO_4$$

sodium   concentrated   manganese   manganese   sodium
chloride   sulphuric   dioxide   sulphate   sulphate
               acid

$$+ 2H_2O + Cl_2$$

water   chlorine

Test for a Soluble Chloride. Dissolve a suspected chloride in
distilled water and add a little nitric acid and then silver nitrate
solution. If a chloride is present you will see a white precipitate of
silver chloride.

$$XCl + AgNO_3 \rightarrow AgCl + XNO_3$$

Divide the precipitate into two parts. Add ammonia to one and
observe that the precipitate dissolves. Allow the other to be
exposed to the light for a few minutes. The precipitate will turn
violet.

Silver chloride is insoluble in nitric acid but soluble in ammonia.
The only two common insoluble chlorides are lead chloride and
silver chloride.

QUESTIONS ON THIS CHAPTER WILL BE FOUND ON PAGE 298.

CHAPTER XXVII

BROMINE AND IODINE

BROMINE

BROMINE was discovered by Balard in 1826. He passed chlorine through the mother liquor obtained after crystallising common salt from sea water. The liquor turned red and from it he was able to isolate bromine and to show that it was an element.

Liebig, some years previously, had received a dark red liquid with a request to examine it, but thinking that it was merely a compound of iodine and chlorine, he did not pay it much attention.

Occurrence. Bromine occurs chiefly as the bromides of potassium, sodium and magnesium usually in association with larger proportions of the chlorides of those metals. Since the bromides are much more soluble in water than the chlorides, a liquid rich in bromides is left by crystallising out the chlorides. Treated in this way, the mother liquors from the Stassfurt deposits in Germany (which consist mainly of carnallite, $KCl.MgCl_2.6H_2O$), after the removal of a large proportion of the potassium chloride, contain about $\frac{1}{4}\%$ of bromide and the bromine is obtained by allowing this solution to come into contact with chlorine, which displaces the bromine:

$$MgBr_2 + Cl_2 \rightarrow MgCl_2 + Br_2$$
$$\text{magnesium} \qquad\qquad\qquad \text{bromine}$$
$$\text{bromide}$$

Laboratory Preparation of Bromine. This experiment must be done in a fume-chamber.

Bromine can be prepared in a way exactly analogous to one of the methods for making chlorine.

Make an intimate mixture of potassium bromide and manganese dioxide and place this in a retort (Fig. 101). Add some concentrated sulphuric acid and warm the mixture. A red gas is given off (together with some misty fumes of hydrogen bromide) which condenses to a red liquid in the cooled receiver. This is bromine.

$$2KBr + MnO_2 + 2H_2SO_4 \rightarrow K_2SO_4 + MnSO_4 + 2H_2O + Br_2$$

potassium manganese concentrated potassium manganese water bromine
bromide dioxide sulphuric sulphate sulphate
acid

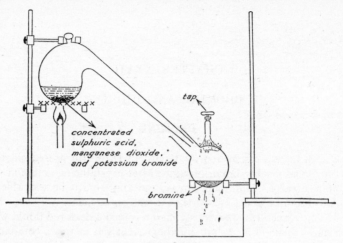

FIG. 101.
Preparation of bromine.

PHYSICAL PROPERTIES OF BROMINE

(1) It is a heavy (density = 3·2), red, volatile liquid (boiling-point 59° C.).

(2) It has a choking irritating smell. (Its name means "a stench".) The liquid causes sores on the flesh, which heal with difficulty.

(3) It is slightly soluble in water, forming a red solution containing about 3% of bromine at ordinary temperatures.

The following *chemical properties* are considered under same headings as those of chlorine.

Bromine as a Bleaching Agent. Bromine is a bleaching agent, not so rapid as chlorine. A piece of damp litmus paper is bleached when placed in the vapour of bromine.

Bromine does not combine with hydrogen as readily as does chlorine. Bromine has an affinity for hydrogen but the affinity is not as marked as in the case of chlorine. A mixture of chlorine and hydrogen will explode when merely exposed to sunlight, but a mixture of bromine and hydrogen needs the application of heat to induce combination, and the compound formed (hydrogen bromide) is not as stable as hydrogen chloride.

$$H_2 + Br_2 \rightarrow 2HBr$$

Bromine as a Bromide Former. Bromine combines readily with most metals and non-metals to form bromides, for example copper, iron, sodium, sulphur. It explodes when mixed with yellow phosphorus, so vigorous is the action. Phosphorus tribromide is made by gradually adding a solution of bromine in carbon tetrachloride to red phosphorus. The solution is used in order to moderate the action.

Bromine as an Oxidising Agent. Bromine is an oxidising agent, but not quite as vigorous as chlorine. It will perform the majority of the oxidations attributed to chlorine. Thus on shaking an acidified solution of ferrous sulphate with a few drops of bromine in a test-tube, the bromine colour soon disappears and the ferrous sulphate has been converted into ferric sulphate.

$$2FeSO_4 + H_2SO_4 + Br_2 \rightarrow Fe_2(SO_4)_3 + 2HBr$$

The Displacing Action of Bromine. Bromine can displace iodine from iodides but cannot displace chlorine from chlorides. Thus, on adding a few drops of bromine to a solution of potassium iodide in water, the characteristic brown colour of the solution of iodine in potassium iodide is seen. On boiling this solution the violet vapour of iodine may be observed.

$$2KI + Br_2 \rightarrow 2KBr + I_2$$

potassium   bromine   potassium   iodine
iodide   bromide

Action of Bromine on the Alkalis. The action of bromine on an alkaline solution is exactly analogous to that of chlorine. Thus:

Cold Caustic Potash

$$2KOH + Br_2 \rightarrow KBr + KOBr + H_2O$$

potassium   potassium
bromide   hypo-
            bromite

Hot Caustic Potash

$$6KOH + 3Br_2 \rightarrow 5KBr + KBrO_3 + 3H_2O$$

potassium
bromate

Summary. Bromine is an element very similar to chlorine but differing from it principally in that bromine is less active than chlorine.

HYDROGEN BROMIDE

As indicated above, hydrogen bromide is not as stable as hydrogen chloride and is decomposed to some extent by the action of heat. This, together with the fact that hot concentrated sulphuric acid is an oxidising agent, makes it impossible to prepare pure hydrogen bromide by the action of heat on a mixture of concentrated sulphuric acid and potassium bromide. The products of such an attempt would be hydrogen bromide, bromine and sulphur dioxide.

It may be made by the action of bromine on a mixture of red phosphorus and water. The chemistry of the action is that bromides of phosphorus are formed which are decomposed by the water.

Preparation of Hydrogen Bromide. Make a paste of red phosphorus and water and place this in the flask (sand may be added to "dilute" the mixture). Bromine is dropped in gradually from a tap-funnel and the reaction proceeds at ordinary temperature

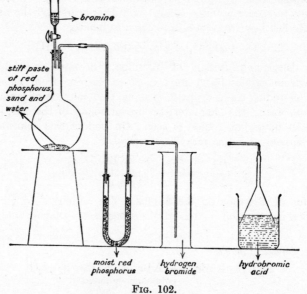

FIG. 102.
Preparation of hydrogen bromide.

(Fig. 102). Heat is evolved during the process and a considerable amount of bromine may be volatilised and would, if not removed, contaminate the hydrogen bromide. The bromine is removed by passing it through a U-tube containing beads smeared with red phosphorus and water. **This U-tube is, in fact, a secondary generating apparatus** so arranged as to offer a large area of phosphorus to the bromine so that it is as completely removed as possible. The misty gas, very similar in appearance to hydrogen chloride, is collected by displacement of air as shown in Fig. 102, the gas being heavier than air. It can also be dissolved in water to form hydrobromic acid by the apparatus shown above.

$$P_4 \ + \ 6Br_2 \ \rightarrow \ 4PBr_3$$
phosphorus   bromine   phosphorus tribromide

$$PBr_3 \ + \ 3H_2O \ \rightarrow \ H_3PO_3 \ + \ 3HBr$$
phosphorous acid   hydrogen bromide

(Alternatively hydrogen bromide may be prepared by heating potassium bromide with conc. sulphuric acid diluted with half its own volume of water.)

Preparation of Hydrogen Bromide from its Elements. The gas can also be made by bubbling hydrogen through a wash-bottle containing bromine and passing the gases through a heated tube containing platinised asbestos, which acts as a catalyst. Any unattacked bromine is absorbed by red phosphorus.

$$H_2 + Br_2 \rightarrow 2HBr$$

Preparation of Hydrogen Bromide by the Action of Hydrogen Sulphide on Bromine-water. A convenient method for making a weak solution of hydrogen bromide is to bubble hydrogen sulphide through bromine-water for some time. Sulphur precipitates and can be filtered off.

$$H_2S + Br_2 \rightarrow 2HBr + S \downarrow$$

Test. Hydrogen bromide turns damp blue litmus paper red, and gives a pale yellow precipitate of silver bromide with a mixture of silver nitrate solution and nitric acid. The precipitate is only slightly soluble in ammonia, and does not turn violet on exposure to light.

$$AgNO_3 + HBr \rightarrow \underset{\substack{silver \\ bromide}}{AgBr} + HNO_3$$

Properties of Hydrogen Bromide. (i) It is a heavy fuming gas with a choking smell (density = 2·8; air = 1).

(ii) It is very soluble in water, forming a strongly acid solution. A saturated solution of hydrogen bromide contains about 70% by weight of hydrogen bromide at ordinary temperatures.

(iii) It is less stable than hydrogen chloride, being more easily decomposed into its elements.

(iv) It is, in its general chemical properties, similar to hydrogen chloride.

Bromides. The bromides are prepared, generally speaking, by the same methods as the chlorides and possess similar properties. They can readily be distinguished from the chlorides by the action of chlorine gas which has no effect on the chlorides but displaces bromine from bromides (see p. 279 for experimental details).

IODINE

Iodine was discovered in 1812 by Courtois. He treated with concentrated sulphuric acid the mother liquors obtained after extracting sodium carbonate from the ash obtained by burning sea weed (kelp). The ash contains a small percentage of iodides and the concentrated sulphuric acid formed hydrogen iodide and oxidised it to iodine. Gay-Lussac and Davy investigated the properties of the black solid, which was called iodine by Gay-Lussac.

Most of the iodine used to-day occurs as sodium iodate ($NaIO_3$) in the sodium nitrate deposits in Chile. The amount is very small (about 0·1%) but after the removal of the sodium nitrate by crystallisation the proportion is much higher in the residues. The iodine is obtained by treatment with sodium hydrogen sulphite.

Laboratory Preparation from Potassium Iodide. Grind together some potassium iodide and manganese dioxide in a mortar and place the mixture in a dish. Add concentrated sulphuric acid and

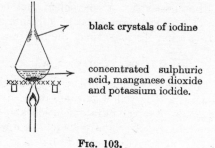

black crystals of iodine

concentrated sulphuric acid, manganese dioxide and potassium iodide.

FIG. 103.
Preparation of iodine.

place an inverted funnel over the dish as shown in Fig. 103. Warm the mixture carefully and the violet vapour of iodine will be seen to condense on the cooler parts of the funnel to black shining plates. The chemistry of the action is similar to the formation of chlorine from common salt. The hydrogen iodide is, however, much more easily oxidised than even hydrogen bromide.

$$MnO_2 + 2KI + 2H_2SO_4 \rightarrow K_2SO_4 + MnSO_4 + 2H_2O + I_2$$
potassium iodide   iodine

Physical Properties of Iodine

(i) It is a black shining solid. Density 4·9.

(ii) It sublimes when heated rapidly, forming a violet vapour from which the black solid can again be obtained by cooling.

(iii) It is almost insoluble in water but readily soluble in potassium iodide solution. This is due to the formation of a compound of potassium iodide and iodine, KI_3, which readily dissolves. This solution is brown. It also dissolves in alcohol and ether, forming brown solutions, and in carbon disulphide and chloroform, forming violet solutions.

The following *chemical properties* of iodine are considered in the same order as those of chlorine and bromine.

Iodine does not bleach, and has little affinity for hydrogen. The effect of heating hydrogen iodide is to decompose the compound into its elements.

Iodine as an Iodide Former. Iodine is a fairly active element and will combine with many metals to form iodides, but it does so much less readily than either chlorine or bromine.

Oxidising Action of Iodine. Iodine is a mild oxidising agent. It will not perform many of the ordinary oxidising actions attributed to chlorine and bromine. It will, however, oxidise hydrogen sulphide to form hydrogen iodide and liberate sulphur.

$$H_2S + I_2 \rightarrow 2HI + S \downarrow$$

Action of Iodine on Alkaline Solutions. The action of iodine with alkalis is similar to the reactions of chlorine and bromine with alkalis. Hypoiodites, iodides and iodates are produced (p. 279).

Displacing Action of Iodine. Iodine cannot displace chlorine or bromine from chlorides or bromides.

Action of Iodine with Starch Solution. Place a 400 c.c. beaker full of water on a tripod and gauze and heat to boiling. Make a paste of a small amount of starch (about 1 gm.) and a little water, and pour this into the *boiling* water and stir. Allow to cool, or if the starch paste is required immediately, pour some of the paste into a boiling-tube and cool under the tap.

Add the smallest possible quantity of a solution of iodine (the test is sensitive to one part in one million) and immediately you will observe a blue colouration. Warm the mixture and the blue colour will disappear, but will return on cooling.

This test is given only by free iodine and is not given by, say, a solution of potassium iodide in water.

Uses of Iodine. The antiseptic properties of iodine have caused a large increase in the demand for iodine during the last few years. It is sold as "tincture of iodine"—a solution of iodine in dilute alcohol. It is used as iodine and iodides in medicine to treat cases of goître, which disease is thought to be due to lack of iodine in the body. Small amounts of iodine have, in fact, been shown to be essential to the human body and all other forms of vertebrate life. Remarkable results have been obtained by giving poultry a small but regular dose of potassium iodide. The production of eggs was wonderfully increased.

HYDROGEN IODIDE

This gas is much less stable than even hydrogen bromide. A solution of hydrogen iodide in water quickly darkens because of the formation of iodine. It is usually prepared by the action of

water on a mixture of red phosphorus and iodine. Since iodine is
a solid and does not volatilise to an appreciable extent during the
reaction, there is no need for a U-tube as in the case of the similar
preparation of hydrogen bromide (Fig. 102).

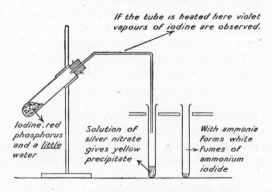

*If the tube is heated here violet
vapours of iodine are observed.*

*Iodine, red
phosphorus
and a little
water*

*Solution of
silver nitrate
gives yellow
precipitate*

*With ammonia
forms white
fumes of
ammonium
iodide*

FIG. 104.
Simple apparatus to show some of the properties of hydrogen iodide.

For class purposes, the reactions of hydrogen iodide can easily be
shown by the very simple apparatus shown in Fig. 104. Grind a
little red phosphorus with iodine in a mortar and introduce the
mixture into a dry boiling-tube. Add about four drops of water,
insert a cork fitted with delivery-tube, and allow the gas to fall
(hydrogen iodide is four times as dense as air) into test-tubes, one
containing silver nitrate solution and the other containing a few
drops of ammonia. The tube may also be heated when the decomposition of the gas is obvious from the violet vapour of iodine which
is observed.

$$P_4 + 6I_2 \rightarrow 4PI_3$$

$$PI_3 + 3H_2O \rightarrow 3HI + H_3PO_3$$

phosphorus   hydrogen phosphorous
tri-iodide   iodide   acid

A solution of hydriodic acid can be more simply obtained by
bubbling sulphuretted hydrogen into a suspension of iodine in water.
The end of the reaction is reached when all the iodine is seen to have
disappeared. The precipitated sulphur is filtered off.

$$H_2S + I_2 \rightarrow 2HI + S \downarrow$$

Test. Add a little chlorine-water to a gas-jar of the gas,
and pour a few drops of the liquid into starch paste.
A blue colour is observed.

Properties

(i) Hydrogen iodide is a fuming gas with a choking smell.

(ii) It is very soluble in water, forming a strongly acid solution, hydriodic acid.

(iii) It is readily dissociated by heat into its elements. The change is reversible.

$$2HI \rightleftharpoons H_2 + I_2$$

(iv) Because of the readiness with which it decomposes it is a vigorous reducing agent—in fact, one of the most vigorous reducing agents known. It will attack any oxidising agent, however mild, with the liberation of iodine. For example, sulphuric acid is reduced to sulphur dioxide, and ferric salts to ferrous salts.

Comparison of the Properties of Chlorine, Bromine and Iodine, to show the Family Resemblance and Gradation of Properties

	CHLORINE.	BROMINE.	IODINE.
Atomic weight .	35·5	80	127
Density . .	1·55	3·2	4·9
Valency . .	usually 1	usually 1	usually 1
Combination with hydrogen	Explosive in sunlight.	Combines on heating.	Does not combine readily.
Bleaching action	Vigorous bleacher	Mild bleacher	Will not bleach.
Preparation .	Action of heat on mixture of manganese dioxide, concentrated sulphuric acid and a chloride.	In a similar manner, using a bromide.	In a similar manner, using an iodide.
Silver salt .	White. Insoluble in water and nitric acid. Soluble in ammonia.	Very pale yellow. Insoluble in water and nitric acid. Slightly soluble in ammonia.	Yellow. Insoluble in water and nitric acid. Insoluble in ammonia.
Solubility of potassium salt at 10° C.	31 gm.	59 gm.	136 gm.
Solubility of sodium salt.	35·6 gm.	80 gm.	168·6 gm.
Melting-point of sodium salt.	805° C.	768° C.	664° C.
Heat of formation of potassium salt.	106 Cals.	95 Cals.	88 Cals.
Heat of solution of potassium salt.	−4·5 Cals.	−5·0 Cals.	−5·1 Cals.
Displacing action on halides.	Displaces bromine and iodine.	Displaces iodine.	Does not displace the other halogens.

Iodides. The iodides are similar to the chlorides and the bromides, but can readily be distinguished by the action of chlorine or bromine, which precipitate iodine.

$$2KI + Cl_2 \rightarrow 2KCl + I_2$$

A solution of silver nitrate and nitric acid gives a decidedly yellow precipitate of silver iodide.

$$NaI + AgNO_3 \rightarrow AgI + NaNO_3$$

sodium   silver
iodide   iodide

This precipitate is insoluble in ammonia.

The iodides are readily oxidised, free iodine being liberated.

The table on p. 297 clearly shows the gradation of properties of the family of elements, chlorine, bromine and iodine.

QUESTIONS ON THE HALOGENS

1. "Chlorine is the product of the oxidation of hydrogen chloride." Illustrate this statement by describing two different processes for the preparation of chlorine, one used in the laboratory and the other a large-scale process. State the various stages in the bleaching of coloured cloth by means of bleaching powder. (N.U.J.B.)

2. Describe a laboratory method for preparing chlorine. What impurities would the gas so prepared be liable to contain, and how would you get rid of them? (O. and C.)

3. How you would prepare chlorine from bleaching powder? What takes place when (a) a mixture of chlorine and hydrogen is exposed to diffused daylight? (b) chlorine is passed into cold, dilute caustic potash solution? (c) chlorine is passed into hot, strong caustic potash solution? (d) chlorine water bleaches litmus solution? (D.)

4. How can it be shown that hydrogen chloride contains half its volume of hydrogen?
   Contrast the behaviour of hydrogen chloride with hydrogen iodide (a) when heated, (b) when mixed with bromine vapour. (O. and C.)

5. Describe how you would prepare a specimen of bleaching powder in the laboratory. What happens when it is treated with (a) dilute hydrochloric acid, (b) an acidified solution of ferrous sulphate? Describe how you would employ your specimen of bleaching powder to bleach a piece of red cloth. (O.)

6. Describe the preparation from iron of (a) ferrous chloride, (b) ferric chloride. How may these compounds be converted one into the other? (O. and C.)

7. Give an account of the experiments you would do in order to investigate the action between lead peroxide and hydrochloric acid. By what tests would you identify the more important products? (L.)

8. Chlorine will react with the substances slaked lime, iron, caustic potash, sulphuretted hydrogen, potassium iodide and water.

Describe briefly the apparatus you would use in carrying out these reactions and state clearly the conditions necessary to bring about the chemical change. Where possible, give an equation for the reaction. (D.)

9. Describe and explain the action of chlorine on (a) metallic sodium, (b) sodium hydroxide solution, (c) potassium iodide solution.

An excess of chlorine water was added to 50 c.c. of a solution of sulphur dioxide. An excess of barium chloride ($BaCl_2$) solution was then added and the resulting precipitate after filtering, washing and drying, weighed 0·5202 gm. Calculate the volume of sulphur dioxide at N.T.P. which was dissolved to make the original solution. (Ba = 137; S = 32.) (L.)

10. Suggest simple experiments by which you could show that (a) ammonia contains hydrogen, (b) carbon dioxide contains carbon, and (c) salt contains chlorine. (N.U.J.B.)

11. (a) Describe with a sketch how you would prepare and collect some dry chlorine.

(b) Assuming that chlorine can be completely converted into ferric chloride ($FeCl_3$) by passing the gas over heated iron, calculate what volume of chlorine, measured at 17° C. and 870 mm. pressure, would be required to produce 32·5 gm. of ferric chloride. (Fe = 56, Cl = 35·5, 2 gm. of hydrogen occupy 22·4 litres at 0° C. and 760 mm. pressure.) (N.U.J.B.)

12. How would you obtain from common salt a concentrated solution of hydrogen chloride?

Explain, giving equations, what takes place when the solution is treated with (a) ammonia, (b) manganese dioxide, (c) ferrous sulphide. (O. and C.)

13. (a) Indicate the chemistry of ONE process of manufacture of each of the following: (i) lime, (ii) chlorine, (iii) bleaching powder. (b) What takes place when carbon dioxide is passed into a suspension of bleaching powder? (N.U.J.B.)

14. Describe how you would collect and prepare a small quantity of liquid bromine. Under what conditions does this element combine with hydrogen? and how does the compound so formed resemble and differ from the corresponding compounds of chlorine and iodine? (L.)

15. How would you make an aqueous solution of hydrochloric acid starting from sodium chloride? Sketch the apparatus you would use. What tests would you apply to show that the solution you have made is (a) acid, (b) hydrochloric acid? Give one test in each case. How would you determine the volume composition of hydrogen chloride? (C. W. B.)

16. Describe the preparation and the collection of dry chlorine. Explain the bleaching action of chlorine and contrast it with that of sulphur dioxide. How would you remove an ordinary inkstain from a white cotton cloth by means of bleaching powder? (L.)

CHAPTER XXVIII

SULPHUR

THE element, sulphur, is a yellow solid. It is usually sold as either "flowers of sulphur", a powder, or "roll sulphur", cylindrical sticks.

Uses of Sulphur. The output of sulphur in the world to-day exceeds 2,000,000 tons annually, about nine-tenths of it being produced by the United States of America. This vast amount is used in the following ways:

1. for the manufacture of sulphuric acid (see p. 320).
2. for dusting vines to prevent the growth of certain kinds of fungus.
3. for the manufacture of calcium bisulphite, $Ca(HSO_3)_2$, which is used as a bleacher of wood-pulp in the manufacture of paper.
4. for the vulcanisation of rubber, a process which converts the soft pliable rubber into the hard, tough substance of which motor tyres and similar products are made.
5. in smaller quantities for the manufacture of dyes, fireworks, sulphur compounds, such as carbon disulphide, CS_2, and medicinally in ointments.

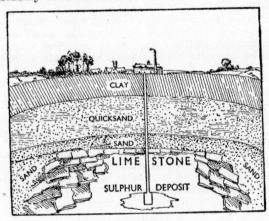

FIG. 105.

American sulphur deposits.

Occurrence. Sulphur occurs:

1. in the States of Louisiana and Texas, U.S.A.
2. in the island of Sicily.

In both cases, the element occurs free. The American deposits are the most important in the world.

Extraction of Sulphur. In America the deposits lie at a depth of about 500 feet with deposits of limestone, clay and sand between the ground level and the sulphur (Fig. 105). It is not necessary to mine the sulphur by sinking shafts as in the case of coal, for sulphur differs from coal in having a fairly low melting-point (115° C.). By utilising this property, the sulphur can be extracted, by a method invented by Frasch, cheaply, rapidly and in a high state of purity.

A hole about 1 foot in diameter is bored down through the clay, sand and limestone to the sulphur beds. This boring is lined with an iron pipe and, inside the pipe, is sunk a device called the sulphur pump. It consists of three concentric tubes which terminate in a reservoir of larger diameter (see Fig. 106). Down the outermost of the three tubes is forced a stream of water at about 170° C. This water must be kept at a pressure of about 140 lbs. per square inch to maintain it in the liquid state, *i.e.*, it is super-heated water, and it is hot enough to melt the sulphur. The molten sulphur flows into the reservoir at the base of the pump and is forced up to the surface through the second of the three tubes by means of a blast of hot compressed air at a pressure of about 200 lbs. per square inch, which is forced down the narrowest tube. The sulphur is run

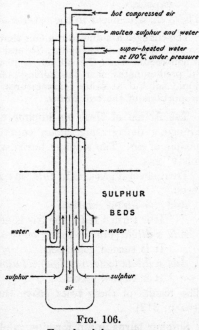

FIG. 106.
Frasch sulphur pump.

into large tanks, where it solidifies and can be separated from the water. Sulphur more than 99% pure is produced by this operation and a single pump may produce up to 500 tons of this high grade sulphur daily.

The output of sulphur from Sicily is small and relatively unimportant.

The Action of Heat on Sulphur when Air is Excluded. The exclusion of air can be sufficiently secured by using for the experiment a test-tube, in which only a very small area of sulphur is exposed.

Place some powdered roll sulphur in a hard glass test-tube and warm it gently, shaking well. Try to avoid local over-heating by rotating the test-tube. The sulphur passes through the following stages as the temperature rises:

1. It melts at about 115° C. to an amber-coloured, mobile liquid.
2. It becomes much darker in colour and, suddenly, at 160° C., very viscous. So viscous does it become that the test-tube may be inverted without loss of sulphur.
3. The sulphur gradually becomes more mobile again and very dark reddish-brown in colour.
4. The sulphur boils at 444° C., giving off light brown sulphur vapour.

These changes occur in the reverse order as the sulphur cools.

The changes are due to the fact that sulphur can exist in two liquid forms, called lambda-sulphur, $S\lambda$, and mu-sulphur, $S\mu$. $S\lambda$ is the form which occurs when the sulphur is just above its melting-point, while $S\mu$ predominates near the boiling-point. The different properties of liquid sulphur at other temperatures are determined by the relative proportions of the two forms.

The Action of Heat on Sulphur with a Plentiful Supply of Air. Plunge a deflagrating spoon containing burning sulphur into a gas-jar of air. The sulphur burns with a blue flame and leaves a misty[1] gas.

Treat several gas-jars in this way and use them for the following tests:

Add blue litmus solution.

It is turned red. The gas is acidic.

Add a dilute (pink) solution of potassium permanganate.

It is turned colourless.

Add a dilute (golden yellow) solution of potassium dichromate.

It is turned green.

The results of these tests prove that the gas is sulphur dioxide (see p. 313).

Sulphur burns in air, forming sulphur dioxide.

$$S + O_2 \rightarrow SO_2$$

Formation of Sulphides from Sulphur. Sulphur will combine directly with many elements forming sulphides. For example, if a

[1] The misty effect is due to traces of sulphur trioxide formed simultaneously.

finely ground mixture of iron filings and sulphur, in the proportions of 56 to 32 by weight (Fe = 56; S = 32), is heated, the two elements will combine vigorously and the whole mass will glow spontaneously when once the combination has been started at one point. A black, or dark grey, residue of *ferrous sulphide* is left.

$$Fe + S \rightarrow FeS$$
ferrous
sulphide

Hot copper foil or wire will similarly glow in sulphur vapour, forming *cuprous sulphide*, Cu_2S.

$$2Cu + S \rightarrow Cu_2S.$$

Carbon combines directly with sulphur to form the important liquid, carbon disulphide, CS_2.

$$C + 2S \rightarrow CS_2$$

A very high temperature is required to bring about the combination, and this is secured by means of the electric furnace, in which an electric current passes between carbon electrodes and raises coke to white heat. Sulphur is also fed into the furnace. It vapourises and combines with the white-hot coke. Carbon disulphide vapour passes off and is condensed.

Carbon disulphide is poisonous and may be used to destroy low and harmful forms of life, such as grain weevils (which feed on stored grain) or cockroaches. It is very inflammable, and must be used with care. It is also an excellent solvent.

Action of Acids on Sulphur. Dilute acids do not act upon sulphur. It is oxidised by hot concentrated sulphuric acid with formation of sulphur dioxide.

$$S + 2H_2SO_4 \rightarrow 3SO_2 + 2H_2O$$

In this reaction the sulphur is oxidised by the acid to sulphur dioxide and the acid is reduced to the same substance. Of the three molecules of sulphur dioxide in the equation, one is the product of oxidation of sulphur and two are the products of reduction of the sulphuric acid. The action is too slow to have practical value.

Sulphur is oxidised by hot concentrated nitric acid, with bromine as the best catalyst, to sulphuric acid.

$$S + 6HNO_3 \rightarrow H_2SO_4 + 6NO_2 + 2H_2O$$

This reaction is fully discussed on p. 345.

ALLOTROPES OF SULPHUR

The following experiments show that sulphur exists in several different forms, called "allotropes". The meaning of this term will be considered more fully after the experiments have been described.

Preparation of Rhombic or Octahedral Sulphur (a-sulphur). Shake some powdered sulphur with carbon disulphide for some time in a test-tube. (Take care to extinguish all flames in the vicinity.) Filter the contents of the test-tube into a dry beaker through a

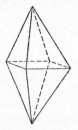

dry filter-paper and funnel. Fasten a filter-paper over the mouth of the beaker, pierce a few pin-holes in it, and set the beaker aside. The carbon disulphide will slowly evaporate, depositing crystals of sulphur, which, because of the slow evaporation, will be large enough for their shape to be seen. They will have the shape shown in Fig. 107.

This variety of sulphur is called *rhombic sulphur* or *octahedral sulphur* or *α-sulphur*.

FIG. 107.
Crystal of rhombic sulphur (simplified).

Note especially that the formation of the crystals takes place at ordinary room temperature.

Preparation of Monoclinic or Prismatic Sulphur (*β*-sulphur). Place powdered sulphur in a very large crucible or an evaporating dish. Heat it and stir, gradually adding more sulphur until the crucible or dish is almost brimful of molten sulphur. Use a small flame for the heating or the sulphur may begin to burn. Then allow the sulphur to cool. After a time, a solid crust will begin to form on the surface. When the crust is continuous, pierce it at two widely separated points with a glass rod and rapidly pour out the liquid sulphur from inside. With a pen-knife, cut through the solid crust all the way round the crucible or dish, near the rim, and lift it out. Underneath will be seen long "needle-shaped" crystals of sulphur. whose shape is shown in Fig. 108. They are crystals of *monoclinic sulphur* or *prismatic sulphur* or *β-sulphur*.

Note that this variety crystallises in close contact with hot, molten sulphur.

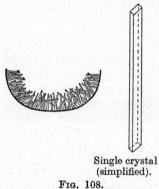

Single crystal (simplified).
FIG. 108.
Monoclinic sulphur.

Preparation of Amorphous Sulphur (δ-sulphur). This variety of sulphur may be prepared in several ways. One is to saturate distilled water with hydrogen sulphide and then expose the solution to the air. Sulphur is deposited as an almost white powder, *amorphous sulphur* or *δ-sulphur*.

$$2H_2S + O_2 \rightarrow 2H_2O + 2S$$

Allotropy and Allotropes. In the experiment just described, we have prepared three different varieties of the element sulphur. They have different properties, *e.g.*, their densities differ (rhombic, 2·08; monoclinic, 1·98), but they all consist of pure sulphur and nothing else. When an element can exist in several different forms in this way it is said to show allotropy. (See p. 410.)

Relation between Monoclinic and Rhombic Sulphur. The factor determining which of these two allotropes will be obtained in an experiment is temperature. In our experiments, rhombic sulphur was crystallised by evaporation of a solution of sulphur in carbon disulphide at ordinary room temperature, while monoclinic sulphur was crystallised in contact with a mass of hot, molten sulphur. Roughly, then, we may say that if the sulphur crystallises while still hot, it does so as the monoclinic allotrope; if it crystallises while cold, the rhombic allotrope is formed.

We can go further. Experiment has shown that the temperature which separates the two varieties is 96° C. If sulphur crystallises above this temperature, monoclinic crystals are formed, and if below it, rhombic. This temperature, 96° C., is therefore called the "transition temperature" between the two varieties.

If rhombic sulphur, stable below 96° C., is kept above that temperature, it changes its crystalline form and becomes monoclinic, while, if monoclinic sulphur, stable above 96° C., is kept below that temperature, it slowly yields rhombic sulphur.

Formation of Plastic Sulphur. Heat some powdered roll sulphur in a test-tube until it is boiling rapidly. (The changes which occur are fully considered on p. 302.) Then pour the boiling sulphur in a thin continuous stream into a beaker full of cold water. It forms long, elastic, light-yellow ribbons of "plastic sulphur", which are insoluble in carbon disulphide. This variety is not a true allotrope of sulphur. If kept for a few days, plastic sulphur becomes hard. This hard variety of sulphur is insoluble in carbon disulphide.

QUESTIONS ON SULPHUR WILL BE FOUND ON PAGE 329.

CHAPTER XXIX

HYDROGEN SULPHIDE AND THE SULPHIDES

HYDROGEN SULPHIDE, H_2S
(also called SULPHURETTED HYDROGEN)

Preparation. Hydrogen sulphide was obtained in the experiment described on p. 9 by the action of dilute hydrochloric acid on ferrous sulphide. This is the most convenient method of preparation, using the apparatus shown in Fig. 109.

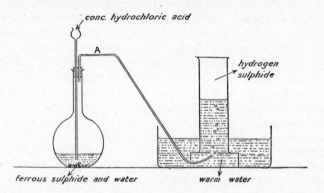

FIG. 109.

Preparation of hydrogen sulphide.

If it is required to prepare the gas starting from sulphur, the best way is to prepare ferrous sulphide first by the method of p. 7 and then to use it in the way about to be described.

As the acid drops on to the ferrous sulphide, effervescence begins and the hydrogen sulphide is collected over hot water. It is rather soluble in cold water (about three volumes of the gas in one volume of water), but, like all gases, it is less soluble in hot water.

$$FeS + 2HCl \rightarrow FeCl_2 + H_2S$$
$$\text{ferrous}$$
$$\text{chloride}$$
$$\text{in solution}$$

Dilute sulphuric acid may also be used.

$$FeS + H_2SO_4 \rightarrow FeSO_4 + H_2S$$

306

Characteristic Test. Soak a strip of filter-paper in lead acetate solution and drop it into a gas-jar of hydrogen sulphide. The paper turns dark brown or black. This colour change is caused by precipitation of black lead sulphide.

$$Pb(C_2H_3O_2)_2 + H_2S \rightarrow PbS \downarrow + 2C_2H_4O_2$$
$$\text{lead acetate} \qquad\qquad\qquad\qquad \text{acetic acid}$$

A purer specimen of hydrogen sulphide may be obtained by gently warming antimony sulphide with hydrochloric acid.

$$Sb_2S_3 + 6HCl \rightarrow 2SbCl_3 + 3H_2S$$

If required dry, the gas may be dried by passing it over calcium chloride and collected by upward displacement of air, as the gas is somewhat denser than the air.

KIPP'S APPARATUS

Kipp's apparatus is a device for obtaining intermittent supplies of a frequently used gas such as hydrogen, carbon dioxide or hydrogen sulphide. (See Fig. 110.)

When the tap A is opened, the acid rises into the bulb B and attacks the ferrous sulphide, producing hydrogen sulphide, which is delivered through A. When the gas is no longer required, A is turned off. The gas is still being generated which raises the pressure in B. The acid is therefore forced out of B and up into C. The generation of hydrogen sulphide now stops because acid and ferrous sulphide are no longer in contact and the apparatus will remain inactive until tap A is again opened to obtain gas.

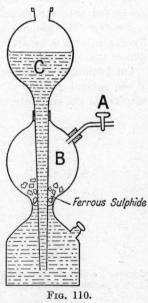

FIG. 110.
Kipp's apparatus.

THE PROPERTIES OF HYDROGEN SULPHIDE

Appearance. The gas is colourless.

Smell. Hydrogen sulphide has a repulsive, rather sweet smell similar to that of a rotten egg. It is, in fact, given off from putrefying eggs and also from decaying cabbages, both of which contain sulphur.

Though very poisonous, the powerful smell of the gas gives ample warning of its presence.

Solubility in Water. Invert a gas-jar of hydrogen sulphide in cold water, remove the cover and shake gently. The rise of the water shows that the gas is fairly soluble. At ordinary temperatures, one volume of water can dissolve about three volumes of hydrogen sulphide.

To the solution in the gas-jar, add blue litmus solution. It is turned claret colour. The solution is weakly acidic. It is known as hydrosulphuric acid, but the name is very seldom used. It is one of the weakest acids known. Hydrogen sulphide is contained in the water of the sulphur springs round which have grown such spas as Harrogate. These "waters" are said to have curative properties. They certainly possess, as a consequence of their hydrogen sulphide content, all the unpleasant taste usually associated with medicines!

Density. The gas has a density of 17 compared with that of hydrogen, and is somewhat denser than air, which is 14·4 times denser than hydrogen.

Combustion of Hydrogen Sulphide with a Plentiful Supply of Air. When several gas-jars of hydrogen sulphide have been collected remove the delivery-tube and fix the tube as shown below (Fig. 111).

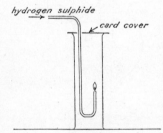

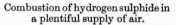

FIG. 111.

Combustion of hydrogen sulphide in a plentiful supply of air.

Apply a lighted taper. The hydrogen sulphide burns with a blue flame similar to that of sulphur. Lower the tube into a wide gas-jar, closing the mouth with a square of cardboard, and, when the flame is extinguished, remove the tube and add a weak, pink, solution of acidified potassium permanganate. On shaking, the solution becomes colourless and remains clear. This test proves the presence of *sulphur dioxide.*

$$2H_2S + 3O_2 \rightarrow 2H_2O + 2SO_2$$

Combustion of Hydrogen Sulphide with a Limited Air Supply. Cut down the air supply to the flame obtained in the last section by putting into it a crucible lid as shown in Fig 112.

After a few seconds, a yellow deposit of sulphur will be seen on the lid. The reduced oxygen supply cannot oxidise the gas completely and free sulphur is deposited.

$$2H_2S + O_2 \rightarrow 2S + 2H_2O$$

Hydrogen Sulphide as a Reducing Agent.
Hydrogen sulphide is a powerful reducing agent as the following experiments show.

Action of Hydrogen Sulphide with Nitric Acid. Dilute some concentrated nitric acid with about one-third of its volume of water in a boiling-tube and pass hydrogen sulphide into it. Brown fumes of nitrogen peroxide are given off, a pale yellow deposit of sulphur appears, and the liquid becomes hot. The hydrogen sulphide has reduced the nitric acid to nitrogen peroxide and has itself been oxidised to sulphur.

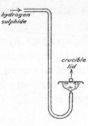

Fig. 112.

Combustion of hydrogen sulphide in a limited supply of air.

$$2HNO_3 + H_2S \rightarrow 2H_2O + 2NO_2 + S$$

Action of Hydrogen Sulphide with Ferric Chloride Solution. Perform the experiment as above, using ferric chloride solution.

A yellow deposit of sulphur appears and, on heating to coagulate the sulphur and filtering, a pale green solution of ferrous chloride is obtained. The hydrogen sulphide has reduced the yellow ferric chloride to green ferrous chloride, being itself oxidised to hydrogen chloride, which dissolves in the water, and sulphur.

$$2FeCl_3 + H_2S \rightarrow 2FeCl_2 + 2HCl + S$$

Action of Air on Hydrogen Sulphide. Pass a stream of hydrogen sulphide into distilled water in a beaker for about half an hour Leave the solution exposed to air. After a few days a white deposit of amorphous sulphur will have appeared. The oxygen of the air has oxidised the hydrogen sulphide to sulphur and water.

$$2H_2S + O_2 \rightarrow 2H_2O + 2S$$

Hydrogen sulphide will reduce concentrated sulphuric acid, depositing sulphur. For this reason, the acid cannot be used to dry it.

$$3H_2S + H_2SO_4 \rightarrow 4H_2O + 4S$$

Acidified potassium permanganate and dichromate solutions are reduced by the gas. The effect differs from that produced by sulphur dioxide because, while either gas decolorises the permanganate and turns the dichromate from yellow to green, hydrogen sulphide leaves also a precipitate of sulphur, while sulphur dioxide does not.

$$2KMnO_4 + 5H_2S + 3H_2SO_4 \rightarrow K_2SO_4 + 2MnSO_4 + 8H_2O + 5S \downarrow$$
$$K_2Cr_2O_7 + 3H_2S + 4H_2SO_4 \rightarrow K_2SO_4 + Cr_2(SO_4)_3 + 7H_2O + 3S \downarrow$$

For the action of hydrogen sulphide with sulphur dioxide, see p. 315, and for its action with the halogen elements, pp. 276, 295.

L

The Action of Hydrogen Sulphide on Salts of Metals

Copper Sulphate. Heat a solution of copper sulphate in a boiling-tube and pass hydrogen sulphide into it. A dark brown precipitate appears, cupric sulphide. Filter the mixture. If sufficient hydrogen sulphide has been passed, the filtrate will be colourless because all the copper, which formerly coloured it, is now precipitated as cupric sulphide. The filtrate is dilute sulphuric acid

$$CuSO_4 + H_2S \rightarrow CuS + H_2SO_4$$
$$\text{cupric}$$
$$\text{sulphide}$$

Lead Nitrate. Experiment as above.

Here, a black precipitate of lead sulphide is produced and the filtrate is dilute nitric acid.

$$Pb(NO_3)_2 + H_2S \rightarrow PbS + 2HNO_3$$
$$\text{lead}$$
$$\text{sulphide}$$

Zinc Sulphate. Experiment as above.

A white precipitate of zinc sulphide is left and the filtrate contains dilute sulphuric acid.

$$ZnSO_4 + H_2S \rightarrow ZnS + H_2SO_4$$

These reactions are all examples of double decomposition (see p. 129).

Hydrogen Sulphide as an Acid. Hydrogen sulphide acts as a weak dibasic acid. It forms with caustic soda, two salts, normal sodium sulphide, Na_2S,

$$2NaOH + H_2S \rightarrow Na_2S + 2H_2O$$

or, with excess of hydrogen sulphide, the acid salt, sodium hydrogen sulphide, NaHS.

$$NaOH + H_2S \rightarrow NaHS + H_2O$$

Caustic potash reacts similarly.

With aqueous ammonia, the gas gives yellow ammonium sulphide, mainly NH_4HS. This compound is used in qualitative analysis.

$$NH_4OH + H_2S \rightarrow NH_4HS + H_2O$$

Laboratory Preparation of Sodium Sulphide. The possible reactions of hydrogen sulphide with sodium hydroxide solution are:

$$2NaOH + H_2S \rightarrow Na_2S + 2H_2O$$
$$2NaOH + 2H_2S \rightarrow 2NaHS + 2H_2O$$

It is clear, from the equations, that the volume of hydrogen sulphide needed to convert a given weight of caustic soda into sodium hydrogen sulphide, NaHS, is twice that required to convert it to sodium sulphide, Na_2S. It is impossible in practice to determine when just enough hydrogen sulphide has been used to convert the caustic soda into sodium sulphide, so the best way of carrying out the preparation is to convert half of the caustic soda into sodium hydrogen sulphide by saturation with hydrogen sulphide, and then to form the normal salt from the acid salt by addition of the other half of the caustic soda.

$$NaOH + H_2S \rightarrow NaHS + H_2O$$
$$NaHS + NaOH \rightarrow Na_2S + H_2O$$

Experiment. Measure out 500 c.c. of bench (about 2N) caustic soda solution, divide it into two equal parts and, into one of them, pass hydrogen sulphide until no more is absorbed and the liquid smells strongly of hydrogen sulphide. Add the other half of the caustic soda solution and obtain crystals of sodium sulphide by the method described on p. 189.

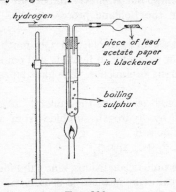

FIG. 113.

Proof of composition of hydrogen sulphide.

Proof that Hydrogen Sulphide contains only Hydrogen and Sulphur. Heat sulphur in a boiling-tube till it is boiling, then pass through it a stream of dry hydrogen by apparatus shown in Fig. 113. The wet lead acetate paper will be turned black. This proves that hydrogen sulphide is present in the gases. Since it can only have been produced by direct combination of hydrogen and sulphur, it must contain these two elements alone.

$$H_2 + S \rightarrow H_2S$$

This is not a practicable preparation of hydrogen sulphide. Only a very small proportion of the hydrogen is converted to hydrogen sulphide.

Formula of Hydrogen Sulphide. This is considered on p. 95.

SULPHIDES

K ⎱ Sulphides of these metals
Na ⎰ are soluble in water.

⎱ Sulphides of these metals
⎰ will not precipitate from acidified solutions.

Ca
Mg
Zn ⎱ Sulphides of these metals
Fe ⎰ are insoluble in water.
Pb
Cu

Sulphides of these metals will precipitate from acidified solutions.

Potassium sulphide, K_2S, is similar to sodium sulphide and is similarly prepared.

Sodium Sulphide, Na_2S. The preparation of this compound by neutralisation of caustic soda by hydrogen sulphide is described on p. 311. Its aqueous solution is alkaline and smells of hydrogen sulphide. When heated with sulphur it forms "polysulphides" of sodium. For example:

$$Na_2S + 4S \rightarrow Na_2S_5$$

In industry, sodium sulphide is prepared by heating sodium sulphate with coke (p. 326).

Uses. (1) For preparing a class of very "fast" dyes.

(2) For stripping the hair from hides.

Calcium Sulphide, CaS. This compound is chiefly important in the form of the "alkali waste" of the Leblanc process (p. 258). Sulphur is recovered from it.

If it contains traces of certain metals, for example, 0·01% bismuth, it is "phosphorescent", that is, after exposure to light, it will emit a violet glow whose intensity gradually diminishes. The glow fades out after some hours.

Zinc Sulphide, ZnS. This compound occurs as the mineral "zinc blende". It may be precipitated by hydrogen sulphide from a *neutral* (or alkaline) solution of a zinc salt.

$$ZnSO_4 + H_2S \rightarrow ZnS + H_2SO_4$$

Like calcium sulphide, and under similar conditions, zinc sulphide is phosphorescent. The luminous paint on watches is usually zinc sulphide, containing about 1 part of a radium salt in 100,000,000 of the sulphide.

Ferrous Sulphide, FeS. This black, insoluble compound is usually employed for the preparation of hydrogen sulphide (p. 306). It is prepared by heating iron with sulphur in the calculated quantities (p. 7).

Iron Disulphide, FeS_2, Iron Pyrites. This occurs as a hard, brassy mineral. There are great masses of it in Spain. It is the cheapest source of sulphur dioxide, which it gives off when burnt in air (p. 320).

Lead Sulphide, PbS. Lead sulphide occurs as the mineral galena, and is precipitated from solutions of lead salts by hydrogen sulphide (p. 310). The most satisfactory test for hydrogen sulphide (p. 306) is the production of a dark brown (almost black) stain of lead sulphide on a filter-paper soaked in lead acetate solution.

$$Pb(C_2H_3O_2)_2 + H_2S \rightarrow PbS \downarrow + 2C_2H_4O_2$$
$$\text{acetic acid}$$

Copper Sulphide, CuS. This is a black insoluble compound precipitated from a solution of a copper salt by hydrogen sulphide (p. 310).

$$CuSO_4 + H_2S \rightarrow CuS + H_2SO_4$$

QUESTIONS ON SULPHIDES WILL BE FOUND ON PAGE 329.

CHAPTER XXX

THE OXIDES AND ACIDS OF SULPHUR AND THE SULPHATES

SULPHUR DIOXIDE, SO$_2$

This compound, which is a gas under ordinary conditions, is conveniently prepared in the laboratory by the apparatus of Fig. 114

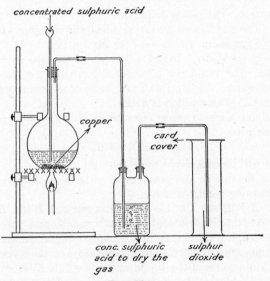

concentrated sulphuric acid

copper

card cover

conc. sulphuric acid to dry the gas

sulphur dioxide

Fig. 114.

Preparation of sulphur dioxide.

There is no action until the mixture in the flask becomes hot. Then rapid effervescence occurs and the sulphur dioxide, being very soluble in water and heavier than air, is usually collected as shown. It may also be collected over mercury.

$$Cu + 2H_2SO_4 \rightarrow CuSO_4 + 2H_2O + SO_2$$

A dark brown mixture is left in the flask. It contains anhydrous copper sulphate and certain impurities. Crystals of copper sulphate may be obtained from it by the method described on p. 189.

Tests. 1. The gas has a very irritating smell and a metallic taste.

2. *Action on Potassium Permanganate Solution.* The solution is turned from purple to colourless by sulphur dioxide. (No precipitate is left as in the case of reduction of the permanganate by hydrogen sulphide.)

$$5SO_2 + 2KMnO_4 + 2H_2O \rightarrow K_2SO_4 + 2MnSO_4 + 2H_2SO_4$$

The explanation of the change in colour is that the potassium permanganate is decomposed and all the products of the reaction give colourless solutions. (The manganese sulphate is too small in amount for its very pale pink colour to be observed.)

PROPERTIES OF SULPHUR DIOXIDE

Appearance. The gas is colourless.

Smell. The gas has an irritating smell and a rather sweet taste. It is fairly poisonous and is used for fumigation.

Solubility in Water. Invert a gas-jar of the gas in cold water and shake. The rapid rise of water shows that the gas is readily soluble in water. Add to the liquid some blue litmus solution. It is turned red. **The solution is acidic.**

The sulphur dioxide reacts chemically with the water to produce *sulphurous acid.*

$$H_2O + SO_2 \rightarrow H_2SO_3$$

This acid will be considered more fully later.

Sulphur dioxide in the presence of water is a vigorous reducer, as the following reactions show:

Action of Sulphur Dioxide with Concentrated Nitric Acid. Put some concentrated nitric acid in a boiling-tube and pass into it a current of sulphur dioxide from a syphon of liquid sulphur dioxide. Brown fumes are evolved (nitrogen peroxide) and the liquid becomes warm. Dilute some of the liquid and add dilute hydrochloric acid and barium chloride solution (the recognised test for a soluble sulphate). The white precipitate of barium sulphate proves the presence of sulphuric acid.

$$BaCl_2 + H_2SO_4 \rightarrow BaSO_4 + 2HCl$$

The concentrated nitric acid has oxidised the sulphur dioxide in the presence of water to sulphuric acid and has been itself reduced to nitrogen peroxide.

$$SO_2 + 2HNO_3 \rightarrow H_2SO_4 + 2NO_2$$

Action of Sulphur Dioxide on Ferric Sulphate Solution. Make a solution of ferric sulphate (or iron ammonium alum) in water in a boiling-tube and pass into it sulphur dioxide as above. The brownish colour of the solution is rapidly converted to pale green.[1] The sulphur dioxide has reduced the brown ferric sulphate to light green ferrous sulphate and has itself been oxidised to sulphuric acid.

$$Fe_2(SO_4)_3 + 2H_2O + SO_2 \rightarrow 2H_2SO_4 + 2FeSO_4$$

Action of Sulphur Dioxide on Potassium Dichromate. Acidify a solution of potassium dichromate in a boiling-tube with dilute sulphuric acid, and pass through it a stream of sulphur dioxide from a syphon of liquid sulphur dioxide. There is a rapid colour change from golden yellow to green, but no precipitate appears (compare the action of hydrogen sulphide, p. 309.)

$$K_2Cr_2O_7 + 3SO_2 + H_2SO_4 \rightarrow K_2SO_4 + Cr_2(SO_4)_3 + H_2O$$

The potassium dichromate has oxidised the sulphur dioxide in the presence of water to sulphuric acid, being itself reduced to green chromium sulphate.

Action of Sulphur Dioxide on Potassium Permanganate. (See test for sulphur dioxide opposite.)

The potassium permanganate oxidised the sulphur dioxide in the presence of water to sulphuric acid, and was itself reduced to manganese sulphate.

$$5SO_2 + 2KMnO_4 + 2H_2O \rightarrow K_2SO_4 + 2MnSO_4 + 2H_2SO_4$$

Bleaching Action of Sulphur Dioxide. Sulphurous acid is a bleaching agent. This may easily be shown by dropping into a gas-jar of the gas (containing some water) a few blue flowers, e.g., blue crocus, iris, or bluebells. After a few minutes, the flowers will have lost their blue colour.

This bleaching is also a reducing action. The sulphurous acid takes up oxygen from the colouring matter of the flowers and forms sulphuric acid; the removal of oxygen from the dye converts it to a colourless compound. Sulphur dioxide is used industrially for bleaching sponges and straw for straw hats. The oxygen of the air may oxidise the reduced colourless compound back to the original coloured compound, which explains why straw hats gradually become yellow with use.

Action of Sulphur Dioxide on Halogen Elements. See p. 278.

Action of Sulphur Dioxide with Hydrogen Sulphide. Add to a gas-jar of sulphur dioxide a little water, invert over it a gas-jar of hydrogen sulphide and allow the gases to mix. A yellow deposit of sulphur will be produced at once.

$$2H_2S + SO_2 \rightarrow 2H_2O + 3S$$

---

[1] The red solution which may be formed is a complex sulphite which decomposes on heating, leaving the products as indicated by the equation above.

Note that, here, the sulphur dioxide is actually acting as an oxidising agent, supplying oxygen to the hydrogen sulphide. As we have seen above, however, sulphur dioxide usually shows reducing properties. Here it has encountered in hydrogen sulphide a more powerful reducer than itself, which takes up its oxygen and causes it to act as an oxidiser.

Class Experiments confirming Properties of Sulphur Dioxide can be performed by test-tube.

Put one or two grams of sodium sulphite crystals into a test-tube, cover them with dilute hydrochloric acid and warm. Dip a *clean* glass tube into a very dilute solution of potassium permanganate and lower it into the gas. Be careful not to lower it into the liquid or into the spray immediately above the liquid. The pink colour is discharged. Remove the tube, *wash well* with water and repeat using the following:—

(a) potassium dichromate solution,
(b) blue litmus solution,
(c) chlorine water,
(d) hydrogen sulphide water,
(e) barium chloride solution,
(f) barium chloride solution acidified with dilute hydrochloric acid.

(See pages 315, 278, for explanations.)

Action of Lead Peroxide on Sulphur Dioxide. Warm some lead peroxide on a deflagrating spoon and lower it into a gas-jar of sulphur dioxide. The lead peroxide glows and white deposit of lead sulphate is left.

$$PbO_2 + SO_2 \rightarrow PbSO_4$$

Liquefaction of Sulphur Dioxide. Sulphur dioxide can readily be liquefied by being dried by concentrated sulphuric acid and passed through a freezing mixture of ice and salt. It liquefies under ordinary atmospheric pressure at about $-10°$ C. It can be kept liquid at ordinary room temperature if under slight pressure, and it is sold in syphons under pressure.

Formula of Sulphur Dioxide. See p. 96.

Sulphur Dioxide in Chemical Industry. Sulphur dioxide is very important as an intermediate compound in the manufacture of sulphuric acid (p. 320). It is prepared by burning sulphur in air.

$$S + O_2 \rightarrow SO_2$$

or by burning iron pyrites in air.

$$4FeS_2 + 11O_2 \rightarrow 2Fe_2O_3 + 8SO_2$$

SULPHUROUS ACID, H_2SO_3

This acid has never been obtained free from water. Any attempt to prepare the pure acid always results in its decomposition into sulphur dioxide and water.

It is prepared by passing sulphur dioxide into water. The gas is readily soluble and it is advisable to prevent "sucking back" by the use of a funnel just touching the water surface (Fig. 115).

The reaction in the flask is the same as described under the preparation of sulphur dioxide (p. 311). It is, of course, not necessary here to dry the sulphur dioxide.

$$Cu + 2H_2SO_4 \rightarrow CuSO_4 + 2H_2O + SO_2$$
$$SO_2 + H_2O \rightarrow H_2SO_3$$

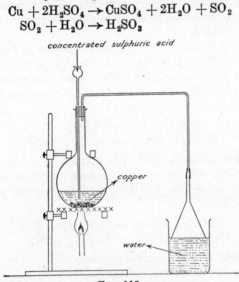

concentrated sulphuric acid

copper

water

FIG. 115.
Preparation of sulphurous acid.

Sulphur dioxide is the anhydride of sulphurous acid and may be called "sulphurous anhydride".

Anhydride. **An anhydride is the oxide of a non-metal, which, when combined with water, forms an acid.**

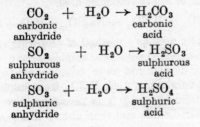

$$CO_2 \quad + \quad H_2O \rightarrow H_2CO_3$$
carbonic   carbonic
anhydride   acid

$$SO_2 \quad + \quad H_2O \rightarrow H_2SO_3$$
sulphurous   sulphurous
anhydride   acid

$$SO_3 \quad + \quad H_2O \rightarrow H_2SO_4$$
sulphuric   sulphuric
anhydride   acid

L*

An anhydride will not always combine directly with water to give the corresponding acid, e.g., silicon dioxide, SiO_2, is the anhydride of silicic acid, H_2SiO_3, though the acid cannot be prepared by direct combination of its anhydride with water. The acid is prepared from one of its salts and, when heated, loses water, leaving silicon dioxide as the residue.

PROPERTIES OF SULPHUROUS ACID

Sulphurous acid is a colourless liquid which smells strongly of sulphur dioxide.

Reducing Action. (i) The acid has all the reducing actions described previously as those of sulphur dioxide in the presence of water (pp. 314–6).

(ii) *Effect of Exposure to Air.* Leave a beaker of sulphurous acid exposed to air for a few days. Then add to it hydrochloric acid and barium chloride solution. The white precipitate of barium sulphate proves that the oxygen of the air has oxidised the sulphurous acid to sulphuric acid.

$$2H_2SO_3 + O_2 \rightarrow 2H_2SO_4$$
$$H_2SO_4 + BaCl_2 \rightarrow BaSO_4 \downarrow + 2HCl$$

Action of Sulphurous Acid with Alkalis. Sulphurous acid is a dibasic acid and with caustic soda forms two sodium salts, the acid salt, sodium bisulphite, $NaHSO_3$, and the normal salt, sodium sulphite, Na_2SO_3.

$$NaOH + H_2SO_3 \rightarrow NaHSO_3 + H_2O$$
$$2NaOH + H_2SO_3 \rightarrow Na_2SO_3 + 2H_2O$$

Caustic potash solution behaves similarly.

Laboratory Preparation of Sodium Sulphite. This is similar to the preparation of sodium sulphide, described on p. 311, using sulphur dioxide instead of hydrogen sulphide.

$$NaOH + H_2SO_3 \rightarrow NaHSO_3 + H_2O$$
$$NaHSO_3 + NaOH \rightarrow Na_2SO_3 + H_2O$$

Sulphites give off sulphur dioxide when acted upon by dilute hydrochloric acid or dilute sulphuric acid.

e.g., $$Na_2SO_3 + H_2SO_4 \rightarrow Na_2SO_4 + H_2O + SO_2$$

This is occasionally used as a method of preparing sulphur dioxide.

Used in dilute acidified solutions, sulphites have all the reducing actions of sulphur dioxide and water, or sulphurous acid (see p. 314).

Preparation of Sulphurous Acid, H_2SO_3, from Sulphur. To convert sulphur into sulphurous acid it is necessary first to oxidise the sulphur to sulphur dioxide and then absorb this gas in water.

This can be done by the apparatus of Fig. 116.

Heat the sulphur and, by means of a filter-pump, draw over it a rapid stream of air. The sulphur burns and the sulphur dioxide

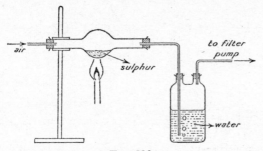

FIG. 116.

Preparation of sulphurous acid from sulphur.

produced is absorbed as it passes through the water in the Woolff's bottle. The liquid left is sulphurous acid. Sulphur vapour may be carried over unburnt and appear as a yellow precipitate in the bottle. Remove it by filtration.

$$S + O_2 \rightarrow SO_2$$
$$H_2O + SO_2 \rightarrow H_2SO_3$$

The method of producing sulphurous acid given on p. 317 is much more convenient in the laboratory, but all the sulphurous acid prepared on the large scale is made by modification of the above method or by burning iron pyrites, FeS$_2$.

$$4FeS_2 + 11O_2 \rightarrow 2Fe_2O_3 + 8SO_2$$

SULPHUR TRIOXIDE, SO$_3$

This compound is a white hygroscopic solid. A sample of it is usually kept in a sealed glass bulb as a laboratory exhibit.

Preparation of Sulphur Trioxide. It is prepared by passing a mixture of dry sulphur dioxide and dry air, or oxygen, over heated platinised asbestos (or vanadium pentoxide). Platinised asbestos is made by soaking asbestos in platinic chloride solution and then igniting it, when platinum is left in a very finely divided form.

$$PtCl_4 \rightarrow 2Cl_2 + Pt$$

The platinum is a catalyst and the best temperature is 450°–500° C. The sulphur trioxide is seen as dense white fumes and may be solidified in a freezing mixture (Fig. 117).

$$2SO_2 + O_2 \rightarrow 2SO_3$$

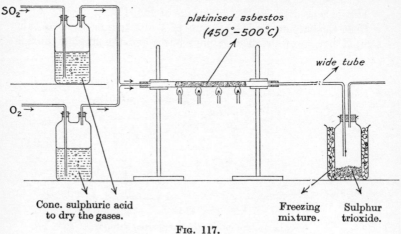

Conc. sulphuric acid
to dry the gases.

Freezing
mixture.

Sulphur
trioxide.

Fig. 117.
Preparation of sulphur trioxide.

Sulphur trioxide is important because it combines vigorously with water, giving sulphuric acid.

$$H_2O + SO_3 \rightarrow H_2SO_4$$

It is the anhydride of this acid and sulphur trioxide may be termed "sulphuric anhydride".

SULPHURIC ACID, H_2SO_4

There is no convenient laboratory method of preparing this compound. It is of very great importance industrially, the output of it being some 9,000,000 tons annually. Two processes are in use for the manufacture of sulphuric acid.

Lead Chamber Process for the Manufacture of Sulphuric Acid. Sulphur dioxide is prepared by burning sulphur or iron pyrites, FeS_2, in air.

$$S + O_2 \rightarrow SO_2$$
$$4FeS_2 + 11O_2 \rightarrow 2Fe_2O_3 + 8SO_2$$

It is converted by the oxygen of the air in the presence of water, into sulphuric acid. Nitric oxide is used as a catalyst or oxygen-carrier.

$$2NO + O_2 \rightarrow 2NO_2$$
$$\text{from}$$
$$\text{air}$$
$$NO_2 + H_2O + SO_2 \rightarrow NO + H_2SO_4$$

The nitric oxide is usually supplied in a modern plant by oxidising ammonia by oxygen of the air. The two gases are passed over heated platinum.

$$2NH_3 + 5O \rightarrow 2NO + 3H_2O$$

This main oxidation of the sulphur dioxide is carried out in large lead chambers, on the floors of which "chamber-acid" (65% sulphuric acid) accumulates. It is not very pure but finds a ready sale where an acid of high purity is not needed. The plant used is made more elaborate by devices for recovery of the nitric oxide, which would otherwise escape, and for its restoration into the reacting gases.

Contact Process for the Manufacture of Sulphuric Acid. Sulphur dioxide (prepared by burning sulphur) and air are passed over platinised asbestos, as catalyst, heated to 450–500° C. About 98% of the possible yield of sulphur trioxide is obtained.

$$2SO_2 + O_2 \rightarrow 2SO_3$$

The platinum is easily "poisoned" by impurities and its catalytic activity lost. For this reason the air and sulphur dioxide are very carefully purified, especially from arsenic compounds, before entering the catalyst chamber.

The sulphur trioxide cannot be satisfactorily absorbed by water. A mist of fine drops of dilute sulphuric acid fills the factory if direct absorption in water is tried. It is dissolved in concentrated sulphuric acid, forming a fuming liquid called "oleum" for which there is some demand. Most of the "oleum" is carefully diluted with the correct amount of water to give ordinary concentrated sulphuric acid.

$$SO_3 + H_2O \rightarrow H_2SO_4$$

PROPERTIES OF SULPHURIC ACID

Sulphuric acid is a dense oily liquid, "Oil of Vitriol". It has several very important properties.

Dilute Sulphuric Acid—as an Acid

It is a dibasic acid and neutralises sodium hydroxide to form two sodium salts, sodium sulphate, Na_2SO_4, and sodium hydrogen sulphate or sodium bisulphate, $NaHSO_4$.

$$2NaOH + H_2SO_4 \rightarrow Na_2SO_4 + 2H_2O$$
$$NaOH + H_2SO_4 \rightarrow NaHSO_4 + H_2O$$

Preparation of Sodium Sulphate and Sodium Bisulphate. It is evident from the previous equations that the amount of sodium hydroxide needed to convert a given amount of sulphuric acid into sodium bisulphate is half that required to convert it to sodium sulphate.

Measure out, say, 100 c.c. of bench (2N) sodium hydroxide solution into a flask, add litmus and then run in carefully from a burette bench

(2N) dilute sulphuric acid, until the solution is neutral (purple). Note the volume of dilute sulphuric acid needed (say x c.c.). This solution now contains sodium sulphate.

$$2NaOH + H_2SO_4 \rightarrow Na_2SO_4 + 2H_2O$$

Then measure out a further 100 c.c. of the same sodium hydroxide solution and add to it, from the burette, $2x$ c.c. of the same acid. This solution now contains sodium hydrogen sulphate.

$$2NaOH + 2H_2SO_4 \rightarrow 2NaHSO_4 + 2H_2O$$

Obtain crystals in the usual way from both solutions (see p. 189).

Similarly, two potassium salts, potassium sulphate, K_2SO_4, and potassium hydrogen sulphate, $KHSO_4$, can be made.

Dilute sulphuric acid also neutralises basic oxides or hydroxides to form salts and water.

e.g.,

$$CuO + H_2SO_4 \quad \rightarrow CuSO_4 + H_2O$$
copper
oxide
$$ZnO + H_2SO_4 \quad \rightarrow ZnSO_4 + H_2O$$
zinc oxide
$$Cu(OH)_2 + H_2SO_4 \rightarrow CuSO_4 + 2H_2O$$
copper
hydroxide
$$Zn(OH)_2 + H_2SO_4 \rightarrow ZnSO_4 + 2H_2O$$
zinc
hydroxide

Action of Dilute Sulphuric Acid with Metals. Some of the common metals displace hydrogen from dilute sulphuric acid, e.g.,

$$Zn + H_2SO_4 \rightarrow ZnSO_4 \quad + H_2$$
$$Fe + H_2SO_4 \rightarrow FeSO_4 \quad + H_2$$
$$Mg + H_2SO_4 \rightarrow MgSO_4 \quad + H_2$$

Copper is, however, without action on this acid. Note that cold, concentrated sulphuric acid, in the complete absence of water, is not attacked by any metal.

Action of Sulphuric Acid with Carbonates. If the sulphate of a metal is soluble, dilute sulphuric acid readily attacks its carbonate with evolution of carbon dioxide, e.g.,

$$Na_2CO_3 + H_2SO_4 \rightarrow Na_2SO_4 + H_2O + CO_2$$
sodium
carbonate
$$MgCO_3 + H_2SO_4 \rightarrow MgSO_4 + H_2O + CO_2$$
magnesium
carbonate

If dilute sulphuric acid is added to marble, $CaCO_3$, however, the effervescence is checked after a few seconds. This is because the calcium sulphate which is formed is only sparingly soluble in water and soon forms a deposit on the surface of the marble separating it from the acid and checking the action.

Concentrated Sulphuric Acid as an Oxidising Agent. The acid exercises this property only when hot and concentrated. It oxidises various substances, as given below, and is itself reduced to sulphur dioxide, *e.g.*,

$$Cu + 2H_2SO_4 \rightarrow CuSO_4 + 2H_2O + SO_2$$
copper
$$Zn + 2H_2SO_4 \rightarrow ZnSO_4 + 2H_2O + SO_2$$
zinc
$$S + 2H_2SO_4 \rightarrow 2H_2O + 3SO_2$$
sulphur
$$C + 2H_2SO_4 \rightarrow CO_2 + 2H_2O + 2SO_2$$
carbon

In all these cases effervescence will occur. The sulphur dioxide given off may be tested by decolorisation of a filter-paper soaked in potassium permanganate solution.

Concentrated Sulphuric Acid possesses an Affinity for Water. The acid has a very great affinity for water. It mixes with water with a very great evolution of heat. The two, when mixed in equal volumes at room temperature, may give a liquid whose temperature is as high as 120° C. This indicates chemical reaction but its nature is not clearly understood. **It is very important when mixing the acid with water to add the acid to the water and NEVER the water to the acid.** It is necessary to stir the liquid as the acid enters to prevent formation of a *lower* layer of acid.

Concentrated sulphuric acid is *hygroscopic, i.e.*, it absorbs water vapour out of the air, increasing in bulk and becoming dilute. This can be shown by the following experiment for which Fig. 118 is

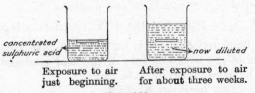

concentrated sulphuric acid

now diluted

Exposure to air just beginning.

After exposure to air for about three weeks.

FIG. 118.

Exposure of concentrated sulphuric acid to the air.

sufficient explanation. The concentrated acid is used for drying gases, *e.g.*, sulphur dioxide, chlorine, hydrogen chloride. It cannot be used to dry a *reducing* gas like hydrogen sulphide, or an *alkaline* gas like ammonia.

So great is the affinity of concentrated sulphuric acid for water that it can decompose many compounds by removing from them the hydrogen and oxygen necessary to form water, with which it then combines. This is called a *dehydrating* action.

Examples of Concentrated Sulphuric Acid Acting as a Dehydrating Agent.

1. *With Sugar.*

Place about a tablespoonful of sugar in a 450 c.c. beaker and cover it with water. Place the beaker in a trough, for safety, and pour in a steady stream of concentrated sulphuric acid. The sugar is charred and a spongy black mass of charcoal rises, filling the beaker. Steam is given off and the whole mass becomes very hot.

The acid has taken out the *elements of water* from the sugar, leaving a black mass of carbon.

$$C_{12}H_{22}O_{11} (+ nH_2SO_4) \rightarrow 12C + (11H_2O + nH_2SO_4)$$

A similar action is the explanation of the very marked corrosive action of the acid on cloth, e.g., cotton. This is cellulose, whose simplest formula is $C_6H_{10}O_5$. As above

$$C_6H_{10}O_5 + nH_2SO_4 \rightarrow 6C + (5H_2O + nH_2SO_4)$$

and a hole appears in the cloth. Similar reactions account for its rapid and serious burning of the skin.

2. *With Oxalic Acid,* $H_2C_2O_4$.

Place a little oxalic acid in a test-tube, add a little concentrated sulphuric acid and warm gently. Effervescence occurs. Apply a lighted splint to the test-tube. The gas burns with a blue flame, showing that carbon monoxide is given off. Extinguish the flame and pass the gas into lime-water held in a boiling-tube. The turbidity shows that carbon dioxide is also present. The reaction is of the same type as those above, and it is used for the large-scale preparation of carbon monoxide (see p. 246).

$$H_2C_2O_4 (+ H_2SO_4) \rightarrow CO + CO_2 + (H_2O + H_2SO_4)$$

Uses of Sulphuric Acid. It is impossible to give a complete list of the uses of the 9,000,000 tons of the acid produced annually. A few of the more important ones are:

(1) For making fertilisers, about 45%.

(2) In refining petroleum, about 20%.

(3) In the manufacture of various chemical compounds, about 12%.

(4) In accumulators, about 6%.

Test for Sulphuric Acid and Soluble Sulphates. To a little dilute sulphuric acid in a boiling-tube add dilute hydrochloric acid and barium chloride solution. A white precipitate of barium sulphate is formed. This is the characteristic test for any soluble sulphate.

$$BaCl_2 + H_2SO_4 \rightarrow 2HCl + BaSO_4 \downarrow .$$

SULPHATES

Sulphates are the salts derived from sulphuric acid by replacing the hydrogen of the acid by a metal.

Methods of Preparation of Sulphates. These are fully dealt with in the chapter, "Acids, Bases and Salts", pp. 180–195. Briefly summarised, they are:

(1) *By the Action of Sulphuric Acid on a Metal.*

   Dilute Acid.

$$Fe + H_2SO_4 \rightarrow FeSO_4 + H_2$$
$$\text{ferrous sulphate}$$

$$Mg + H_2SO_4 \rightarrow MgSO_4 + H_2$$
$$\text{magnesium sulphate}$$

$$Zn + H_2SO_4 \rightarrow ZnSO_4 + H_2$$
$$\text{zinc sulphate}$$

   Hot Concentrated Acid.

$$Cu + 2H_2SO_4 \rightarrow CuSO_4 + 2H_2O + SO_2$$
$$\text{copper sulphate}$$

(2) *By the Action of Dilute Sulphuric Acid on the Oxide, Hydroxide or Carbonate of the Metal.*

For example:
$$CuO + H_2SO_4 \rightarrow CuSO_4 + H_2O$$
$$Zn(OH)_2 + H_2SO_4 \rightarrow ZnSO_4 + 2H_2O$$
$$Na_2CO_3 + H_2SO_4 \rightarrow Na_2SO_4 + H_2O + CO_2$$
$$\text{sodium sulphate}$$

(3) *By Double Decomposition.*

This is limited in application to the preparation of insoluble sulphates. Only two common sulphates are insoluble, barium sulphate and lead sulphate.

$$Pb(NO_3)_2 + H_2SO_4 \rightarrow PbSO_4 \downarrow + 2HNO_3$$
$$\text{lead sulphate}$$

$$BaCl_2 + H_2SO_4 \rightarrow BaSO_4 \downarrow + 2HCl$$
$$\text{barium sulphate}$$

Ammonium Sulphate, $(NH_4)_2SO_4$, "sulphate of ammonia". This compound is very widely used as a nitrogenous fertiliser. It may be made in the laboratory by neutralisation of dilute sulphuric acid with ammonia (p. 192). In industry, it is produced by the action of ammonia and carbon dioxide on the mineral "anhydrite", calcium sulphate, in the presence of water.

$$CaSO_4 + 2NH_3 + CO_2 + H_2O \rightarrow CaCO_3 \downarrow + (NH_4)_2SO_4$$

The chalk is filtered off and the ammonium sulphate crystallised.

Potassium Sulphate, K_2SO_4. This compound may be prepared in the laboratory by neutralisation of caustic potash solution by dilute sulphuric acid (p. 192). In industry, it is usually prepared by heating potassium chloride with concentrated sulphuric acid.

$$2KCl + H_2SO_4 \rightarrow K_2SO_4 + 2HCl \uparrow$$

Unlike most soluble sulphates, it crystallises without water of crystallisation.

Sodium Sulphate, Na_2SO_4. This salt is usually met with in the form of transparent crystals of the decahydrate, $Na_2SO_4.10H_2O$, Glauber's salt. In the laboratory, it may be made by neutralising caustic soda solution by dilute sulphuric acid (p. 192). In industry, it is prepared by heating common salt with concentrated sulphuric acid (the first stage of the Leblanc process, p. 258).

It is used in medicine, in the Leblanc process for making washing soda, in the manufacture of glass, and, by heating with coke, for the manufacture of sodium sulphide.

$$Na_2SO_4 + 4C \rightarrow Na_2S + 4CO$$

Calcium Sulphate, $CaSO_4$. This salt occurs naturally as anhydrite, $CaSO_4$, and gypsum, $CaSO_4.2H_2O$. Gypsum is soluble in water to the extent of about 2·5 gm. in 1 litre of water at ordinary temperatures and is responsible for most of the "permanent" hardness in water (p. 164).

Gypsum is chiefly employed for the manufacture of plaster of Paris.

Plaster of Paris, $(CaSO_4)_2.H_2O$, calcium sulphate hemihydrate. This compound is made by heating gypsum in large steel vessels of several tons capacity. The gypsum is stirred mechanically and the temperature is maintained between 100° C. and 200° C.

$$2(CaSO_4.2H_2O) \rightarrow (CaSO_4)_2.H_2O + 3H_2O$$
plaster of Paris

When mixed with water, plaster of Paris sets to a hard interlacing mass of fine needles of gypsum, expanding at the same time. It is used for making casts for statuary (the expansion during setting ensures a fine impression), in surgery to maintain joints in a fixed position and in cements and wall-plasters.

Magnesium Sulphate, $MgSO_4$. Magnesium sulphate heptahydrate, $MgSO_4.7H_2O$, is the familiar substance, "Epsom salt". It occurs in springs at Epsom and Bath and is usually prepared from the mineral, kieserite, $MgSO_4.H_2O$, found at Stassfurt. It acts as a mild purgative.

In the laboratory it may be prepared by the method described on p. 189.

Zinc Sulphate, $ZnSO_4$. This salt is usually encountered as the heptahydrate, $ZnSO_4.7H_2O$, "white vitriol". It can be prepared in the laboratory from zinc, zinc oxide or zinc carbonate, and its preparation is fully described on p. 188.

Its transparent crystals are very soluble in water (138 gm. in 100 gm. water at $10°$ C.) and the salt is used as an emetic and for the treatment of certain skin diseases.

Ferrous Sulphate, $FeSO_4$. Ferrous sulphate heptahydrate, $FeSO_4.7H_2O$, is known as "green vitriol". It is usually prepared in the laboratory by the action of iron (wire, filings or borings) on dilute sulphuric acid (p. 189).

In industry, it is obtained by the action of air and water on the mineral, iron pyrites, FeS_2.

$$2FeS_2 + 7O_2 + 2H_2O \rightarrow 2FeSO_4 + 2H_2SO_4$$

The sulphuric acid is neutralised by scrap iron and the ferrous sulphate is crystallised.

$$Fe + H_2SO_4 \rightarrow FeSO_4 + H_2$$

Action of Heat. On heating, ferrous sulphate first loses its water of crystallisation, the original green crystals being converted into a dirty-yellow anhydrous solid.

$$FeSO_4.7H_2O \rightarrow FeSO_4 + 7H_2O$$

When more strongly heated, it gives off sulphur dioxide (test—decolorisation of potassium permanganate solution) in addition to white fumes of sulphur trioxide, and leaves a reddish-brown solid, ferric oxide, Fe_2O_3, "jewellers' rouge". This is used in pigments (venetian red, red ochre) and as a polishing powder.

$$2FeSO_4 \rightarrow Fe_2O_3 + SO_3 + SO_2$$

Sulphuric acid was prepared by Glauber (1648) by distilling ferrous sulphate crystals. The sulphur trioxide given off in the second stage reacted with the water driven off in the first.

$$H_2O + SO_3 \rightarrow H_2SO_4$$

Ferrous sulphate is used in the brown ring test for nitrates (p. 343) and it gives a similar colour with nitric oxide (p. 354).

Like all ferrous salts, ferrous sulphate is a reducing agent; for example, it reduces nitric acid, in the presence of sulphuric acid, to nitric oxide. This is one of the best methods of preparation of pure nitric oxide.

$$6FeSO_4 + 3H_2SO_4 + 2HNO_3 \rightarrow 3Fe_2(SO_4)_3 + 4H_2O + 2NO$$
$$\text{ferric sulphate}$$

When exposed to air, ferrous sulphate crystals become covered with a brownish deposit of a basic ferric sulphate, by a reaction of the type:

$$12FeSO_4 + 6H_2O + 3O_2 \rightarrow 4 \left\{ Fe_2(SO_4)_3.Fe(OH)_3 \right\}$$
$$\text{(from the air)} \qquad \text{basic ferric sulphate}$$

Large quantities of ferrous sulphate are used with gallic acid in the manufacture of ink. This recipe has been known for more than 2,000 years.

Ferric Sulphate, $Fe_2(SO_4)_3$. This salt may be prepared by oxidising ferrous sulphate by nitric acid in the presence of sulphuric acid (equation above).

It forms alums, for example $K_2SO_4.Fe_2(SO_4)_3.24H_2O$, which are more important than ferric sulphate itself, because they can be more readily purified by crystallisation.

Copper Sulphate (cupric sulphate), $CuSO_4$. "Blue vitriol", $CuSO_4.5H_2O$, is copper sulphate pentahydrate. The preparation of the salt from copper is fully described on p. 189; it may also be prepared from the oxide or carbonate of the metal and dilute sulphuric acid, p. 193.

On the large scale, it is made by first heating scrap copper with sulphur,

$$Cu + S \rightarrow CuS$$

and then oxidising the cupric sulphide by heating it with access of air,

$$CuS + 2O_2 \rightarrow CuSO_4$$

The sulphate is then crystallised.

When heated, the pentahydrate loses water of crystallisation and leaves white anhydrous copper sulphate (p. 170).

$$CuSO_4.5H_2O \rightarrow CuSO_4 + 5H_2O$$

The formation of the blue pentahydrate from the anhydrous salt is used as a test for water.

Use. Copper sulphate is used in making washes such as "Bordeaux mixture" (11 parts of lime and 16 parts of copper sulphate in 1,000 parts of water), used in spraying vines and potatoes to kill moulds which would injure the plants. It is also used in the manufacture of certain green pigments.

SULPHITES

The general properties of sulphites are discussed on p. 318.

Calcium Bisulphite, $Ca(HSO_3)_2$, is prepared by passing sulphur dioxide into milk of lime (a paste of slaked lime and water) and is used for bleaching the pulp in paper-making.

$$Ca(OH)_2 + 2SO_2 \rightarrow Ca(HSO_3)_2$$

QUESTIONS

1. Give an account of the preparation and properties of hydrogen sulphide.

   If a specimen of hydrogen sulphide were contaminated with hydrogen, how could you obtain the hydrogen sulphide free from hydrogen? (C.)

2. Starting from sulphur, describe how you could prepare specimens of (a) plastic sulphur, (b) sulphur dioxide, (c) sulphur trioxide, and (d) hydrogen sulphide. (N.U.J.B.)

3. Starting with roll sulphur, how would you prepare:—
   (a) Rhombic crystals of sulphur?
   (b) Monoclinic (prismatic) crystals of sulphur
   (c) Plastic sulphur?

   Mention two other elements which, like sulphur, exist in more than one variety. (C.)

4. Describe *one* laboratory method of preparing and collecting hydrogen sulphide, and mention a suitable drying agent. What is the effect of passing hydrogen sulphide into solutions of (a) copper sulphate, (b) ferric chloride, (c) chlorine, (d) ammonia, (e) litmus?

   Briefly describe what happens when hydrogen sulphide burns in (a) excess of air, (b) a deficit of air. (B.)

5. Give an account of the important properties of hydrogen sulphide. A specimen of this gas prepared from ferrous sulphide is found on analysis to contain 10 per cent by volume of free hydrogen. Assuming that the ferrous sulphide contained no other impurity than metallic iron, calculate the percentage of free iron present. (L.)

6. From what sources is sulphur obtained? How can sulphur be used for the preparation of (a) sulphuric acid, (b) sulphurous acid? (O. and C.)

7. How would you prepare in the laboratory sulphuretted hydrogen gas? Sketch the apparatus. What is the effect of the gas on (a) a solution of lead nitrate, (b) sulphur dioxide, (c) bromine water? (N.U.J.B.)

8. Give a short account of the chemical reactions which take place in the manufacture of sulphuric acid.

   Describe experiments illustrating the action of this acid on metals. (O. and C.)

9. Describe the properties of sulphuric acid.

   Why is this compound regarded as (a) an acid, (b) a dibasic acid? (O. and C.)

10. How would you prepare a quantity of dry sulphur dioxide? How may it be shown that the formula for this gas is SO_2? (N.U.J.B.)

11. Describe briefly two distinct methods which could be used for the preparation of sulphur dioxide.

    How is sulphur dioxide converted into sulphuric acid in the "contact" process?

    What simple experiment shows that sulphur dioxide contains its own volume of oxygen?

12. Describe the preparation and collection of dry sulphur dioxide in the laboratory. Mention, without giving details of the manufacturing plant. how it is prepared on the industrial scale. What is

the action of sulphur dioxide on (a) water, (b) oxygen, (c) chlorine, (d) hydrogen sulphide, (e) nitrogen peroxide? (B.)

13. Describe the preparation and collection of sulphur dioxide. Describe an experiment to show that sulphur dioxide contains its own volume of oxygen. What additional information would you require in order to determine the molecular formula of sulphur dioxide? Show clearly how you would use the results of the experiment, and the additional information in determining this formula.

(Atomic weights: H = 1, C = 12, N = 14, O = 16, Na = 23, Cl = 35·5, Ca = 40.)

(N.U.J.B.)

14. Describe the reaction which takes place when copper is heated with concentrated sulphuric acid. The resulting gas is passed into (a) litmus solution, (b) chlorine water, (c) a solution of hydrogen sulphide. What would be observed in each case? and what explanations would you give of the results obtained? (L.)

15. Describe fully how to prepare and collect in the laboratory sulphur dioxide from sulphuric acid. How would you show the action of this gas on (a) chlorine water, (b) moist hydrogen sulphide?

What takes place when a solution of the gas is allowed to stand in contact with air?

Explain the above reactions by equations or otherwise. (N.U.J.B.)

16. What is meant by the term allotropy? Describe the preparation of two allotropic forms of sulphur.

Starting from sulphur, how would you obtain fairly pure samples of (a) sulphur dioxide; (b) sulphur trioxide? (C.W.B.)

17. Describe, with a diagram, how you would prepare and collect hydrogen sulphide in the laboratory.

Describe how hydrogen sulphide reacts with (a) sulphur dioxide, (b) ferric chloride solution.

When electric sparks from an induction coil are passed for some time through a volume of hydrogen sulphide the gas is decomposed, sulphur is deposited on the sides of the vessel and on cooling to the original conditions hydrogen remains, the volume of which is equal to that of the hydrogen sulphide. The vapour density of the hydrogen sulphide being 17 calculate *from these facts* the formula of hydrogen sulphide. (H, 1 ; S, 32.) (N.U.J.B.)

18. Explain the construction and the working of a Kipp's apparatus for generating hydrogen sulphide. Describe and explain the effect of passing the gas through aqueous solutions of (a) copper sulphate, (b) blue litmus, (c) chlorine. What happens if the resulting solution from (b) is boiled? (L.)

CHAPTER XXXI

NITROGEN AND AMMONIA

NITROGEN

Occurrence. About four-fifths of the atmosphere is free nitrogen. The element also occurs combined in the form of sodium nitrate, Chile saltpetre, $NaNO_3$, as a mineral deposit in Chile, and distributed everywhere in the soil in minute quantities as ammonium sulphate, $(NH_4)_2SO_4$, and sodium nitrate, $NaNO_3$, potassium nitrate, KNO_3, and calcium nitrate, $Ca(NO_3)_2$. (The very great importance of these compounds of nitrogen in maintaining the fertility of the soil is discussed on p. 356.)

Combined nitrogen is always found as a constituent of the living matter of plants and animals.

Preparation of Nitrogen from the Atmosphere. The gases present in dry air are oxygen, about 21% by volume, carbon dioxide, about 0·03% by volume, and "atmospheric nitrogen", about 79% by

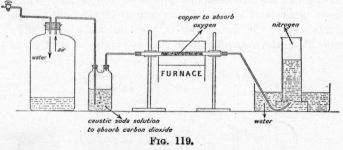

FIG. 119.

Preparation of nitrogen from the air.

volume. The first two of these gases can be removed and the nitrogen collected by the apparatus of Fig. 119.

The equations are:

Absorption of carbon dioxide $\quad 2NaOH + CO_2 \rightarrow Na_2CO_3 + H_2O$
Absorption of oxygen $\quad\quad\quad 2Cu + O_2 \rightarrow 2CuO$

If the nitrogen is required dry, it may, after leaving the heated copper, be passed through a U-tube containing glass beads wetted

331

with concentrated sulphuric acid to dry it and then collected over mercury.

The product of this experiment is not pure nitrogen. It contains about 1% by volume of the "rare gases", chiefly argon, the removal of which is not possible by chemical methods. The presence of these gases makes "atmospheric nitrogen" denser than the pure gas.

Another method of preparing "atmospheric nitrogen" is to absorb both carbon dioxide and oxygen together by shaking air with a solution of pyrogallol in caustic soda solution. The caustic soda absorbs the carbon dioxide and the pyrogallol absorbs the oxygen to form an oxidation product of itself.

This method is, however, only suitable for the preparation of small samples of "atmospheric nitrogen".

Preparation of Nitrogen by Heating Ammonium Nitrite. A solution of ammonium nitrite readily decomposes on slight warming to give nitrogen. This decomposition occurs slowly at ordinary temperatures, so that neither ammonium nitrite itself, nor its solution in water, should be kept in stock. The compound is prepared as required by a double decomposition reaction between sodium nitrite and ammonium chloride.

$$\underset{\text{69 gm.}}{NaNO_2} + \underset{\text{53·5 gm.}}{NH_4Cl} \rightarrow NaCl + \underset{\substack{\text{ammonium} \\ \text{nitrite}}}{NH_4NO_2}$$

Weigh out the two compounds in these proportions. 14 gm. of sodium nitrite and 11 gm. of ammonium chloride will be suitable weights. Place the compounds in a round flask, add 350 c.c. of water, fit up the apparatus as in Fig. 120 and heat gently. As the

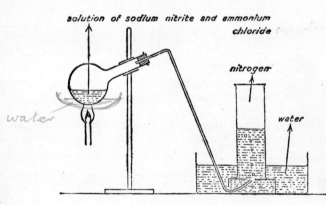

Fig. 120.

Preparation of nitrogen by a chemical method.

solution becomes warm, rapid effervescence occurs and the nitrogen evolved may be collected over water.

$$NH_4NO_2 \rightarrow N_2 + 2H_2O$$

Other Chemical Methods of Preparation of Nitrogen are
The action of chlorine on ammonia.

$$3Cl_2 + 8NH_3 \rightarrow N_2 + 6NH_4Cl$$

(See p. 91.)
Passing ammonia gas over heated copper oxide (see p. 337).

$$2NH_3 + 3CuO \rightarrow 3Cu + N_2 + 3H_2O$$

Reduction of oxides of nitrogen by heated copper, e.g.,

$$2Cu + 2NO \rightarrow 2CuO + N_2$$
$$\text{nitric} \atop \text{oxide}$$

These methods are all much less convenient than the heating of ammonium nitrite.

Tests for Nitrogen. At ordinary temperatures, nitrogen is so inert that no positive tests can be applied. We can only show a given gas to be nitrogen by elimination of other possibilities.

Lighted Splint. Place a lighted splint into a gas-jar of the gas. It is extinguished and the gas does not burn. It cannot, therefore, be any gas which supports combustion, e.g., oxygen, nitrous oxide, or any combustible gas, e.g., hydrogen sulphide, carbon monoxide, hydrogen.

Smell. The gas has no smell. This distinguishes it from gases such as sulphur dioxide, ammonia, hydrochloric acid gas.

Action of Lime-water. After the above tests the only gas with which nitrogen may be confused is carbon dioxide. To distinguish it from this, add lime-water and shake. Nitrogen leaves the lime-water unchanged; with carbon dioxide, the lime-water is turned milky.

Properties of Nitrogen. Nitrogen is colourless and odourless. It is slightly lighter than air and only slightly soluble in water (about 2 volumes of the gas dissolve in 100 volumes of water at ordinary temperature).

Under ordinary conditions the gas is very inert, but, by applying the results of much research, it has been made to combine with both oxygen and hydrogen to give nitric oxide and ammonia respectively.

$$N_2 + O_2 \rightleftharpoons 2NO$$
$$N_2 + 3H_2 \rightleftharpoons 2NH_3$$

The very important industrial application of these reactions is discussed on pp. 340, 358.

Nitrogen will combine directly with many metals forming nitrides, *e.g.*,

$$3Mg + N_2 \rightarrow Mg_3N_2$$
$$\text{magnesium}$$
$$\text{nitride}$$

To illustrate this, burn some magnesium ribbon in a crucible and allow the product to cool. Add a few drops of water and smell the mixture. The choking smell is that of ammonia. It is evolved by the action of water on the magnesium nitride which was formed, in small amount, by combination of the magnesium with nitrogen of the air.

$$Mg_3N_2 + 6H_2O \rightarrow 2NH_3 + 3Mg(OH)_2$$
$$\text{magnesium} \quad \text{water} \quad \text{ammonia} \quad \text{magnesium}$$
$$\text{nitride} \qquad\qquad\qquad\qquad \text{hydroxide}$$

AMMONIA

This hydride of nitrogen, NH_3, can be made in very small amounts by heating nitrogenous organic materials such as hoofs and horns of animals. Its old name was, in fact, "spirit of hartshorn".

Preparation of Ammonia. Ammonia may be prepared in the laboratory by heating any ammonium salt with an alkali. Usually a mixture of ammonium chloride and slaked lime (the cheapest alkali) is used. Both are solids so they must be thoroughly ground first to give a very fine mixture in which the reaction can occur satisfactorily.

$$Ca(OH)_2 + 2NH_4Cl \rightarrow CaCl_2 + 2H_2O + 2NH_3$$
$$\text{74 gm.} \quad 2 \times 53{\cdot}5 \text{ gm.}$$
$$\text{107 gm.}$$

An excess of the slaked lime is preferable. Weigh out 25 gm. of slaked lime and 16 gm. of ammonium chloride. Grind the mixture well in a mortar, place it in a round flask of resistance glass and set up apparatus as in Fig. 121. The neck of the flask should slope towards A as shown, because water will condense and, if allowed to run back on to the hot flask, might break it. Heat the flask. Ammonia gas is evolved. **It is dried by a rather unusual drying agent, quicklime,** CaO, because it reacts with all the usual drying agents. Concentrated sulphuric acid is acidic and would absorb the gas, forming a salt, *e.g.*,

$$2NH_3 + H_2SO_4 \rightarrow (NH_4)_2SO_4$$

while it reacts with calcium chloride, forming solid complex compounds, *e.g.*,

$$CaCl_2 + 4NH_3 \rightarrow CaCl_2.4NH_3$$

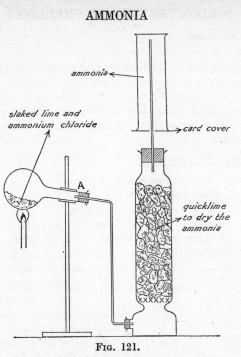

ammonia ←

slaked lime and
ammonium chloride

→ card cover

A

quicklime
→ to dry the
ammonia

Fig. 121.

Preparation of ammonia gas.

Ammonia is lighter than air and very soluble in water, so it is collected as shown by downward displacement of air or over mercury.

Instead of slaked lime, caustic soda or caustic potash solution may be used, in which case the flask would be placed in the vertical position and heated on a tripod and gauze.

$$NaOH + NH_4Cl \rightarrow NH_3 + H_2O + NaCl$$

or   or

$$KOH \qquad\qquad\qquad\qquad\qquad KCl$$

Ammonium sulphate is commonly used instead of ammonium chloride.

$$Ca(OH)_2 + (NH_4)_2SO_4 \rightarrow CaSO_4 + 2H_2O + 2NH_3$$
$$2NaOH + (NH_4)_2SO_4 \rightarrow Na_2SO_4 + 2H_2O + 2NH_3$$

To Obtain Ammonia Gas in Quantity. If several gas-jars of ammonia are required, it is very convenient to fill these by heating a concentrated solution of the gas in water. In this case the flask containing the ammonium chloride and slaked lime in the previous experiment is replaced by a vertical flask containing a strong solution of ammonia. *N.B. This is not, strictly speaking, a preparation of ammonia gas but merely obtaining the gas from its solution in water.*

Tests for Ammonia.

Smell. A characteristic choking smell. The choking smell is due to the fact that the gas temporarily paralyses the respiratory muscles and breathing is checked. In large quantities, the gas causes asphyxiation.

Action with Litmus. Expose damp red litmus paper to the gas. It is turned blue. **Ammonia is the only common alkaline gas.**

PROPERTIES OF AMMONIA

Appearance. A colourless gas.

Density. Lighter than air.

Density relative to Hydrogen, 8·5.

Density of air relative to Hydrogen, 14·4.

Solubility of Ammonia in Water. The Fountain Experiment. The very great solubility of ammonia in water is illustrated in the fountain experiment (Fig. 122).

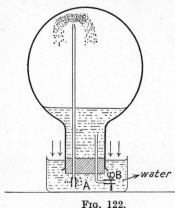

Fig. 122.
Fountain experiment.

Replace the gas-jar of Fig. 121 by a dry, thick-walled flask of about 1½ litres capacity and pass ammonia into it for some time. (It is better to supply another flask with fresh reaction mixture, to give off a satisfactory stream of ammonia.) Fit the flask with a rubber stopper carrying tubes and clips as shown. Place the tubes and clips under water, open clip B for a moment, close it and allow the few drops of water which have entered to run down into the round part of the flask. Then replace the tubes and clips under water and open clip A. A fountain will at once play, as in sketch, and **will continue until the flask is as full of water as it was formerly full of ammonia.**

The alkaline nature of ammonia can be shown in this experiment by adding a little litmus solution to the water in the trough and making it turn red by the addition of a drop of acid. When the ammonia dissolves in the litmus solution, the latter is turned blue.

Explanation. Ammonia has the highest solubility of all known gases (about 800 vols. of gas in 1 volume of water at 15° C.). The first few drops of water, which entered when clip B was opened, dissolved nearly 800 times their own volume of ammonia. This reduced the gas pressure inside the flask to only a fraction of its former value, atmospheric pressure. As soon as the clip A was opened, the water was forced into the flask because the atmospheric pressure from outside overcame the resistance of the reduced gas pressure inside the flask. The water, entering as a fountain, dissolved the remaining ammonia, maintaining the fountain until only air was left in the flask. (A thin-walled flat-bottomed flask must not be used for this experiment; the reduction of pressure inside would almost certainly cause it to collapse inwards.)

Action of Ammonia with Hydrochloric Acid Gas. Place a gas-jar of ammonia over a gas-jar of hydrochloric acid gas, remove the covers and allow the gases to mix. Dense white fumes will be seen which will settle to a white solid, sal-ammoniac or ammonium chloride, on the sides of the gas-jar.

$$NH_3 + HCl \rightarrow NH_4Cl$$

Ammonia as a Reducing Agent

Action of Ammonia on Chlorine. This is fully considered on p. 91.

Action of Ammonia on Heated Copper Oxide. Set up the apparatus as shown in Fig. 123. The colourless liquid collecting at A is water

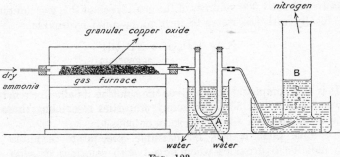

FIG. 123.

Action of ammonia on heated copper oxide.

(for tests, see p. 153) and the colourless gas at B is nitrogen (for tests see p. 333). The ammonia has **reduced** the copper oxide to copper and has itself been **oxidised** to nitrogen and water.

$$3CuO + 2NH_3 \rightarrow 3Cu + 3H_2O + N_2$$

Combustion of Ammonia. Ammonia will burn in an atmosphere of air slightly enriched by oxygen but not in air alone. The chief products are nitrogen and water.

$$4NH_3 + 3O_2 \rightarrow 2N_2 + 6H_2O$$

Liquefaction of Ammonia Gas. Ammonia gas can be liquefied at ordinary temperatures by compression. The colourless liquid boils at about $-33°$ C. under ordinary atmospheric pressures.

Formula of Ammonia Gas—see p. 91.

Ammonium Hydroxide, NH_4OH. Set up apparatus as in Fig. 124,

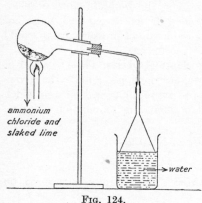

ammonium
chloride and
slaked lime

water

Fig. 124.
Preparation of ammonium hydroxide
solution.

and heat the flask gently as in the preparation of ammonia gas. The rim of the inverted funnel should just touch the surface of the water. This is a device to prevent the water from "sucking back" into the flask. After a time the water in the beaker will be found to have acquired the smell of ammonia gas which has dissolved in it. The solution is known as *ammonium hydroxide.* At $0°$ C. and ordinary pressure, one volume of water dissolves about 1,000 volumes of the gas. Much of this gas combines chemically with the water to form ammonium hydroxide.

$$NH_3 + H_2O \rightarrow NH_4OH$$
ammonium
hydroxide

It is this compound which gives the solution its alkaline reaction towards litmus (p. 336) and **many properties resembling those of typical alkalis** such as caustic soda or potash.

Like them it will, for example, precipitate insoluble metallic hydroxides when mixed with solutions of salts of the metals,

e.g., $3KOH + FeCl_3 \rightarrow 3KCl + Fe(OH)_3 \downarrow$
            ferric   ferric
            chloride   hydroxide
$3NH_4OH + FeCl_3 \rightarrow 3NH_4Cl + Fe(OH)_3 \downarrow$

and neutralise acids forming *ammonium* salts which can be crystallised out and are generally similar to ordinary metallic salts.

e.g., $NaOH + HCl \rightarrow NaCl + H_2O$
            sodium   sodium
            hydroxide   chloride

$$NH_4OH + HCl \rightarrow NH_4Cl + H_2O$$
ammonium   ammonium
hydroxide   chloride

$$2NaOH + H_2SO_4 \rightarrow Na_2SO_4 + 2H_2O$$
sodium
sulphate

$$2NH_4OH + H_2SO_4 \rightarrow (NH_4)_2SO_4 + 2H_2O$$
ammonium
sulphate

Notice that the group, (NH_4), participates as a whole in these reactions without splitting in any way, and its compounds, in which it exercises unit valency, are like typical metallic salts. **This means that the group (NH_4) is a basic radical, and, acting as a whole, exhibits metallic chemical properties.** Distinguish carefully between NH_3, the formula of ammonia gas, which is stable and capable of a separate chemical existence, and NH_4, the formula of the ammonium radical, which is incapable of separate existence and occurs only in combination.

Ammonia gas is the *basic anhydride* of the base ammonium hydroxide and forms this base when combined with water.

$$NH_3 + H_2O \rightarrow NH_4OH$$

just as sulphur trioxide is the acidic anhydride of sulphuric acid.

$$SO_3 + H_2O \rightarrow H_2SO_4$$

Ammonia gas reacts directly with acids forming salts, but no water is then produced, *e.g.*,

$$NH_3 + HCl \rightarrow NH_4Cl$$
$$2NH_3 + H_2SO_4 \rightarrow (NH_4)_2SO_4$$

Uses of Ammonium Hydroxide and Ammonia Gas. (1) Ammonium hydroxide solution is used in "smelling salts". It has a slightly stimulating effect on the action of the heart and so may prevent fainting.

(2) It is used in laundry work. It removes temporary hardness by precipitating the calcium of calcium bicarbonate as chalk,

$$Ca(HCO_3)_2 + 2NH_4OH \rightarrow CaCO_3 \downarrow + (NH_4)_2CO_3 + 2H_2O$$

and also assists in the cleansing of woollens, such as under-clothing, by reacting with the acids left behind by evaporation of perspiration and removing them as soluble salts. (The "liquid ammonia" sold for laundry work is a solution of ammonium hydroxide, made by dissolving ammonia gas in water, and should not be confused with the liquid, free from water, obtained by compression of gaseous ammonia.)

(3) Liquid ammonia is used in refrigerators.

(4) Much gaseous ammonia is now converted, by oxidation, to nitric acid (see p. 359).

LARGE SCALE MANUFACTURE OF AMMONIA GAS

Ammonia gas always occurs in the crude gaseous product of distillation of coal. It is dissolved out by "scrubbing" the gas with water and, after purification, usually converted into ammonium sulphate.

The Haber Process. This process "fixes" nitrogen of the air as the compound, ammonia. Hydrogen is manufactured from water (p. 215) and mixed with nitrogen, derived from the air, in the proportion of three volumes of hydrogen to one volume of nitrogen. The gases are dried and then passed over finely divided reduced iron as catalyst at 450° C. and a pressure of 200 atmospheres. The issuing gas contains about 6% of ammonia, which is absorbed in water. The uncombined nitrogen and hydrogen are returned to the catalyst chamber.

$$N_2 + 3H_2 \rightleftharpoons 2NH_3.$$

This process came into large scale operation in Germany in 1914 and, since ammonia can be converted into nitric acid, made her independent of explosives throughout the Great War. A large factory for manufacture of ammonia by a modified Haber process has recently been erected at Billingham, near Middlesbrough. Haber died in exile in 1934. The very great agricultural importance of his process is discussed later (p. 357).

PROPERTIES OF AMMONIUM SALTS

Action of Ammonium Salts with Alkalis. Any ammonium salt, when heated with an alkali, gives off ammonia gas (see p. 334).

e.g.,
$$NH_4Cl + KOH \rightarrow KCl + H_2O + NH_3$$
$$(NH_4)_2SO_4 + 2NaOH \rightarrow Na_2SO_4 + 2H_2O + 2NH_3$$
$$(NH_4)_2SO_4 + Ca(OH)_2 \rightarrow CaSO_4 + 2H_2O + 2NH_3$$

This readily distinguishes ammonium salts from those of any metal.

Action of Heat on Ammonium Salts

Sublimation. Ammonium salts are always decomposed by heat and, sometimes, sublime. The best example of *sublimation* is provided by ammonium chloride.

Place a little ammonium chloride in a dry test-tube and heat gently. The effects shown in Fig. 125 will be observed.

Usually when a vapour is cooled, it condenses first to a liquid, and, later, on further cooling, solidifies, *e.g.*, steam → water → ice.

The characteristic feature of sublimation is that, on cooling, the vapour condenses directly to the solid without the intermediate liquid state. Usually, the converse is also true, that the subliming solid is converted directly to vapour on heating without an intermediate liquid stage, but in some cases (for example, that of iodine) melting may occur.

Very few substances sublime. Among those which sublime are a few ammonium salts (especially the chloride) iodine and naphthalene. Sublimation is a very effective means of purifying them, because their impurities are very unlikely to sublime. The white sublimate of ammonium chloride in Fig. 125 will be a purer sample of the compound than the original material used for the experiment. For thermal dissociation, see p. 128.

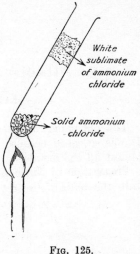

White sublimate of ammonium chloride

Solid ammonium chloride

FIG. 125.
Action of heat on ammonium chloride.

Decomposition of Ammonium Salts by Heat. Ammonium salts of acids having a high proportion of oxygen are usually decomposed by heat, *e.g.*

(i) *Ammonium Nitrite.*

$$NH_4NO_2 \rightarrow N_2 + 2H_2O$$

This reaction is fully dealt with on p. 332.

(ii) *Ammonium Nitrate.*

$$NH_4NO_3 \rightarrow \underset{\substack{\text{nitrous}\\\text{oxide}}}{N_2O} + 2H_2O$$

This reaction is fully considered on p. 353.

QUESTIONS ON THIS CHAPTER WILL BE FOUND ON PAGE 359.

M

CHAPTER XXXII

NITRIC ACID AND THE NITRATES

NITRIC ACID, HNO₃

THE old name for nitric acid was "aqua fortis"—strong water. It was so called because it attacks so many substances, including almost all the metals.

Preparation of Nitric Acid. Set up the apparatus of Fig. 126. Into the bulb of the retort put some potassium nitrate crystals

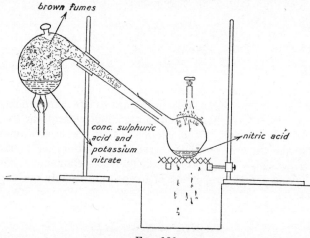

FIG. 126.

Preparation of nitric acid.

and add concentrated sulphuric acid. Heat the retort gently. The potassium nitrate gradually dissolves and effervescence occurs.

$$KNO_3 + H_2SO_4 \rightarrow KHSO_4 + HNO_3$$

potassium
hydrogen
sulphate

The nitric acid distils and collects in the cooled receiver as a yellow liquid, while drops of the acid can be seen running down the bulb and neck of the retort. The brown fumes are nitrogen peroxide formed by slight decomposition of the nitric acid by heat,

$$4HNO_3 \rightarrow 2H_2O + 4NO_2 + O_2$$
nitrogen
peroxide

and they impart a yellow colour to the acid by dissolving in it.

This reaction is a general one. Any metallic nitrate, when heated with concentrated sulphuric acid, gives off nitric acid, e.g.,

$$NaNO_3 + H_2SO_4 \rightarrow NaHSO_4 + HNO_3$$
sodium nitrate

$$Pb(NO_3)_2 + H_2SO_4 \rightarrow PbSO_4 + 2HNO_3$$
lead nitrate

Manufacture. Some nitric acid is manufactured by the above laboratory process. Iron retorts are used, because this metal is only slightly attacked by the acid, which is condensed in silica condensers. The nitrate employed is sodium nitrate, $NaNO_3$, "Chile saltpetre" (see p. 348). Another method of manufacture is Birkeland and Eyde's Process (p. 358). Nitric acid is used mainly for the manufacture of explosives and dyes.

Test for Nitric Acid and Soluble Nitrates. Crush a few potassium nitrate crystals in a mortar and put them into a test-tube and add water to a depth of about one inch. Shake to dissolve the potassium nitrate. Add a little dilute sulphuric acid and then two or three crystals of ferrous sulphate, which have also been crushed. Shake to dissolve them. Hold the test-tube in a slanting position and pour a slow continuous stream of concentrated sulphuric acid down the side. (**Care!**) It will form a separate layer underneath the aqueous layer and, at the junction of the two, a brown ring will be seen **This brown ring is the characteristic test for nitric acid or a soluble nitrate.**

Explanation. The concentrated sulphuric acid and the nitrate yield nitric acid.

$$KNO_3 + H_2SO_4 \rightarrow KHSO_4 + HNO_3$$

The nitric acid is then reduced by some of the ferrous sulphate to nitric oxide, NO.

$$6FeSO_4 + 2HNO_3 + 3H_2SO_4 \rightarrow 3Fe_2(SO_4)_3 + 4H_2O + 2NO$$
ferric sulphate

The nitric oxide reacts with more ferrous sulphate to give the brown compound $(FeSO_4)_2.NO$, which appears as the brown ring.

$$2FeSO_4 + NO \rightarrow (FeSO_4)_2.NO$$

PROPERTIES OF NITRIC ACID

Nitric acid is a colourless, fuming liquid of specific gravity 1·5 and boiling point 85° C. at ordinary atmospheric pressure. The ordinary concentrated nitric acid, as sold, contains about 65% by weight of the pure acid and 35% of water. The pure acid is corrosive and destroys organic matter very readily. The skin is stained yellow by it and, if the acid is left in contact with it for even a very short time, the skin is destroyed.

Chemical Properties of Nitric Acid. Nitric acid can behave chemically in two ways:

It is (1) a very strong acid.

(2) a powerful oxidiser.

Nitric Acid Acting as an Acid

(a) Nitric acid neutralises bases, forming nitrates. *e.g.,*

$$KOH + HNO_3 \rightarrow KNO_3 + H_2O$$

dilute potassium hydroxide   dilute nitric acid   potassium nitrate

$$CuO + 2HNO_3 \rightarrow Cu(NO_3)_2 + H_2O$$

copper oxide   dilute nitric acid   copper nitrate

$$Zn(OH)_2 + 2HNO_3 \rightarrow Zn(NO_3)_2 + 2H_2O$$

zinc hydroxide   dilute nitric acid   zinc nitrate

A full account of reactions of this type is given in Chapter XVI, pp. 180, 195.

It is very useful to remember that all metallic nitrates are soluble in water.

(b) It is characteristic of strong acids that, when dilute, they will react with the more electropositive metals, liberating hydrogen, *e.g.,*

$$Zn + 2HCl \rightarrow ZnCl_2 + H_2$$
$$Fe + H_2SO_4 \rightarrow FeSO_4 + H_2$$

We would expect nitric acid to react in the same way. It probably does; but the reaction is complicated by the fact that nitric acid is also a powerful oxidising agent.

Nitric Acid as an Oxidising Agent

Any hydrogen initially produced by the action of a metal upon nitric acid is at once oxidised by more of the acid to water and the reduction products of the acid are liberated.

The typical reaction of nitric acid on a metal is given by the equation

$$3Cu + 8HNO_3 \rightarrow 3Cu(NO_3)_2 + 4H_2O + 2NO$$

copper   copper nitrate   water   nitric oxide

It will be more fully considered, and full experimental details given, when it is used for the preparation of nitric oxide (p. 353). Other oxides of nitrogen may be produced with acid of different concentrations and metals other than copper.

The important point is, that if a metal acts upon nitric acid under ordinary experimental conditions, the product is always an oxide of nitrogen and never hydrogen.

As the acid changes in concentration, other oxides of nitrogen, or even nitrogen itself, or ammonia, may be obtained by more vigorous reduction of the acid. The ammonia would be at once converted to ammonium nitrate. Nitric acid attacks all commonly known metals except gold and platinum.

The Oxidising Action of Nitric Acid on Sulphur. In an evaporating dish, place some concentrated nitric acid and powdered sulphur with a little bromine (CARE ! !) as catalyst. Place the dish in the fume-chamber on a tripod. Warm gently. There is vigorous effervescence with evolution of brown fumes of nitrogen peroxide. When the effervescence subsides, add water and filter off the excess sulphur. To some of the filtrate add dilute hydrochloric acid and barium chloride solution. A white precipitate (barium sulphate) shows that sulphuric acid is present.

The nitric acid has oxidised the sulphur to sulphuric acid and has itself been reduced to nitrogen peroxide.

$$S + 6HNO_3 \rightarrow 2H_2O + H_2SO_4 + 6NO_2$$
$$H_2SO_4 + BaCl_2 \rightarrow BaSO_4 \downarrow + 2HCl$$

The Oxidising Action of Nitric Acid on a Ferrous Salt. Dissolve a few crystals of ferrous sulphate in dilute sulphuric acid in a test-tube. Add a little concentrated nitric acid and heat.[1] Brown fumes of nitrogen peroxide are seen and a brown or yellow solution is left, instead of the original pale green solution.

The nitric acid has oxidised the green ferrous sulphate to brown or yellow ferric sulphate and has itself been reduced to nitric oxide which, in the air, forms nitrogen peroxide (p. 354).

$$6FeSO_4 + 3H_2SO_4 + 2HNO_3 \rightarrow 3Fe_2(SO_4)_3 + 4H_2O + 2NO$$
$$2NO + O_2 \rightarrow 2NO_2$$
$$\text{of the}$$
$$\text{air}$$

An important point to notice about nitric acid as an oxidiser is that it introduces no solid into a mixture. The acid itself is volatile and its reduction products, oxides of nitrogen, are gaseous, while the other product, water, can also be evaporated off. Thus, it leaves no solids to complicate purification of the product of oxidation.

[1] Before heating, the solution will be very dark brown or black. For an explanation of this, see the "brown ring" test, p. 343.

Other oxidising actions of nitric acid are:
Carbon to carbon dioxide.

$$C + 4HNO_3 \rightarrow 2H_2O + 4NO_2 + CO_2$$

Red phosphorus to orthophosphoric acid.

$$P + 5HNO_3 \rightarrow H_3PO_4 + 5NO_2 + H_2O$$
$$\text{orthophosphoric}$$
$$\text{acid}$$

The Action of Heat on Concentrated Nitric Acid. A clay pipe is used for this experiment because a fairly high temperature is needed and the liquid nitric acid would break a heated glass tube. Fit up apparatus as in Fig. 127, omitting, for the present, the

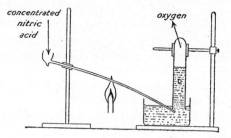

FIG. 127.
Decomposition of nitric acid by heat.

boiling-tube, and raising the end of the pipe stem above the water level.

Heat the pipe stem to red heat at one point with a bunsen burner and pour concentrated nitric acid into the bowl of the pipe. Clouds of brown fumes emerging from the pipe stem show that *nitrogen peroxide* is produced.

Now, complete the apparatus as in Fig. 127, making sure that the end of the pipe stem is **the least possible distance below the water level** and starting with the boiling-tube full of water. As the nitric acid runs over the red-hot pipe stem, a colourless gas collects in the boiling-tube. Test it with a glowing splint. It is rekindled. The gas is *oxygen*. (Nitrogen peroxide, also produced as above, is soluble in water.)

The third product of the decomposition of the acid is water.

$$4HNO_3 \rightarrow 2H_2O + 4NO_2 + O_2$$

K Na	Nitrates of these metals are decomposed by heat to the *nitrite* and *oxygen*.	
Ca Mg Zn Fe Pb Cu	Nitrates of these metals are decomposed on heating to the *oxide of the metal, nitrogen peroxide* and *oxygen*.	All nitrates are soluble in water.
Hg Ag	Nitrates of these metals are decomposed on heating to the *metal, nitrogen peroxide* and *oxygen*.	

Ammonium Nitrate, NH_4NO_3. This compound may be made in the laboratory by neutralisation of ammonia by nitric acid (p. 193).

$$NH_4OH + HNO_3 \rightarrow NH_4NO_3 + H_2O$$

It is colourless and very soluble in water. When it dissolves, heat is absorbed and, by dissolving a large quantity of the salt in water, a liquid of low temperature is rapidly obtained and may be used as a "freezing-mixture".

Ammonium nitrate is decomposed by heat into nitrous oxide and water (p. 351).

$$NH_4NO_3 \rightarrow N_2O + 2H_2O$$

If the experiment is carried out in a test-tube, the usual test for nitrous oxide (rekindling of a glowing splint) will be masked by the steam which is also given off. If the heating is carried on to decompose all the ammonium nitrate, there will be no residue and the last traces of the salt will decompose with explosion.

A mixture of ammonium nitrate and aluminium powder is used as an explosive, "ammonal". When it is detonated, the following reaction occurs.

$$2Al + 3NH_4NO_3 \rightarrow Al_2O_3 + 3N_2 + 6H_2O$$

The gaseous nitrogen and steam, having a volume many times greater than that of the original solids, produce a very high pressure and hence an explosion.

Potassium Nitrate, KNO_3 (nitre, saltpetre). In the laboratory, this salt may be obtained by neutralisation (p. 193).

$$KOH + HNO_3 \rightarrow KNO_3 + H_2O$$

On the industrial scale, it is prepared by double decomposition between potassium chloride (from the Stassfurt deposits) and sodium nitrate (from Chile).

$$KCl + NaNO_3 \rightarrow KNO_3 + NaCl$$

Boiling saturated solutions of potassium chloride and sodium nitrate are used and sodium chloride, being the least soluble of the four salts at this temperature, crystallises and is filtered off. On cooling to ordinary temperature, potassium nitrate crystallises as it is the least soluble of the four salts at this temperature.

When heated, potassium nitrate melts to a colourless liquid and decomposes slowly, liberating oxygen (test: glowing splint rekindled) and leaving, when cool, a pale yellow solid, potassium nitrite.

$$2KNO_3 \rightarrow 2KNO_2 + O_2$$

Potassium nitrate is chiefly used for the making of fireworks and gunpowder, which usually contains about one part of charcoal, one part of sulphur and six parts of potassium nitrate (by weight). When ignited, the mixture burns rapidly, producing nitrogen, oxides of carbon and sulphur and other gases. These hot gases occupy a much greater volume than the original solids, and a very great pressure is set up which is used for propulsion or disruption.

Sodium Nitrate, $NaNO_3$ (Chile saltpetre). Large deposits of sodium nitrate, mixed with clay, occur in Chile, as "caliche". The material is broken up by blasting. The sodium nitrate is extracted by dissolving it out in water and evaporating the solutions by the heat of the sun. The area where the nitrates are found is practically rainless and water is supplied for the process by pipe-lines.

In the laboratory, sodium nitrate may be prepared by neutralising caustic soda with nitric acid (p. 193).

$$NaOH + HNO_3 \rightarrow NaNO_3 + H_2O$$

When heated, sodium nitrate behaves exactly like potassium nitrate (see last section).

$$2NaNO_3 \rightarrow 2NaNO_2 + O_2$$

The most important use of sodium nitrate is its application to the land as a fertiliser (see p. 357). It is rapid in action and is applied in Spring.

The Chilean deposits used to be the only source of nitrogenous "chemical" fertiliser, but the Haber (p. 340) and Birkeland-Eyde processes (p. 358) now furnish alternative supplies.

Large quantities of sodium nitrate are also used for the manufacture of nitric acid (p. 343), potassium nitrate (see above), and sodium nitrite. This substance is used extensively in the manufacture of aniline dyes, and is made by heating sodium nitrate with carbon or lead. The presence of these reducing agents hastens the conversion of the nitrate to the nitrite, a process which is slow if heat alone is employed.

$$NaNO_3 + Pb \rightarrow NaNO_2 + PbO$$
$$2NaNO_3 + C \rightarrow 2NaNO_2 + CO_2$$

Calcium Nitrate, $Ca(NO_3)_2$. This compound may be made in the laboratory by the action of nitric acid upon slaked lime or chalk.

$$Ca(OH)_2 + 2HNO_3 \rightarrow Ca(NO_3)_2 + 2H_2O$$
$$CaCO_3 + 2HNO_3 \rightarrow Ca(NO_3)_2 + H_2O + CO_2$$

It is usually met with as the tetrahydrate, $Ca(NO_3)_2.4H_2O$, which forms white deliquescent crystals.

In industry, some calcium nitrate (mixed with lime) is used as a fertiliser, "air saltpetre". It is prepared from the nitric acid of the Birkeland-Eyde process.

For the action of heat on calcium nitrate, see below.

Nitrates of Magnesium, Zinc, Lead, Copper. These compounds are all prepared, as explained in Chapter XVI, by the action of nitric acid on the metal or on its oxide, hydroxide or carbonate. Except lead nitrate, which crystallises anhydrous, they all form hydrated crystals. All the crystals are white in colour except those of copper nitrate, which are blue.

The most important property of these nitrates is the reaction they undergo when heated. This is described below.

Action of Heat on Nitrates of Heavy Metals; for example: *lead nitrate.*

Place a little lead nitrate in a test-tube and heat it. A series of sharp cracking sounds, almost small explosions, is heard. (This effect is called *decrepitation*.) Later, the lead nitrate melts and effervesces, giving off brown fumes (*nitrogen peroxide*). Test the gas with a glowing splint. The splint is rekindled. Hence *oxygen* is also present. The solid residue is reddish-brown when hot and yellow when cold. It is litharge (lead monoxide), and will probably be found to be fused into the glass.

$$2Pb(NO_3)_2 \rightarrow 2PbO + 4NO_2 + O_2$$

This reaction is typical of the action of heat on the nitrates of common heavy metals. (Note that it is also exactly analogous to the action of heat on nitric acid, p. 346.)

The following equations express the reaction for other nitrates of heavy metals. In all cases, the experimental observations are

M*

exactly as above except for the colours of the oxides, which are stated. With the nitrates given below there is no decrepitation.

$$2Ca(NO_3)_2 \rightarrow 2CaO + 4NO_2 + O_2$$
white   calcium
oxide
(white)

$$2Mg(NO_3)_2 \rightarrow 2MgO + 4NO_2 + O_2$$
white   magnesium
oxide
(white)

$$2Zn(NO_3)_2 \rightarrow 2ZnO + 4NO_2 + O_2$$
white   zinc oxide
(yellow when hot;
white when cold)

$$2Cu(NO_3)_2 \rightarrow 2CuO + 4NO_2 + O_2$$
green   copper oxide
(black)

Mercuric and Silver Nitrates. The oxides of mercury and silver are decomposed by heat, therefore the nitrates of these two metals have the free metals when heated.

$$2AgNO_3 \rightarrow 2Ag + 2NO_2 + O_2$$
silver

$$Hg(NO_3)_2 \rightarrow Hg + 2NO_2 + O_2$$
mercury

QUESTIONS ON THIS CHAPTER WILL BE FOUND ON PAGE 359.

CHAPTER XXXIII

THE OXIDES OF NITROGEN

NITROUS OXIDE, N_2O

THIS compound is most conveniently prepared by the action of heat on ammonium nitrate (Fig. 128).

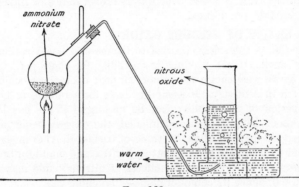

FIG. 128.

Preparation of nitrous oxide

On heating, the ammonium nitrate melts and effervesces. Nitrous oxide and steam are given off. Nitrous oxide is fairly soluble in cold water and is collected over warm water. Most of the steam is condensed to water as the bubbles pass up the gas-jar.

$$NH_4NO_3 \rightarrow N_2O + 2H_2O$$
$$\text{nitrous}$$
$$\text{oxide}$$

Ammonium nitrate will explode, on heating, if the amount of material in the vessel becomes very small, but the reaction is quite safe unless this happens. If desired, the gas may be prepared by heating any mixture of salts which, by double decomposition, will yield ammonium nitrate—e.g., a mixture of potassium nitrate and ammonium sulphate, finely ground.

$$(NH_4)_2SO_4 + 2KNO_3 \rightarrow 2NH_4NO_3 + K_2SO_4$$

This mixture is less liable to explode.

Test for Nitrous Oxide

The gas rekindles a brightly glowing splint.

It may be distinguished from oxygen by the following tests:

Nitrous oxide has a sweet and sickly smell (oxygen has no smell).

Invert a gas-jar of nitrous oxide over cold water and shake it. The level of water in the gas-jar will rise, showing the gas to be fairly soluble in water. Oxygen is almost insoluble in water and no rise would be observed.

Nitrous oxide does not give brown fumes with nitric oxide. If a little oxygen is bubbled up into a volume of nitric oxide enclosed over water, brown fumes of nitrogen peroxide are formed.

PROPERTIES OF NITROUS OXIDE

The gas is colourless, neutral to litmus and has a rather sweet, sickly smell. It can produce insensibility for short periods and is used as an anæsthetic for minor surgical operations, such as are required in dentistry. Insensibility lasts for a minute or two only. The period of insensibility can be prolonged if the gas is mixed with about 20% oxygen and inhaled, the oxygen being necessary to keep the patient alive. A trace of carbon dioxide must also be present to stimulate the respiratory centres and maintain breathing. Patients recovering from the effects of nitrous oxide may become hysterical; hence its common name—"laughing gas".

Density. Nitrous oxide has a density of 22 compared with hydrogen. (Molecular weight of nitrous oxide = 44.)

Solubility. The gas is fairly soluble in cold water.

Nitrous Oxide as a Supporter of Combustion

Action on a Glowing Splint. If the splint is glowing brightly, it will be rekindled by nitrous oxide, but, if only feebly glowing, it will be extinguished.

To be rekindled, the glowing portion of the splint must be hot enough to decompose some nitrous oxide into nitrogen and oxygen. The mixture will then be rich enough in oxygen to stimulate the combustion of the splint and cause it to burst into flame. A feebly glowing splint will not be hot enough to decompose the nitrous oxide, and so will be extinguished, having no free oxygen with which to burn.

Combustion of a Candle, Sulphur, Carbon, and Phosphorus.

These materials are placed on deflagrating spoons and made to burn by heating in a bunsen flame. (The candle is, of course, merely lighted.) When plunged into nitrous oxide, they all burn more vigorously than in air, the candle with its familiar yellow flame, sulphur with a blue flame, and phosphorus with a bright yellow flame. The oxides of the burning elements are formed and gaseous nitrogen.

$$\text{candle wax} \begin{cases} C + 2N_2O \rightarrow CO_2 + 2N_2 \\ H_2 + N_2O \rightarrow H_2O + N_2 \end{cases}$$

$$C + 2N_2O \rightarrow CO_2 + 2N_2$$
carbon
dioxide

$$S + 2N_2O \rightarrow SO_2 + 2N_2$$
sulphur
dioxide

$$4P + 10N_2O \rightarrow P_4O_{10} + 10N_2$$
dense white
fumes;
phosphorus
pentoxide

Feebly burning sulphur may be extinguished by nitrous oxide. For the explanation of this, see the action of nitrous oxide on a glowing splint (above).

Formula of Nitrous Oxide. See p. 93.

NITRIC OXIDE, NO

Nitric oxide is produced, mixed always with other oxides of nitrogen, by the action of nitric acid on most metals. The commonest reaction used is that of moderately concentrated nitric acid on copper. Set up the apparatus shown in Fig. 129. Cover the copper with water and add concentrated nitric acid, renewing it as the action slackens. Vigorous effervescence occurs and the flask

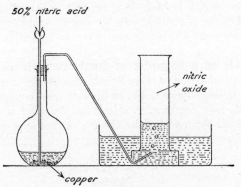

FIG. 129.

Preparation of nitric oxide.

is filled with brown fumes. These are nitrogen peroxide produced partly by the action of the acid upon the copper and partly by the oxidation of the main product, nitric oxide, by the oxygen of the air in the flask.

$$2NO + O_2 \rightarrow 2NO_2$$
nitrogen
peroxide

The brown fumes dissolve in the water over which the nitric oxide is collected as a colourless gas. A green solution of copper nitrate is left in the flask.

$$3Cu + 8HNO_3 \rightarrow 3Cu(NO_3)_2 + 4H_2O + 2NO.$$

Tests for Nitric Oxide

Exposure to Air. Remove the cover from a gas-jar of nitric oxide. **Reddish-brown fumes are at once produced by oxidation of the gas by oxygen of the air.**

$$2NO + O_2 \rightarrow 2NO_2$$

Nitric oxide is the only gas to give this action.

Action on Ferrous Sulphate Solution. Prepare a cold solution of ferrous sulphate in dilute sulphuric acid. Pour it into a gas-jar of nitric oxide. The dark brown or black colouration is caused by formation of a black compound, $(FeSO_4)_2.NO$.

$$2FeSO_4 + NO \rightarrow (FeSO_4)_2.NO$$

(The gas can be obtained in a pure state by heating this compound.)

PROPERTIES OF NITRIC OXIDE

Nitric oxide is colourless and almost insoluble in water. Its density is 15 times that of hydrogen; it is slightly heavier than air of which the density is 14·4. It is neutral to litmus.

The smell of the gas is unknown because it combines with oxygen of the air (see tests above); it can never be collected by displacement of air.

Nitric Oxide as a Supporter of Combustion. Nitric oxide will support the combustion of those burning materials whose flames are hot enough to decompose it and so liberate free oxygen with which the materials may combine. A splint, candle, sulphur and glowing charcoal are all extinguished by the gas, but it supports the combustion of strongly burning phosphorus.

$$P_4 + 10NO \rightarrow P_4O_{10} + 5N_2$$
white fumes;
phosphorus
pentoxide

Formula of Nitric Oxide. See p. 93.

NITROGEN PEROXIDE, NO_2 or N_2O_4

Preparation. Nitrogen peroxide is given off, together with oxygen, when nitrates of heavy metals are heated. The most suitable nitrate to use is lead nitrate, because it crystallises without water of crystallisation, which is found in crystals of most nitrates and which would interfere with the preparation.

The lead nitrate decrepitates and melts on heating. It effervesces, giving a brown gas nitrogen peroxide, and oxygen. The nitrogen peroxide is liquefied in the freezing mixture (Fig. 130)

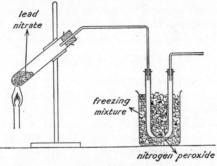

FIG. 130.

Preparation of nitrogen peroxide.

and collects in the U-tube as a green liquid (yellow if pure), oxygen passing on as gas and escaping. Litharge remains in the tube as a yellow solid fused into the glass.

$$2Pb(NO_3)_2 \rightarrow 2PbO + 4NO_2 + O_2$$

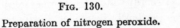

lead nitrate litharge nitrogen oxygen
         peroxide

PROPERTIES OF NITROGEN PEROXIDE

Nitrogen peroxide is usually seen as a reddish-brown gas, though the boiling-point of liquid nitrogen peroxide (22° C.) is above the usual atmospheric temperatures. It has a pungent, irritating smell and is a rather dangerous gas on account of its tendency to set up septic pneumonia if inhaled. It should not be allowed to escape in quantity into the open laboratory.

Action of Nitrogen Peroxide with Water. Pour a little of the liquid nitrogen peroxide prepared above into a dry gas-jar in the fume cupboard and allow the liquid to vaporise. Add water and shake. The brown fumes dissolve, leaving a pale blue liquid. Add to it blue litmus solution. The litmus is turned red. This is because the solution contains nitric and *nitrous* acids.

$$2NO_2 + H_2O \rightarrow HNO_3 + HNO_2$$

nitric   nitrous
acid   acid

Similarly with caustic soda, the gas gives a mixture of sodium nitrate and sodium nitr*ite*.

$$2NaOH + 2NO_2 \rightarrow NaNO_3 + NaNO_2 + H_2O$$

sodium   sodium
nitrate   nitrite

Nitrogen Peroxide as a Supporter of Combustion. Like the other two oxides of nitrogen we have considered, nitrogen peroxide will support the combustion of a burning substance whose flame is hot enough to decompose it and supply free oxygen. It will support, for example, the combustion of *strongly-burning* phosphorus

$$2P_4 + 10NO_2 \rightarrow 2P_4O_{10} + 5N_2$$

but not that of sulphur or a candle.

The use of nitrogen peroxide in the manufacture of sulphuric acid is discussed on p. 320.

Dissociation of Nitrogen Peroxide. At 150° C., nitrogen peroxide is very dark brown in colour. Its vapour density is 23, and its molecular weight is therefore 46, corresponding to the formula NO_2 ($N = 14$; $O = 16$). As the temperature falls, the vapour density of the gas gradually increases, until at 22° C. it approaches 46, corresponding to a molecular weight of 92 and a formula of N_2O_4. At the same time it becomes lighter in colour.

This must mean that, on heating, nitrogen peroxide dissociates, and, at any temperature between 22° C. and 150° C., contains both N_2O_4 and NO_2 molecules, the proportion of the latter increasing, as the temperature rises to 150° C., when only NO_2 molecules are present.

heat
$N_2O_4 \quad \rightleftharpoons \quad 2NO_2$
light yellow   cool   dark brown

For a more complete consideration of dissociation, see p. 128.

THE IMPORTANCE OF NITROGEN COMPOUNDS IN THE LIFE OF PLANTS

Fixation of Atmospheric Nitrogen. The fertility of soil depends in part on the presence in the soil of certain chemical elements. These elements are potassium, nitrogen and phosphorus, together with traces of iron, sulphur and others. We shall consider, for the present, nitrogen alone.

Every time a crop is taken from a given patch of soil, some of the nitrogen previously contained in the soil is removed in the form of complex organic compounds, which are part of the tissue of the plant. This nitrogen was absorbed from the soil as dissolved nitrates by the roots of the plant and this is the only manner in which the vast majority of plants can absorb and use nitrogen. It is obvious that unless nitrogen is continually supplied to the soil to balance the loss suffered by removal of crops, the fertility of the soil will decrease and its yield become meagre.

The soil receives some nitrogen by natural means. Certain plants, for example peas and beans, always have colonies of bacteria on their roots which are able to convert the nitrogen of the air into compounds which pass into the soil. Electrical discharges in the atmosphere, such as lightning, cause some slight combination of

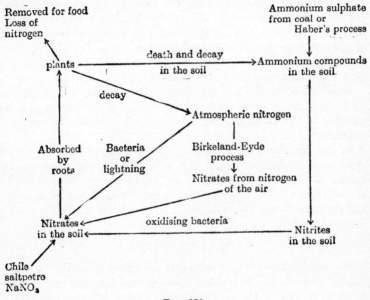

FIG. 131.

The nitrogen cycle.

oxygen and nitrogen and this leads to the passage of nitrogen into the soil as nitrates, dissolved in rain water. This is a natural counterpart of Birkeland and Eyde's process which is described later. Nitrogen-fixing bacteria, living free in the soil, are another important agency supplying nitrogen to the soil from the air. Nitrogenous fertilisers are also used to make good the loss of nitrogen. These fertilisers fall into the following classes:

1. Ammonium sulphate derived from the ammonia produced when coal is distilled.

2. Sodium nitrate from the deposits of this substance in Chile— "Chile saltpetre", $NaNO_3$.

3. Farmyard manure.

4. Fertilisers produced by manufacture, using the nitrogen of the air. These fertilisers include *ammonium sulphate*, for which the ammonia is prepared from nitrogen of the air by Haber's process (p. 340) and *nitrates*, also obtained from nitrogen of the air by the Birkeland-Eyde process which will shortly be described. The nitrogen of the air is inexhaustible so that adequate supplies of nitrogenous fertilisers are now assured for ever.

Though most plants can only use nitrogen as nitrates, it need not actually be supplied to the soil in this form. Bacteria in the soil will carry out the oxidation of any nitrogen compound to nitrates and the plants can then utilise it.

The sum total of all these processes is called the *"Nitrogen Cycle"*. A simplified form of it is given in Fig. 131.

Birkeland-Eyde Process for Fixation of Atmospheric Nitrogen. "Fixation" is the name given to the process of converting gaseous nitrogen of the air into a nitrogen compound, usually for use as a fertiliser.

In the Birkeland-Eyde process, nitrogen and oxygen of the air are passed through a circular disc of electrical flame, produced by spreading an ordinary electric arc by means of very powerful electromagnets. This flaming disc is some 6 or 7 feet in diameter and its temperature about 3,500° C. Under these conditions a little nitric oxide is formed.

$$N_2 + O_2 \rightarrow 2NO$$

The air, leaving the high temperature region, may contain about 2% of nitric oxide. It is quickly cooled and the nitric oxide combines with some of the excess oxygen to form nitrogen peroxide.

$$2NO + O_2 \rightarrow 2NO_2$$

This nitrogen peroxide is then absorbed in water trickling down high towers under conditions chosen to give nitric acid as the chief product.

$$4NO_2 + O_2 + 2H_2O \rightarrow 4HNO_3$$
$$\text{from air}$$

The nitric acid is then neutralised with lime and the calcium nitrate, mixed with excess of lime to prevent deliquescence, is sold as a fertiliser.

$$2HNO_3 + Ca(OH)_2 \rightarrow Ca(NO_3)_2 + 2H_2O$$

Haber's Process for Fixation of Atmospheric Nitrogen. Fixation of atmospheric nitrogen by Haber's Process has already been considered (p. 340).

The product, ammonia, may be converted into ammonium sulphate (p. 325) or oxidised by passing it with air over platinum as catalyst at red heat.

$$4NH_3 + 5O_2 = 4NO + 6H_2O$$

The nitric oxide may then be converted to nitric acid as above.

QUESTIONS

1. Describe the usual laboratory method of making nitric acid, and give an account of its action on (a) one base, (b) one metal, (c) one non-metallic element, (d) one carbonate. (B.)

2. Describe shortly how you would obtain, starting with *nitric acid*, specimens of (a) oxygen, (b) nitric oxide, (c) nitrous oxide, and (d) nitrogen peroxide. (N.U.J.B.)

3. Give equations illustrating the effect of heat upon nitrates.
   Describe concisely the properties of the gaseous products of these reactions. (O. and C.)

4. Describe the preparation and collection of nitric oxide in the laboratory and give an account of its chief properties. How would you prove that it consists of nitrogen and oxygen?
   Explain, very briefly, how it is formed in the earth's atmosphere, and indicate how the acid subsequently produced becomes "fixed" in the soil as nitrate. (B.)

5. How would you prepare nitrous oxide? Give an account of the properties and uses of this gas. Draw and describe the apparatus you would use to show that nitrous oxide contains its own volume of nitrogen. (D.)

6. Describe the preparation and properties of nitric oxide. Three litres of a mixture of nitrous and nitric oxides were passed over red-hot copper, and 2·2 litres of nitrogen collected. Calculate the composition of the mixture. (O. and C.)

7. How would you prepare and collect some nitric oxide free from nitrogen?
   Describe and account for what you would observe during the preparation. What happens when this gas is (a) passed into ferrous sulphate solution, and (b) mixed with oxygen? (N.U.J.B.)

8. Given ammonium nitrate how would you proceed to obtain a sample of (a) nitrous oxide, (b) ammonia?
   How would you obtain from ammonia a sample of nitrogen? What is the reaction between an aqueous solution of ammonia and (a) ferric chloride solution, (b) dilute sulphuric acid? (C.W.B.)

9. How is nitrogen usually prepared and collected in the laboratory? How is nitrogen obtained industrially?
   Outline the industrial method by which nitrogen may be converted into (a) ammonia, (b) nitric acid.
   How and under what conditions does copper oxide react with ammonia? (N.U.J.B.)

CHAPTER XXXIV

PHOSPHORUS

Occurrence. Phosphorus is a very active non-metal and is not found uncombined in nature. It was first isolated by Brandt, a Hamburg chemist, in 1669, who obtained it by distilling concentrated urine with sand. It is extracted nowadays from bones and mineral phosphates. The residue left after burning away the organic matter from bones contains calcium phosphate, $Ca_3(PO_4)_2$. This substance also occurs as the mineral, apatite.

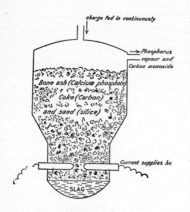

FIG. 132.

Extraction of phosphorus.

Extraction. A charge of calcium phosphate, sand and coke is fed continuously into an electric furnace, Fig. 132. At the very high temperature obtained (the electric current is merely to produce the high temperature; there is no electrolysis) the following reaction takes place:

$$2Ca_3(PO_4)_2 + 6SiO_2 + 10C \rightarrow 6CaSiO_3 + 10CO + P_4$$
$$\text{calcium silicate}$$
$$\text{slag}$$

The phosphorus distils over with the carbon monoxide and the vapour is led below the surface of water, when the phosphorus solidifies to a white solid. The calcium silicate is formed as a molten slag which is run off from time to time.

Chemistry of the Action. Most salts can be considered as being made up of a basic and acidic oxide.

$$2Ca_3(PO_4)_2 \equiv 6CaO.P_4O_{10}$$

Silica is an acidic oxide, hence

$$6CaO + 6SiO_2 \rightarrow 6CaSiO_3$$
$$\text{calcium silicate}$$
$$(cf. \text{ calcium carbonate})$$

360

The carbon (a reducing agent) reduces the oxide of phosphorus to the element

$$P_4O_{10} + 10C \rightarrow P_4 + 10CO$$

On adding these equations together the main equation will be obtained.

PROPERTIES

Phosphorus exists in two chief allotropic forms, white phosphorus and red phosphorus. The latter is the stable form. (See p. 411.)

Yellow phosphorus is a white solid which becomes pale yellow on exposure to light. It is of density 1·8 gm./c.c. and is soluble in carbon disulphide. It smoulders in air owing to oxidation and this action causes it to glow in the dark.

$$4P + 3O_2 \rightarrow P_4O_6$$

It is usually kept below the surface of water. **Great care should be taken in handling it, for it gives off a very poisonous vapour and catches fire very readily.** It burns in air or oxygen, giving off white fumes of oxides of phosphorus. This variety of phosphorus is formed when the vapour of phosphorus is suddenly cooled.

Red phosphorus is the stable variety at all temperatures. It is not poisonous as is yellow phosphorus, and does not catch fire so readily. It can be made by heating yellow phosphorus in an inert atmosphere (usually with a little iodine to act as catalyst) to a temperature of about 250° C. It is insoluble in carbon disulphide.

Phosphorus is used in the match industry, in rat poisons and in making smoke bombs.

Match Industry. In earlier days, matches contained white phosphorus and an oxidising agent and the mixture was caused to burn by rubbing on sand paper. The use of white phosphorus in industry caused hundreds of work-people to suffer from phosphorus poisoning, which took the form of the rotting of the bones of the face and jaw ("phossy-jaw"). Its use was then forbidden by law and matches nowadays consist of compounds of phosphorus (sulphides as a rule) and oxidising agents. The friction of rubbing on a rough surface generates enough heat to start the combustion. In "safety" matches the phosphorus (red variety) is on the side of the box and thus the match-head, which contains the oxidising agent, is useless without the box.

Chemical Properties of Phosphorus. Phosphorus will combine readily with oxygen, chlorine and sulphur. It is a reducing agent and readily attacks oxidising agents with the formation of oxides of phosphorus which are soluble in water forming acids. It is attacked by alkalis forming phosphine. Phosphorus forms two series of compounds, exhibiting valencies of 3 and 5. The following experiments illustrate these actions.

Preparation of Phosphine. (Phosphoretted Hydrogen, PH₃.) Fit up the apparatus as shown in Fig. 133 in a fume chamber. Place caustic soda solution and a few small pieces of yellow phosphorus in the flask, sweep out the air by means of coal-gas and warm the mixture. A gas is given off, phosphine, and on coming into contact

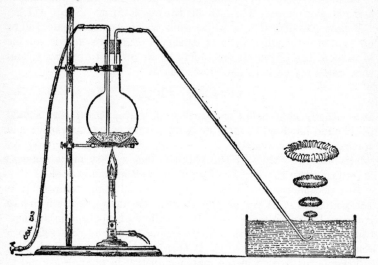

Fig. 133.

Preparation of phosphine.

with the air it ignites spontaneously (the ignition is due to an impurity) and forms white vortex rings of oxides of phosphorus.

$$3NaOH + P_4 + 3H_2O \rightarrow 3NaH_2PO_2 + PH_3$$
$$\text{sodium} \qquad \text{phosphine}$$
$$\text{hypophosphite}$$

Phosphine is a colourless gas with a garlic-like odour and is extremely poisonous. It shows similarities to ammonia, forming salts, for example, PH₄Cl, phosphonium chloride (*cf.* ammonium chloride).

Phosphorus Trichloride, PCl₃, is made by allowing dry chlorine to react with warm yellow phosphorus in an inert atmosphere.

$$P_4 + 6Cl_2 \rightarrow 4PCl_3$$

Phosphorus trichloride is a liquid (boiling-point, 76° C.) which fumes in air owing to the action of moisture upon it. The liquid is attacked by water forming phosphorous acid.

$$PCl_3 + 3H_2O \rightarrow H_3PO_3 + 3HCl$$
phosphorous
acid

Phosphorus pentachloride, PCl_5, is made from phosphorus trichloride by the action of chlorine upon it. A yellowish solid separates out. It sublimes when heated, decomposing into the trichloride and chlorine, but on cooling forms the original pentachloride.

$$PCl_5 \underset{\text{cool}}{\overset{\text{heat}}{\rightleftharpoons}} PCl_3 + Cl_2$$
phosphorus phosphorus chlorine
pentachloride trichloride

It also attacks water vigorously forming phosphoric acid,

$$PCl_5 + 4H_2O \rightarrow H_3PO_4 + 5HCl$$
phosphoric
acid

Phosphorus trioxide, P_4O_6 (phosphor*ous* oxide), is made by burning phosphorus in a limited supply of air and passing the mixture of trioxide and pentoxide through a tube surrounded by a water jacket at 50° C., and containing a loose cotton-wool plug. The pentoxide remains solid and is retained by the plug. The trioxide vapour passes on and is condensed in a freezing mixture.

$$P_4 + 3O_2 \rightarrow P_4O_6$$
phosphorous
oxide
$$P_4 + 5O_2 \rightarrow P_4O_{10}$$
phosphoric
oxide

Phosphorous oxide is a white volatile solid which readily reacts with water to form phosphorous acid.

$$P_4O_6 + 6H_2O \rightarrow 4H_3PO_3$$
phosphorous
acid

Phosphorus pentoxide, P_4O_{10} (phosphor*ic* oxide), is made by igniting phosphorus in a plentiful supply of air. A small piece of phosphorus is placed in a crucible on a plate of glass under a bell-jar containing dry air. The phosphorus is ignited. It burns with a brilliant flame and a white solid finally settles on the plate. This is quickly scraped into a dry bottle.

$$P_4 + 5O_2 \rightarrow P_4O_{10}$$

It can be purified by heating it in a current of dry oxygen. The latter converts any trioxide formed into pentoxide.

Phosphorous pentoxide is a white solid which reacts vigorously with water, and is one of the best drying agents known. With hot water it forms phosphoric acid.

$$P_4O_{10} + 6H_2O \rightarrow 4H_3PO_4$$
$$\text{phosphoric acid}$$

Acids of Phosphorus. Many acids of phosphorus exist, the chief of which are phosphorous and phosphoric acids.

Phosphorous acid, H_3PO_3, can be made as indicated above by the action of water on either phosphorous oxide or phosphorus trichloride.

It is a crystalline solid (melting-point, 70° C.) and can form salts, the phosphites.

Preparation of Phosphoric Acid, H_3PO_4, from Phosphorus. Heat a small amount of red phosphorus in a dish with fairly conc. nitric acid (1 : 1, acid and water) for some time on a water bath in a fume chamber. Dilute with water and filter off any unattacked red phosphorus. The product is a solution of phosphoric acid, H_3PO_4. It may be concentrated, and any nitric acid removed, by heating it till the temperature reaches 200 °C., above which it decomposes. The nitric acid is reduced to oxides of nitrogen and there is a copious evolution of brown fumes during the experiment. The presence of a phosphate can be shown by warming a portion of the filtrate with nitric acid and excess ammonium molybdate. A yellow colouration or precipitate of ammonium phosphomolybdate indicates the presence of a phosphate.

$$P_4 + 20HNO_3 \rightarrow 4H_3PO_4 + 20NO_2 + 4H_2O$$
$$\text{phosphoric} \quad \text{nitrogen}$$
$$\text{acid} \quad \text{peroxide}$$

Phosphoric acid is a colourless syrupy liquid and forms salts, the phosphates.

Phosphatic Fertilisers. Phosphorus is an element essential to soil fertility. Plants absorb it from the soil and, if the crop is consumed by man, phosphorus passes into his bone structure and protoplasm. Much of it is lost to the soil in general by sewage disposal and by depositing human remains in cemeteries.

The loss must be made good. Bone-meal and basic slag are used, both of which contain calcium phosphate, $Ca_3(PO_4)_2$. This compound is, however, almost insoluble in water and becomes available to the plants very slowly. A more soluble material, quicker in action, can be made by stirring calcium phosphate with an appropriate weight of 65% sulphuric acid. An acid calcium phosphate is formed.

$$Ca_3(PO_4)_2 + 2H_2SO_4 \rightarrow Ca(H_2PO_4)_2 + 2CaSO_4$$

The product is dried and sold as "superphosphate".

QUESTIONS

1. Describe a method (a) for the preparation of white phosphorus from calcium phosphate, (b) for the conversion of white phosphorus into the red form.

   Compare and contrast the properties of these two forms of phosphorus. What reaction, if any, has each form with chlorine, and with caustic soda solution? (D.)

2. Compare the properties of the two forms of phosphorus. How may phosphorus be converted into *two* of the following: (a) phosphorus pentachloride, (b) phosphine, (c) phosphorus pentoxide? (O. and C.)

3. Describe with necessary detail how you would prepare from phosphorus reasonably pure specimens of (a) orthophosphoric acid, (b) phosphorus trichloride. (O.)

4. Show by giving three chemical properties in each case that sodium is a metal and that phosphorus is a non-metal.

   Starting with metallic sodium and yellow phosphorus, describe fully how you would prepare specimens of (a) phosphine, and (b) sodium phosphate. (L.)

5. How does phosphorus react with (a) oxygen, (b) chlorine, (c) sodium hydroxide?

   Describe how the products behave when brought into contact with water. (O. and C.)

6. Describe the preparation of (a) phosphorus trichloride, and (b) phosphine. Show how the latter is related to ammonia. (L.)

7. How is phosphorus obtained from bone ash? State how white phosphorus can be converted into red phosphorus, and name three respects in which they differ from one another. Write the formulæ of two chlorides, one hydride, and two oxides of phosphorus. How does the highest oxide of phosphorus react with water and for what purposes is this oxide used? (L.)

8. Contrast, tabulating your answer, *six* properties of two allotropes of phosphorus. Starting with one of these forms, briefly describe the preparation of the other form from it. How is phosphine usually prepared in the laboratory? Give details. (L.)

CHAPTER XXXV

EXTRACTION, PROPERTIES AND USES OF THE COMMON METALS

METALS AND NON-METALS

THESE are the first two classes into which elements can be divided. **The classification is not perfect,** but it serves to group together elements which have certain broad characteristics in common. These are summed up in the following table.

METALS	NON-METALS
Physical Properties.	
Metals are of high density.	Non-metals are of low density.
Metals have a lustre, and can be polished.	Non-metals have no metallic lustre, and cannot be polished.
Metals are malleable * and ductile.*	Non-metals are brittle.
Metals have great tensile strength (that is, they can withstand great strains).	Non-metals have little tensile strength.
Metals have high melting-points.	Non-metals have low melting-points.
Metals are good conductors of heat and electricity.	Non-metals are poor conductors of heat and electricity.
Metals are usually sonorous (that is, a metallic bar when struck will ring).	Non-metals are not sonorous.
Chemical Properties.	
Metallic oxides are **BASIC.**	Non-metallic oxides are **ACIDIC.**
Metals will replace the hydrogen of acids, forming salts.	Non-metals do not form salts.
Chlorides of metals are true salts.	Chlorides of non-metals are not true salts and often react readily with water.
Metals do not combine readily with hydrogen.	Non-metals form stable compounds with hydrogen.

* Malleable—can be beaten into sheets.
Ductile —can be drawn into wire.

There are exceptions to the list. Mercury, for example, is a liquid; sodium and potassium have a low specific gravity, a low melting-point and possess little tensile strength.

The non-metal, graphite, on the other hand, is quite a good conductor of electricity.

The following table shows in diagrammatic form how some of the properties of metals and non-metals are connected with one another.

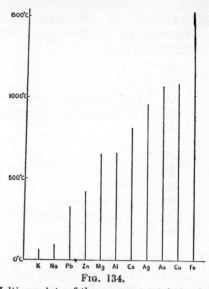

FIG. 134.

Melting-points of the common metals (excluding mercury). The metals are represented by their symbols.

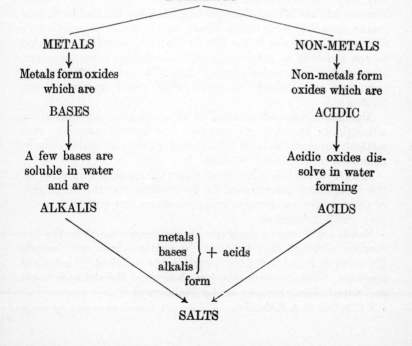

ELEMENTS

METALS

Metals form oxides which are

BASES

A few bases are soluble in water and are

ALKALIS

NON-METALS

Non-metals form oxides which are

ACIDIC

Acidic oxides dissolve in water forming

ACIDS

metals
bases } + acids
alkalis
form

SALTS

EXTRACTION OF METALS FROM THEIR NATURALLY OCCURRING COMPOUNDS. PROPERTIES AND USES OF THE METALS.

K
Na
Ca } Very reactive. Never found as free element.
Mg } Extracted by electrolysis. All isolated after 1807.
Al
Zn
Fe
Pb
Cu
Hg } Not very reactive. May be found in nature as the free
Ag } element. Known for a very long time.
Au

N.B. In this chapter the physical properties of the metals are arranged in the same order throughout. Any property which is not in accordance with metallic properties generally, is shown by an asterisk.

The electrochemical series shown above indicates (in a very rough way only) the inverse order in which the elements were isolated. Thus metals low in the series such as gold, silver and lead have been known since very early times. Metals high in the series proved very difficult to isolate and it was Davy's work on electrolysis which led to the isolation of potassium, sodium, calcium, magnesium and aluminium over a period of years from 1807 (when Davy isolated potassium and sodium) to about 1850 (when aluminium was isolated).

Aluminium was not obtained in the first place by electrolysis although its manufacture nowadays is entirely confined to that method, but it was isolated by the action of the very active element potassium on aluminium chloride.

In view of what we have learnt about the electro-chemical series, this order seems quite natural for we should expect the compounds of the very active elements such as sodium and potassium to be very stable substances.

Metals low down in the series are frequently found as the free element, although they may also be obtained from ores because the amounts found as the free metal are not sufficient for industrial purposes. Gold, however, the last element of the series, is found and mined almost entirely as the free element.

Extraction is a Reduction. Metals are found as a rule as their oxides or salts, chiefly sulphides and carbonates, and therefore the process by which the metal is obtained must be **reduction,** since there is bound to be a **decrease in the proportion of the non-metallic part of the substance.** Thus iron is found as hæmatite impure ferric oxide, Fe_2O_3, and, as the process ends with the production of metallic iron, then the oxygen must have been removed.

$$Fe_2O_3 + 3CO \rightarrow 2Fe + 3CO_2$$

In this case carbon monoxide is the reducing agent.

The reduction in the case of the first members of the series is brought about by electrolysis, which can be regarded as a very powerful oxidation and reduction process which often results in the formation of the elements present in the compound electrolysed (see Electrolysis, p. 109). As far as the metals are concerned the process is one of reduction, although no reducing agent (in the ordinary sense of the term) is used.

The usual reducing agents employed for the less electropositive metals are carbon in the form of coke, and carbon monoxide (made from the coke by passing a limited amount of air over the hot coke). You may ask why the usual laboratory reducing agents are not employed; for example, hydrogen. The reason is that, in an industrial process the chief concern is cost, and coke easily wins on that score.

POTASSIUM AND SODIUM

Occurrence. These metals occur chiefly as the chloride, sodium as common salt in the huge salt deposits of Cheshire, and elsewhere, and potassium chloride as carnallite (together with magnesium chloride) in the deposits in Stassfurt (see p. 289). Other sources of the elements are:

sodium carbonate . . in Africa and in ash of sea plants.
sodium nitrate . . Chile saltpetre in Chile.
sodium chloride . . in sea-water and many salt lakes.
potassium nitrate . . saltpetre found in India.
potassium carbonate . in the ash of land plants.

POTASSIUM

Potassium is obtained by a method similar to that shown below for sodium, that is, by the electrolysis of fused caustic potash.

Physical Properties of Potassium.

State	.	Solid.
Appearance	.	White metal, possessing a lustre.
Density	.	0·86 gm. per c.c.*
Malleability	.	Malleable and ductile.
Tensile strength	.	Does not possess tensile strength to any appreciable extent.*
Melting-point	.	62° C.*
Conduction of heat and electricity	.	Good conductor of heat and electricity.

* Properties marked with an asterisk are not in accordance with the general properties of metals.

In chemical properties potassium is very similar to sodium, but it is slightly more reactive. Thus, when a small piece of potassium is placed on water it darts about, melts and gives off hydrogen which at once ignites and burns with the oxygen of the air, giving a lilac-coloured flame.

$$2K + 2H_2O \rightarrow 2KOH + H_2$$

Flame Test for Potassium (see p. 287).

Compounds of potassium (especially the chloride) colour the bunsen flame lilac and the colour is still visible through blue glass.

Hence, although the lilac colour of potassium is easily masked by the presence even of traces of sodium, the potassium colour is visible when viewed through blue glass.

In general, the salts of potassium are less soluble in water than the corresponding salts of sodium (the principal exceptions are potassium hydroxide, potassium carbonate and bicarbonate). This accounts for the use in medicine of such substances as potassium permanganate, potassium iodide, potassium chlorate, where one would expect the cheaper sodium salt to be used. The extra cost of preparing the potassium salt instead of the cheaper sodium salt is outweighed by the ease of obtaining the potassium salt from its solution because of its lower solubility.

SODIUM

Extraction of Sodium. Sodium is not obtained directly from its naturally occurring compound, common salt, but from sodium hydroxide, which is made from common salt by electrolysis of brine (see p. 206). The reason is this: since sodium (and potassium) will attack water to liberate hydrogen, it is essential to exclude all traces of water from the apparatus. The solids, common salt and sodium hydroxide, will not conduct an electric current, but, when they have been heated and melted, both liquids become conductors. So far there seems little difference between them. **Common salt, unfortunately, does not melt until a temperature of 800° C. is reached, whereas caustic soda melts at about 300° C.** At the former temperature much of the sodium would volatilise and come off as a gas, and great difficulty would be experienced in preventing its oxidation by the atmosphere. This makes sodium chloride very unsuitable as a source of sodium. Davy isolated potassium, and sodium a few days later, in 1807, by electrolysis of caustic potash and caustic soda respectively.

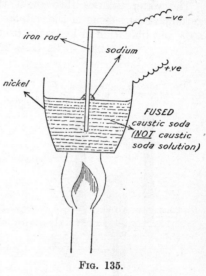

Electrolysis of Fused Caustic Soda. A few sticks of solid caustic soda are placed in a nickel crucible and the solid is heated until it melts and forms a liquid. (Do not confuse this with a solution of caustic soda in water—if a solution were used there would be no sodium formed at all. See p. 373.) An iron rod which is connected to the negative

Fig. 135.

Preparation of sodium.

terminal of a battery is dipped into the molten caustic soda and the positive wire is attached to the crucible (Fig. 135). A current of electricity is passed and after a time small silvery globules of sodium collect round the negative pole or cathode. Hydrogen is given off at the cathode also, and serves to prevent the oxidation of the sodium by the atmosphere. Oxygen is evolved from the anode or positive pole.

The explanation of the action is:

The sodium hydroxide ionises

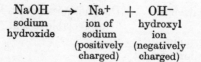

$$NaOH \rightarrow Na^+ + OH^-$$

sodium	ion of	hydroxyl
hydroxide	sodium	ion
	(positively	(negatively
	charged)	charged)

The ions of sodium become ordinary sodium on losing their electric charge at the cathode.

At the anode, the hydroxyl groups react to give water and oxygen and the latter is liberated.

$$\begin{matrix} OH \\ OH \end{matrix} \rightarrow H_2O \quad + \quad O$$

hydroxyl   water   atom of oxygen
groups   (pairs of these link up to form
(these cannot exist   molecules and come off
as such)   as oxygen gas)

The water diffuses throughout the fused caustic soda and is decomposed by some of the sodium with the formation of caustic soda and liberation of hydrogen from the cathode.

$$2Na + 2H_2O \rightarrow 2NaOH + H_2$$

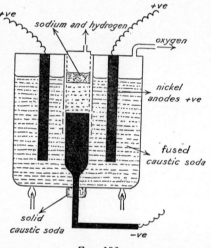

FIG. 136.

Extraction of sodium from caustic soda.

Industrial Process. This is an adaptation by Castner of the electrolytic process. The crucible is replaced by an iron container with an iron rod as cathode and nickel cylinder as anode (Fig. 136). The sodium is liberated into a cylindrical nickel gauze from which it is removed from time to time. The principle of the method is the same as that of the method described above. The oxygen and hydrogen liberated at the same time are valuable by-products.

Physical Properties of Sodium.

State . . .	Solid.
Appearance . .	White, silvery, shining metal. Rapidly tarnishes.
Density . .	0·97 gm. per c.c.*
Malleability . .	Very malleable. Can be cut with a knife.
Tensile strength .	Does not possess tensile strength to any appreciable extent.*
Melting-point .	97° C.*
Conduction of heat and electricity .	Conducts both heat and electricity.

* Properties marked with an asterisk are not in accordance with the general properties of metals.

Action of Sodium on Exposure to Air. Sodium is attacked by the oxygen of the air to form sodium oxide. The moisture present combines with some of the oxide to form the hydroxide and finally, after a time, the carbon dioxide of the air combines with the sodium hydroxide to form sodium carbonate.

$$4Na + O_2 \rightarrow 2Na_2O$$
$$Na_2O + H_2O \rightarrow 2NaOH$$
$$2NaOH + CO_2 \rightarrow Na_2CO_3 + H_2O$$

If heated in air or oxygen, sodium burns with a golden yellow flame to form sodium peroxide.

$$2Na + O_2 \rightarrow Na_2O_2$$

Action of Sodium on Water. Place a small piece of sodium (a piece the size of a very small pea will be *ample*) on the surface of water in a large dish or trough. The sodium will dart about and melt to a silvery ball of molten sodium, liberating hydrogen and forming sodium hydroxide (see p. 157).

$$2Na + 2H_2O \rightarrow 2NaOH + H_2$$
$$\text{sodium}$$
$$\text{hydroxide}$$

If a light is applied the hydrogen given off will burn with a golden-yellow flame. Sodium and potassium are so readily attacked by the oxygen and water-vapour of the atmosphere that they are usually kept below the surface of petroleum oil.

Flame Colouration. Sodium compounds impart a persistent golden-yellow colouration to the flame (see flame test, p. 287). This colour is invisible when viewed through blue glass. The above serves as a very definite and delicate test for the presence of sodium in a compound.

Uses of Sodium. Sodium is used in the manufacture of sodium cyanide for gold extraction, and also to make sodium peroxide. A liquid alloy of sodium and potassium is used in making high temperature thermometers.

CALCIUM

Occurrence. Calcium occurs abundantly and very widely distributed as—*calcium carbonate*, $CaCO_3$, which is found as chalk, limestone, marble, calcite, Iceland spar and aragonite.

It also occurs as—

Calcium sulphate as gypsum, $CaSO_4.2H_2O$, and as anhydrite $CaSO_4$.

It occurs, less abundantly, as fluorspar, calcium fluoride, and as calcium phosphate.

N

Extraction. Calcium is obtained by the electrolysis of fused calcium chloride. (Notice that whereas sodium and potassium are obtained from the hydroxide, calcium cannot be obtained from the hydroxide by electrolysis. The reason is that if calcium hydroxide is heated strongly it becomes quicklime and, if that is heated strongly, it merely becomes white hot and does not melt. Quicklime is one of the most refractory substances known.)

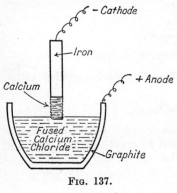

FIG. 137.

Extraction of calcium.

Calcium chloride, which is obtained as a by-product from the Solvay process (see p. 256), is placed in a graphite (carbon) container which is the anode of the cell (Fig. 137). The cathode is an iron rod which just dips below the surface of the calcium chloride. The calcium chloride is melted and the electrolysis is begun. As the calcium forms on the iron rod, the latter is withdrawn and an irregular stick of calcium is gradually formed. Chlorine is evolved at the anode. If the anode were made of metal it would be attacked by the chlorine, but chlorine has no effect on carbon, and the gas is a valuable by-product.

$$CaCl_2 \rightarrow Ca + Cl_2$$
calcium   calcium   chlorine
chloride

Physical Properties of Calcium.

State . . .	Solid.
Appearance . .	Silvery, shining, metal which rapidly tarnishes in air owing to formation of film of oxide.
Density . .	1·55 gm. per c.c.*
Malleability . .	Malleable and ductile.
Tensile strength .	Possesses fair tensile strength.
Melting-point .	810° C.
Conduction of heat and electricity .	Good conductor of heat and electricity.

* Properties marked with an asterisk are not in accordance with the general properties of metals.

Action of Air on Calcium. Calcium is not as reactive as sodium and potassium, and it is not necessary to keep it below the surface of petroleum.

A white film of oxide is formed on the surface on exposure to air.

Calcium will burn with a brick-red flame if heated in the air and forms quicklime, calcium oxide.

$$2Ca + O_2 \rightarrow 2CaO$$

Action of Calcium on Water (see p. 157).

Calcium is attacked by water liberating hydrogen and forming a solution of calcium hydroxide.

$$Ca + 2H_2O \rightarrow Ca(OH)_2 + H_2$$

The action is not so vigorous as that of sodium or potassium and a test-tube full of water can safely be placed over a piece of calcium in a dish containing water, and the hydrogen can be collected.

Flame Colouration (see p. 287).

Calcium compounds (especially the chloride) colour the flame brick red.

Uses. Calcium is being used more and more in certain technical processes as a reducing agent.

GENERAL IDEAS ON EXTRACTION OF METALS FROM THEIR ORES

The three metals already described are obtained from their compounds by electrolysis. We now come to those metals which have been obtained for many years and which are used in far greater quantities than the more electropositive elements.

The metals zinc, iron, lead and copper are found chiefly as the impure carbonates and sulphides, and iron is also found as the impure oxide. The following processes are amongst those commonly used in the extraction of metals from their ores *although all the processes are not used in connection with each individual metal.*

Concentration of Ores. Very often, as ores are found contaminated with earthy impurities, methods are employed to pick out the richer ores, or those worth working up, and to reject the poorer grades. This may be done by hand, or the earthy matter may be washed away by means of a stream of water, leaving the heavier ores. In the case of copper ores, the latter drop through a magnetic separator where metallic ores are deflected into one pile, whilst the lower grade ores and earthy impurities are not deflected and pass straight on.

Roasting in Air. Since many ores contain either the sulphide or carbonate of the metal, a preliminary roasting in air will remove the sulphur as sulphur dioxide and drive off carbon dioxide from the carbonate. Thus:

$$2ZnS + 3O_2 \rightarrow 2ZnO + 2SO_2$$

zinc   zinc   sulphur
sulphide   oxide   dioxide

$$ZnCO_3 \rightarrow ZnO + CO_2$$

zinc   zinc
carbonate   oxide

The oxides are usually easier to deal with than the sulphides or carbonates.

Reduction Process. The roasted ore must now be reduced. The reduction in the case of zinc and iron is by means of carbon. In some cases (*e.g.*, lead and copper), by a suitable adjustment of the roasting process, it is possible to oxidise some of the sulphide to oxide, and then by adding more of the ore to supply sufficient sulphide to react with the oxygen of the oxide, leaving the metal in both cases.

Purification. The product of the reduction process is seldom a pure specimen of the metal. Purification may be carried out electrolytically (as in the case of copper and zinc). By electrolysis a very pure product is usually obtainable. In other cases the impure metal is heated in a hearth open to the air, when impurities oxidise and rise to the surface as a scum and can be removed.

ZINC

Occurrence. Zinc occurs in various parts of the world, as
     Zinc carbonate, $ZnCO_3$, Calamine, and
     Zinc sulphide, ZnS, Zinc blende.

The ores are first roasted in air when the oxide is formed whether the ore is calamine or zinc blende.

$$ZnCO_3 \rightarrow ZnO + CO_2$$
$$2ZnS + 3O_2 \rightarrow 2ZnO + 2SO_2$$

The sulphur dioxide is frequently used for the manufacture of sulphuric acid.

The ore is now mixed with coke and placed in a fireclay retort to the end of which there is attached a fireclay condenser (Fig. 138). On the end of this condenser is placed an iron "prolong" which collects any zinc which escapes the condenser. The mixture is heated by means of producer-gas for about twenty-four hours. The zinc oxide is reduced to metallic zinc, the carbon becoming carbon monoxide, which burns at the mouth of the condenser.

$$ZnO + C \rightarrow Zn + CO$$

zinc   carbon   zinc   carbon
oxide   monoxide

The zinc distils out of the retort and the bulk of it condenses to molten zinc in the condenser, and is removed from time to time. Owing to the presence of air in the retort, some of the zinc burns to zinc oxide and condenses on the upper part of the condenser as

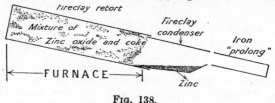

FIG. 138.
Extraction of zinc.

"zinc dust" (this is a mixture of zinc and zinc oxide). The impure zinc obtained in this way is purified by electrolysis. It is frequently "granulated" by running the molten metal into water. (In this granulated form the zinc offers a larger area for action with, e.g., dilute acids.)

Physical Properties of Zinc.

State . . . Solid.
Appearance . . Bluish-white metal. Can be polished.
Density . . 7·0 gm. per c.c.
Malleability . . Malleable at temperatures between 100° and 150° C.
Tensile strength . Possesses high tensile strength.
Melting-point . 420° C.
Conduction of heat
and electricity . Good.

Action of Zinc on Exposure to Air. Zinc is only very slightly attacked by air owing to the formation of a film of oxide which prevents further action. If heated in air, it will burn with a bluish-green flame forming the oxide.

$$2Zn + O_2 \rightarrow 2ZnO$$

Action of Acids. Ordinary samples of zinc are attacked readily by the mineral acids. Very pure zinc is only slowly attacked, and in recent years the purity of even the commercial zinc is so high that very often the action of dilute sulphuric acid on zinc is slow at first. The common actions are expressed by the equations:

$$\underset{\text{zinc}}{Zn} + \underset{\substack{\text{dilute}\\\text{sulphuric}\\\text{acid}}}{H_2SO_4} \rightarrow \underset{\substack{\text{zinc}\\\text{sulphate}}}{ZnSO_4} + \underset{\text{hydrogen}}{H_2}$$

With hot concentrated sulphuric acid, sulphur dioxide is formed.

$$Zn + 2H_2SO_4 \rightarrow ZnSO_4 + 2H_2O + SO_2$$

$$\underset{\substack{\text{zinc} \\ \text{hydrochloric} \\ \text{acid}}}{Zn} + \underset{\text{dilute}}{2HCl} \rightarrow \underset{\substack{\text{zinc} \\ \text{chloride}}}{ZnCl_2} + \underset{\text{hydrogen}}{H_2}$$

$$3Zn + 8HNO_3 \rightarrow 3\underset{\substack{\text{zinc} \\ \text{nitrate}}}{Zn(NO_3)_2} + 4H_2O + \underset{\substack{\text{nitric} \\ \text{oxide}}}{2NO}$$

(In the last case other oxides of nitrogen and even ammonia, which combines to form ammonium nitrate, may be formed.)

Action of Alkalis on Zinc. Zinc is attacked by a hot strong solution of either caustic soda or caustic potash. (Zinc oxide is amphoteric, see p. 211.) Hydrogen is evolved and sodium or potassium zincate solution is left.

$$\underset{\substack{\text{sodium} \\ \text{hydroxide}}}{Zn + 2NaOH} \rightarrow \underset{\substack{\text{sodium} \\ \text{zincate}}}{Na_2ZnO_2} + \underset{\text{hydrogen}}{H_2}$$

Action of Water on Zinc. Water does not attack zinc to any appreciable extent. Zinc at a red heat is attacked by steam with the formation of hydrogen

$$Zn + H_2O \rightarrow \underset{\substack{\text{zinc} \\ \text{oxide}}}{ZnO} + \underset{\text{hydrogen}}{H_2}$$

Uses of Zinc

Galvanising. As previously stated, zinc is not attacked to any appreciable extent by the air or water. It is therefore used extensively to protect iron from rusting, and many household articles, for example wash tubs, small baths, wire netting, are "galvanised" to prevent the rusting of the sheet iron of which they are made. The article to be galvanised is cleaned in acid and then dipped in molten zinc and withdrawn. A layer of zinc, formed on top of the iron, protects it. Furthermore, if the layer of zinc is broken, although rusting takes place where the iron surface is exposed, the rusting does not spread.

In the formation of alloys, for example, brass contains copper and zinc (2 : 1).

Small Batteries. Zinc has an extensive use as the negative pole of small dry batteries. If you examine the dry battery of your electric torch you will find that the outer casing (other than cardboard) is made of zinc.

IRON

Occurrence. The occurrence of iron, a metal of immense importance, has had a profound effect upon the development of the countries in which it is found. Your geography book will tell you how important it has been to this country that iron ore and coal (which is necessary for the extraction of large quantities of the metal) have been found comparatively close together. The chief ores are the following:

Hœmatite, found in Great Britain, United States, France, Germany, Belgium and Spain, is impure ferric oxide Fe_2O_3.

Magnetite, or magnetic iron ore, Fe_3O_4, occurs in Sweden and North America.

Spathic iron ore, ferrous carbonate, $FeCO_3$, is found in Great Britain.

Iron is widely diffused and is present in many soils.

Extraction. Since the demand for iron is so great (64 million tons of pig-iron are made yearly), iron has often to be made from poorer grade ores, containing a certain amount of earthy impurities. The ores are first roasted in air when ferric oxide, Fe_2O_3, is the main product.

This impure oxide is mixed with coke and limestone and introduced into a blast furnace (Fig. 139). The blast furnace is a tall structure about 100 ft. high and 20 ft. in diameter at the widest part. It contains a firebrick lining inside an iron shell, and a blast of hot air can be introduced low down in the furnace through several pipes known as tuyères. A well at the bottom of the furnace serves to hold the molten iron and slag until these can be run off. The mixture of ore, coke and limestone is fed in continuously from the top, and a blast furnace, once started, is kept going for months at a time, until repairs are necessary or work lacking.

Chemistry of the Action

As the hot air comes into contact with the white-hot coke, the latter burns to form carbon dioxide.

$$C + O_2 \rightarrow CO_2$$
$$\text{carbon} \qquad \text{carbon}$$
$$\text{(coke)} \qquad \text{dioxide}$$

The above reaction liberates a very large quantity of heat, and it is this heat which keeps up the high temperature necessary for the reduction process.

As the gas is forced higher up the furnace the supply of oxygen (from the air) becomes less and the carbon dioxide coming into contact with white-hot coke is reduced to carbon monoxide.

$$CO_2 + C \rightarrow 2CO$$

This carbon monoxide at the high temperature (about 1,000°) **reduces** the iron oxide to metallic iron forming carbon dioxide.

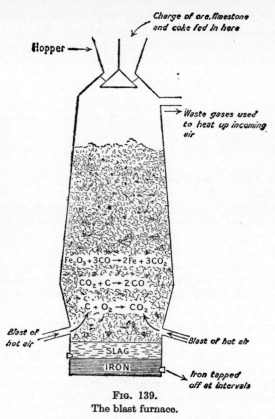

Fig. 139.
The blast furnace.

$$Fe_2O_3 + 3CO \rightarrow 2Fe + 3CO_2$$

ferric   carbon   iron   carbon
oxide   monoxide   dioxide

The molten iron runs to the bottom of the furnace.

Action of the Limestone. The limestone, which has been introduced together with the ore, is first decomposed at this high temperature to form quicklime.

$$CaCO_3 \rightarrow CaO + CO_2$$

calcium   carbon
oxide   dioxide

The earthy impurities contain a certain amount of silica (SiO_2), which is an acidic oxide, and this combines with the basic oxide, quicklime, to form calcium silicate.

$$SiO_2 + CaO \rightarrow CaSiO_3$$

silica   lime   calcium silicate

(compare $CO_2 + CaO \rightarrow CaCO_3$)

The earthy impurities and this calcium silicate form a molten slag which does not mix with the iron but floats above it and can be run off separately. At one time this slag was a waste material, and the countryside has been defaced by the presence of huge slag heaps. The slag is being increasingly used at the present time for making roads.

By courtesy of Messrs. Wellman and Co

PLATE X.

An open-hearth furnace, being charged with raw material for steel-making. The furnace shown has a capacity of 80 tons, taking about ten hours for melting and refining the charge.

The molten iron is run off into moulds made in sand, where it is allowed to cool in long bars about 3 ft. long and 4 in. in diameter. It is known as "cast iron" or "pig iron".

Cast iron is impure iron and contains varying amounts of impurities, such as carbon (4%), with smaller quantities of silicon, phosphorus and sulphur. This impure iron melts at a lower temperature than pure iron and is brittle. It cannot be welded, and possesses little tensile strength. (Thus it could not be used for bridges or motor-car construction.) It is, however, used extensively for small castings, such as fire-grates, railings, hot-water pipes, bunsen burner bases and for many other purposes where little strain is imposed.

N*

Wrought iron is the purest form of iron, and is obtained from cast iron by heating it with ferric oxide in a furnace by a process known as "puddling". The oxygen of the iron oxide oxidises the impurities, carbon and sulphur, to the gaseous oxides which escape, and phosphorus to phosphates and silicon to silicates, and these form as a slag. The semi-molten mass is then hammered and rolled so that the slag is squeezed out and a mass of almost pure iron remains.

Wrought iron has a higher melting-point than cast iron. It is malleable and can be forged, hammered and welded when hot. It is tough and fibrous, and can withstand some strain, but is not elastic, and, if subjected to great strain, it will bend. It cannot be tempered. It is used to make iron nails, sheeting, ornamental work, horse shoes and agricultural implements. It has been replaced to a large extent in recent years by mild steel, which can be made more cheaply.

Steel consists of iron containing a small percentage of carbon (or other substances). The amount of carbon is carefully controlled.

Steel is made to a large extent to-day by the Siemens open hearth process. (This accounts for about 90% of the steel made in Great Britain.) It will be seen that the majority of the impurities of cast iron are non-metals, the oxides of which are acidic. The object of the Siemens process is to oxidise the impurities to their acidic oxides, and these combine with a basic lining supplied to the furnace. In this process pig iron, scrap iron and iron oxide (the last of these supplies the oxygen for oxidation of impurities) are melted in an open hearth which has been lined with a basic material (carbonates of calcium and magnesium are used, the oxides being formed at this high temperature). The amount of carbon is regulated at from 0·5% to 1%, and small quantities of various metals such as manganese, nickel, chromium or tungsten, are added according to the quality of the steel and the use to which the steel will be put.

Properties of Steel. Steel is hard, tough and strong. If cooled gradually, steel can subsequently be hammered into shape or drilled, because is it fairly soft. By heating it and suddenly cooling it, the steel becomes very hard indeed, of very high tensile strength, and elastic. By reheating the steel to carefully regulated temperature, steels of different degrees of hardness and brittleness can be obtained. This is called "tempering".

Steel has a most extensive use in the manufacture of all kinds of products, from battleships and bridges to knives and needles. Modern motor-cars frequently have a pressed steel frame, roads are reinforced with steel mesh, buildings are frequently erected round a frame of steel. So extensive are the uses of steel that it would be difficult to imagine a civilised world without it. At the present time the chemist is continuously providing the engineer with differing types of steel which the engineer adapts to increasingly diverse purposes. It would be difficult to predict the future of the stainless and rustless steels which are being made more cheaply and used more extensively.

Physical Properties of Pure Iron.

State . . . Solid.
Appearance . Pure iron is a white metal and can be polished.
Density . . 7·9 gm. per c.c.
Malleability . . Extremely malleable.
Tensile strength . High.
Melting-point . 1,525° C.
Conduction of heat and electricity . Good.

Iron can also be magnetised.

Action of Iron on Exposure to Air. In the presence of air and moisture, iron readily rusts, forming a reddish-brown solid which consists mainly of hydrated ferric oxide ($Fe_2O_3 . x\, H_2O$).

If finely divided (for example iron filings), it will burn in air or oxygen to form the magnetic oxide of iron, Fe_3O_4.

$$3Fe + 2O_2 \rightarrow Fe_3O_4$$

Action of Steam on Heated Iron. Iron, at a red heat, is attacked by *excess* of steam, forming magnetic oxide of iron (triferric tetroxide) and hydrogen,

$$3Fe + 4H_2O \rightarrow Fe_3O_4 + 4H_2$$
$$\text{triferric}$$
$$\text{tetroxide}$$

The above action is reversible (see p. 127).

[Note that if air and water act together on iron, ferric oxide is formed, but if either of these substances acts separately the product is triferric tetroxide.]

Action of Acids on Iron.

1. *Dilute Sulphuric and Hydrochloric Acids.* Iron is attacked by these dilute acids in accordance with the following equations:

$$Fe + H_2SO_4 \rightarrow FeSO_4 + H_2$$
ferrous
sulphate

$$Fe + 2HCl \rightarrow FeCl_2 + H_2$$
ferrous
chloride

The ferrous salt is obtained because the hydrogen which is given off during the action is a reducing agent.

2. *Nitric Acid.* Dilute nitric acid gives a series of complex reactions in which oxides of nitrogen and even ammonia are formed.

Passive State. If a piece of clean iron is dipped into concentrated nitric acid there is apparently no action and the iron no longer behaves as a piece of ordinary iron; for example, it will not displace copper from copper sulphate solution nor is it attacked by dilute nitric acid, which normally does attack it. If, however, the piece of iron is scratched while in contact with, say, dilute nitric acid, a vigorous reaction occurs. This "passive state" is supposed to be due to a protective layer of oxide formed on the iron by the strong oxidising agent, concentrated nitric acid.

Iron will readily combine with sulphur and chlorine when heated with them to form ferrous sulphide (p. 7) and ferric chloride (p. 278) respectively.

Ferrous and Ferric Compounds. Iron exercises two valencies and forms two sets of compounds; it may be either divalent, as in *ferrous* compounds, or trivalent, as in *ferric* compounds. The formulæ of the important ferrous and ferric compounds are:

	Ferrous. Valency of iron = 2	*Ferric.* Valency of iron = 3
Oxide . . .	FeO	Fe_2O_3
Hydroxide . .	$Fe(OH)_2$	$Fe(OH)_3$
Chloride . .	$FeCl_2$	$FeCl_3$
Sulphate . .	$FeSO_4$	$Fe_2(SO_4)_3$
	Soluble *ferrous* compounds give *green* solutions.	Soluble *ferric* compounds give *yellow* or *brown* solutions.

Solutions of pure ferrous compounds are distinguished from those of pure ferric compounds by the colour difference just mentioned, though, in dilute solution, the green colour of the ferrous salts is very pale. Ferric hydroxide and ferric oxide are both brown, while ferrous hydroxide, as usually precipitated, is green. Ferrous oxide is so readily oxidised by oxygen of the air that it cannot be kept under ordinary laboratory conditions.

A Simple Test for a Ferrous Salt. Dissolve a little ferrous sulphate in water. To the solution, add sodium hydroxide (caustic soda) solution. A dirty-green, gelatinous precipitate of ferrous hydroxide is formed. This reaction is typical of a ferrous salt.

$$FeSO_4 + 2NaOH \rightarrow Fe(OH)_2 \downarrow + Na_2SO_4$$
$$\text{ferrous hydroxide}$$

Where it is exposed to the air, the precipitate will become brown because it is oxidised to ferric hydroxide.

$$2Fe(OH)_2 + O + H_2O \rightarrow 2Fe(OH)_3$$

A Simple Test for a Ferric Salt. Using ferric chloride solution, repeat the test just given. In this case, the precipitate is reddish brown and is ferric hydroxide. This reaction is typical of a ferric salt.

$$FeCl_3 + 3NaOH \rightarrow Fe(OH)_3 \downarrow + 3NaCl$$
$$\text{ferric hydroxide}$$

Conversion of a Ferrous Salt to a Ferric Salt. The conversion of a ferrous salt to a ferric salt is an *oxidation* and is brought about by *oxidising agents.* This point is fully discussed on p. 130.

To a solution of ferrous sulphate, which is green, add dilute sulphuric acid. Warm the mixture and add cautiously a few drops of concentrated nitric acid. (A dark brown colouration will probably appear. For an explanation of this see the "brown ring" test, p. 343.) Heat the mixture. Brown fumes of nitrogen peroxide are given off and a brown or yellow solution remains. It contains ferric sulphate (test as described above).

The nitric acid has oxidised the ferrous sulphate to ferric sulphate and has itself been reduced to nitric oxide, which, on exposure to air, gives nitrogen peroxide.

$$2FeSO_4 + H_2SO_4 + O \rightarrow Fe_2(SO_4)_3 + H_2O$$
$$\uparrow$$
$$\text{from nitric acid}$$

or fully,

$$6FeSO_4 + 2HNO_3 + 3H_2SO_4 \rightarrow 3Fe_2(SO_4)_3 + 4H_2O + 2NO$$

Ferrous chloride is converted by the oxidising agent, chlorine, to ferric chloride.

$$2FeCl_2 + Cl_2 \rightarrow 2FeCl_3$$
$$\text{ferrous} \qquad \text{ferric}$$
$$\text{chloride} \qquad \text{chloride}$$
$$\text{(green)} \qquad \text{(yellow)}$$

Conversion of a Ferric Salt to a Ferrous Salt. The conversion of a ferric salt to a ferrous salt is a *reduction*, and is brought about by *reducing agents* (see p. 343).

To a solution of ferric chloride (yellow), add hydrochloric acid and zinc. There is vigorous effervescence with evolution of hydrogen. Leave the mixture for 20 to 30 minutes. The colour of the liquid is now green. It contains ferrous chloride. (Test, after filtering, as described above.)

The reducing agent here is the "nascent" hydrogen produced by the action of the zinc upon the hydrochloric acid. It is much more active than ordinary gaseous hydrogen, which will not reduce a ferric salt in aqueous solution.

$$2HCl + Zn \rightarrow ZnCl_2 + \underset{\text{nascent}}{2H}$$

$$\underset{\substack{\text{ferric} \\ \text{chloride}}}{2FeCl_3} + \underset{\text{nascent}}{2H} \rightarrow \underset{\substack{\text{ferrous} \\ \text{chloride}}}{2FeCl_2} + 2HCl$$

Other reducing agents will convert ferric salts to ferrous salts. The action of two common ones is represented in the following equations with an indication of the colour changes involved.

$$\underset{\text{yellow}}{2FeCl_3} + \underset{\substack{\text{hydrogen} \\ \text{sulphide}}}{H_2S} \rightarrow \underset{\text{green}}{2FeCl_2} + 2HCl + \underset{\substack{\text{yellow} \\ \text{precipitate}}}{S \downarrow}$$

$$\underset{\text{yellow}}{Fe_2(SO_4)_3} + SO_2 + 2H_2O \rightarrow \underset{\text{green}}{2FeSO_4} + 2H_2SO_4$$

LEAD

Occurrence. Lead occurs as galena, lead sulphide, PbS, and is distributed widely in the earth's crust, being found to some extent in most parts of the world. It has been known for a very long time —lead pipes were used by the Romans in this country.

Extraction. The galena is roasted with excess of air to form litharge.

$$2PbS + 3O_2 \rightarrow 2PbO + 2SO_2$$

The litharge is then reduced to lead by heating with carbon in a small blast furnace.

$$PbO + C \rightarrow Pb + CO$$

Some iron is added to reduce any remaining galena,

$$PbS + Fe \rightarrow Pb + FeS$$

and lime to combine with earthy impurities and form a molten slag. The molten ferrous sulphide and slag are tapped off separately from the lead.

Physical Properties of Lead.

State . . . Solid.
Appearance . . Bluish white.
Density . . 11·4 gm. per c.c.
Malleability . . Very malleable. Can be cut with a knife. Has a metallic lustre but speedily tarnishes.
Tensile strength . Fair.
Melting-point . 327° C.
Conduction of heat and electricity. Good conductor of heat and electricity.

Action of Air and Water on Lead. Lead is attacked by air and water together, a white layer being formed on the lead which consists of a mixture of lead hydroxide and lead carbonate. Lead is used extensively as piping to carry water supplies and cases of poisoning have been traced to the removal of this layer of hydroxide and carbonate by the water passing through. If the water is slightly "hard" (see p. 162) a protective coat appears to be formed and none of the lead is removed. In many water supplies nowadays, the water is specially hardened by the addition of lime to prevent any of these poisonous effects.

If lead is strongly heated in air it forms litharge, a yellow powder,

$$2Pb + O_2 \rightarrow 2PbO$$

but if heated to a carefully regulated temperature of about 450° C. red lead is formed,

$$3Pb + 2O_2 \rightarrow Pb_3O_4$$
$$\text{triplumbic}$$
$$\text{tetroxide}$$
$$\text{(red lead)}$$

Action of Acids on Lead. Dilute sulphuric acid and dilute hydrochloric acid have no action on lead.

Hot concentrated sulphuric acid attacks lead (compare copper):

$$Pb + 2H_2SO_4 \rightarrow PbSO_4 + 2H_2O + SO_2$$
$$\qquad\qquad \text{lead} \qquad\qquad \text{sulphur}$$
$$\qquad\qquad \text{sulphate} \qquad\quad \text{dioxide}$$

Nitric acid attacks it forming nitric oxide (chiefly),

$$3Pb + 8HNO_3 \rightarrow 3Pb(NO_3)_2 + 4H_2O + 2NO$$
$$\text{Dilute nitric} \qquad \text{lead} \qquad \text{water} \quad \text{nitric}$$
$$\text{acid} \qquad\quad \text{nitrate} \qquad\qquad \text{oxide}$$

The only satisfactory laboratory method of obtaining lead in solution is by the action of dilute nitric acid to form lead nitrate solution.

Uses of Lead

(1) Lead is used extensively in the manufacture of water and gas piping and as lead sheet for roofing. It is particularly valuable for piping as it is easily repaired and joints are quickly made. It is also soft and bends easily at corners. It is also used in the manufacture of lead shot, solder, pewter and type-metal.

(2) For Paint. If lead is exposed to the action of acetic acid, air, water-vapour and carbon dioxide, it is converted into a basic carbonate known as white lead $(Pb(OH)_2 . 2PbCO_3)$ and as such is used for paint.

(3) Lead is used in the manufacture of electrical accumulators and as a covering material for cables.

COPPER

Occurrence. Native copper or boulder copper is found as the element round the shores of Lake Superior but most of the copper used in industry occurs as copper pyrites, $CuFeS_2$.

Extraction from Boulder Copper. This is merely refined, very often on the spot, by building a container round the mass of copper,

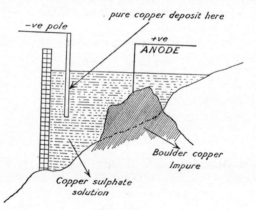

FIG. 140.

Purification of boulder copper where the metal is found.

filling the container with copper sulphate solution and making the impure native copper the anode of a cell (Fig. 140). A strip of copper is made the cathode and pure copper deposits on this from the anode as the electrolysis proceeds. (See electrolysis of copper sulphate solution, p. 124.)

Extraction of Copper from Copper Pyrites. The extraction from sulphur-containing ores is long and tedious since the copper must be of a high degree of purity, otherwise it is useless for electrical purposes. The chemistry of the process is too difficult for inclusion here.

Physical Properties of Copper.

State . . . Solid.
Appearance . . A red metal possessing a lustre and can be polished.
Density . . 8·95 gm. per c.c.
Malleability . . Very malleable and ductile.
Tensile strength . The metal is of fairly high tensile strength.
Melting-point . 1,100° C.
Conduction of heat and electricity. It is an excellent conductor of both heat and electricity.

Action of Air and Water on Copper. Copper is not attacked by pure air or water, but when exposed to the atmosphere it is slowly attacked on the surface with the formation of a green solid. This is probably a basic sulphate.

When heated in the air, copper forms a layer of black copper oxide on the surface.

$$2Cu + O_2 \rightarrow 2CuO$$

Action of Acids on Copper. Copper has no action on either dilute sulphuric acid or dilute hydrochloric acid.

With dilute nitric acid, oxides of nitrogen are liberated, chiefly nitric oxide, and a blue or bluish-green solution of copper nitrate remains.

$$3Cu + 8HNO_3 \rightarrow 3Cu(NO_3)_2 + 4H_2O + 2NO$$

dilute nitric acid   copper nitrate   water   nitric oxide

With hot concentrated sulphuric acid sulphur dioxide is liberated and copper sulphate is formed.

$$Cu + 2H_2SO_4 \rightarrow CuSO_4 + 2H_2O + SO_2$$

Flame Colouration (see p. 287). The chloride of copper colours the flame a characteristic green colour, often with a bluish zone. This colouration is seen when a little salt is put into a fire. (Coal often contains small quantities of copper pyrites.)

Uses of Copper

1. For conduction of electric current. Being the cheapest good conductor of electricity, copper is used extensively for making wire for electrical purposes. It must be very pure because traces of impurity greatly increase its electrical resistance.
2. For coinage and ornamental work, being only slightly attacked by the atmosphere.

3. Alloys. Copper is often alloyed with other metals. The chief alloys are brass (copper and zinc), bronze (copper and tin), German silver (copper, zinc and nickel), and coinage metal, "copper" (copper and tin), "silver" (silver, copper, zinc and nickel).

QUESTIONS

1. What are the chief chemical properties which distinguish the metals from the non-metallic elements?
   Give *three* distinct methods by which metals can be converted into their oxides, using iron, copper and zinc as examples, and state how the oxides of these metals may be distinguished from one another. (B.)
2. Illustrate, by reference to two chemical and to four physical properties, the chief differences between the metals and the non-metals. Describe briefly how a metal may be isolated from (a) a naturally occurring sulphide, *and* (b) a naturally occurring carbonate. (N.U.J.B.)
3. Give the chemistry of the extraction of iron from hæmatite (ferric oxide). How would you prepare (a) ferric oxide starting from ferric chloride, (b) anhydrous ferrous chloride starting from iron? (N.U.J.B.)
4. Name the products, if any, formed when
   (a) air is passed over heated (i) iron, (ii) copper, (iii) carbon.
   (b) steam is passed over heated (i) iron, (ii) copper, (iii) carbon.
   (c) hydrogen is passed over heated (i) black iron oxide, (ii) copper oxide.
   Give the equations for
   (d) ONE of these reactions which shows simultaneous oxidation and reduction.
   (e) TWO of these reactions which together illustrate one reversible change. (N.U.J.B.)
5. Explain what is meant by the statement that iron forms two series of salts. Describe how you would prepare from metallic iron *one* member of each of these series, and give *one* physical and *one* chemical distinguishing test for (a) ferrous, (b) ferric salts. (B.)
6. Outline the chemistry of the extraction of (a) zinc from zinc carbonate (calamine), (b) lead from lead sulphide (galena).
   State two general methods of preparing salts, and illustrate each method by reference to the preparation of a zinc salt. (N.U.J.B.)
7. The chief ore of zinc is zinc blende, ZnS. Outline the chemistry of the extraction of zinc from this ore. State *two* important uses of zinc. Starting from zinc, how would you prepare specimens of (a) zinc oxide and (b) crystalline zinc sulphate? (N.U.J.B.)
8. Describe the electrolytic process for the refining of copper. Name four distinct uses of copper.
   Starting with cupric oxide, how would you obtain (a) a dry crystalline specimen of copper sulphate, (b) a sample of metallic copper? (C.W.B.)

CHAPTER XXXVI

ALUMINIUM

Occurrence. Compounds of this metal are quite abundant. Some of the better known are:

Mica, felspar $K_2Al_2Si_6O_{15}$
Kaolin (china clay) $Al_2Si_2O_7 \cdot 2H_2O$ (used in making porcelain)
Corundum Al_2O_3
Cryolite Na_3AlF_6
Bauxite $Al_2O_3 \cdot 2H_2O$

Extraction. Bauxite is first purified.* It is then electrolysed as below, in solution in molten cryolite.

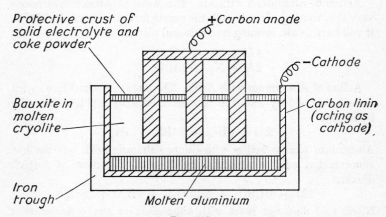

FIG. 141.
Extraction of aluminium.

* The crude bauxite is first heated under pressure with caustic soda solution. Undissolved ferric oxide (impurity) is filtered off.
$$Al_2O_3 + 2NaOH \rightarrow 2NaAlO_2 + H_2O$$
Silica (impurity) also dissolves
$$SiO_2 + 2NaOH \rightarrow Na_2SiO_3 + H_2O$$
To the filtered solution, freshly prepared aluminium hydroxide is then added. This induces precipitation of this compound by hydrolysis, but the silica remains in solution.
$$NaAlO_2 + 2H_2O \rightleftharpoons NaOH + Al(OH)_3$$
The aluminium hydroxide is filtered, washed and heated to give the pure oxide.
$$2Al(OH)_3 = Al_2O_3 + 3H_2O.$$

The iron trough is long and many anodes dip into it at intervals. The solid surface crust is broken from time to time and more bauxite is stirred in. If bauxite is kept continually in excess, the cryolite is unchanged and can be used indefinitely.

$$2Al_2O_3 \rightarrow 4Al + 3O_2$$
$$\text{at} \qquad \text{at}$$
$$\text{cathode} \quad \text{anode}$$

Oxygen liberated at the anode burns the carbon electrodes away. This is a considerable expense in the process. Aluminium is tapped off from time to time and is very pure.

PHYSICAL PROPERTIES OF ALUMINIUM

State:	solid.
Appearance:	silvery white.
Density:	2.69 gm. per c.c.
Malleability:	can be rolled into foil.
Tensile strength:	moderate (high in alloys).
Melting point:	659° C.
Conduction of heat and electricity:	good.

Action of Aluminium with Air. The metal acquires a continuous, very thin coating of oxide and this resists further action. At 800° C., it will burn in air, forming its oxide and nitride.

$$4Al + 3O_2 \rightarrow 2Al_2O_3$$
$$2Al + N_2 \rightarrow 2AlN.$$

Action of Aluminium with Acids. The metal attacks dilute hydrochloric acid slowly and the concentrated acid rapidly, liberating hydrogen.

$$2Al + 6HCl \rightarrow 2AlCl_3 + 3H_2$$

Aluminium has no action with dilute sulphuric acid, but the hot, concentrated acid is attacked by it with liberation of sulphur dioxide.

$$2Al + 6H_2SO_4 \rightarrow Al_2(SO_4)_3 + 6H_2O + 3SO_2$$

Nitric acid does not react with aluminium at any concentration. This is probably because it produces on the metal a thin layer of insoluble oxide, which protects the metal from further attack. (See passive iron, p. 384.)

Action of Aluminium with Caustic Alkali Solution. The metal, especially in powder form, reacts violently with bench caustic soda solution, liberating hydrogen and leaving sodium aluminate in solution. (Caustic potash similar.)

$$2Al + 2NaOH + 2H_2O \rightarrow 2NaAlO_2 + 3H_2$$

USES OF ALUMINIUM

(1) *In alloys.* The metal is a constituent of several light alloys.

They combine high tensile strength with lightness, and have been much used in aircraft construction. *Duralumin* (Al, Mg, Cu, Mn), *magnalium* (Mg, Al) and *aluminium bronze* (Al, Cu) are well known.

(2) *In cooking utensils.* Cheapness, lightness, good appearance, good conductivity for heat and resistance to attack by cooking solutions have combined to make aluminium very popular in the kitchen. Aluminium vessels must not be exposed to alkaline solutions (see above).

(3) *In overhead electric cables.* The lightness of aluminium is very favourable here. Thick cables of low resistance can be employed without undue weight.

(4) *In aluminium paint.* The powdered metal is used, with oils.

(5) *In Thermit processes.* The reactions between aluminium powder and oxides of other metals are commonly very exothermic. If a mixture of ferric oxide and aluminium powder, known as "thermit", is "fired" by burning a piece of magnesium ribbon stuck into it, a violent reaction will occur. Molten iron is produced with a slag of aluminium oxide floating on it.

$$Fe_2O_3 + 2Al \rightarrow 2Fe + Al_2O_3$$

This reaction has been used in welding steel parts *in situ* by means of the molten metal produced, and in incendiary bombs in the early part of World War II. Similar reactions are also used in isolating certain metals, e.g. chromium.

$$Cr_2O_3 + 2Al \rightarrow 2Cr + Al_2O_3$$

Aluminium Hydroxide, $Al(OH)_3$. This is a colourless, gelatinous solid. It can be precipitated by adding dilute ammonia to a solution of an aluminium salt. The precipitate is then filtered, washed and allowed to dry.

$$Al_2(SO_4)_3 + 6NH_4OH \rightarrow 2Al(OH)_3 \downarrow + 3(NH_4)_2SO_4.$$

Amphoteric Nature. If freshly prepared, the hydroxide is soluble in dilute mineral acid, forming a salt and water only, and so is *basic.*

$$Al(OH)_3 + 3HCl \rightarrow AlCl_3 + 3H_2O$$

It is also soluble in caustic alkali solution, again forming a salt and water only, and so is *acidic.*

$$Al(OH)_3 + NaOH \rightarrow NaAlO_2 + 2H_2O$$

Showing both basic and acidic character, it is *amphoteric.*

From the above it is obvious that caustic alkali solution, when added to an aluminium salt solution, will react in two stages:

(1) The production of a colourless, gelatinous precipitate of aluminium hydroxide

$$Al_2(SO_4)_3 + 6NaOH \rightarrow 2Al(OH)_3 \downarrow + 3Na_2SO_4$$

(2) When the alkali is added *in excess*, this precipitate redissolves to give a colourless solution of sodium aluminate.

$$Al(OH)_3 + NaOH \rightarrow NaAlO_2 + 2H_2O$$

Uses. This hydroxide has the property of readily absorbing colouring matter, e.g. if precipitated in a solution containing litmus, it will give a blue "lake" as precipitate. This makes it useful as a mordant for certain dyes. It will also carry down bacteria from water and finds a use in treating sewage. Precipitated in the fibres of cloth, it makes the cloth waterproof.

Aluminium Oxide, Al_2O_3. This is a white solid. It is most conveniently prepared by first adding dilute ammonia to an aluminium salt solution. This precipitates aluminium hydroxide.

$$Al_2(SO_4)_3 + 6NH_4OH \rightarrow 2Al(OH)_3 + 3(NH_4)_2SO_4$$

The precipitate is then filtered, washed, dried and heated.

$$2Al(OH)_3 \rightarrow Al_2O_3 + 3H_2O$$

If prepared at the lowest temperature possible, it shows both basic and acidic properties:

basic $Al_2O_3 + 6HCl \rightarrow 2AlCl_3 + 3H_2O$
acidic $Al_2O_3 + 2NaOH \rightarrow 2NaAlO_2 + H_2O$
sodium
aluminate

It strongly heated, it passes into a form which insoluble in both acid and alkali.

Uses. The most important form of this oxide is *bauxite*, Al_2O_3. $2H_2O$, from which the metal is extracted, p. 391. It also occurs in an impure form as *emery* and is used as an abrasive.

Coloured by the presence of impurities, this oxide occurs as the gems, *ruby* (iron and titanium), *sapphire* (chromium) and *amethyst* (manganese).

Aluminium Chloride, $AlCl_3$. This is a pale yellow solid. Being readily hydrolysed by water, it fumes in damp air with evolution of hydrogen chloride. If required anhydrous, it must be prepared by *heating* aluminium foil in *dry* chlorine or *dry* hydrogen chloride. The apparatus is the same as for ferric chloride (p. 278).

$$2Al + 3Cl_2 \rightarrow 2AlCl_3$$
$$2Al + 6HCl \rightarrow 2AlCl_3 + 3H_2$$

The anhydrous solid reacts rather violently with water. It forms the hydrate, $AlCl_3.6H_2O$, and, with excess water, dissolves and hydrolyses considerably.

$$AlCl_3 + 3H_2O \rightleftharpoons Al(OH)_3 + 3HCl$$

On evaporation to dryness, the solution leaves hydroxide as residue.

Aluminium Sulphate, $Al_2(SO_4)_3.18H_2O$. This is a white solid. It is conveniently prepared by dissolving the oxide or hydroxide of the metal in dilute sulphuric acid, leaving the acid in slight excess to counter hydrolysis. The sulphate can be obtained by evaporation to small bulk and cooling, but it does not crystallise well.

$$2Al(OH)_3 + 3H_2SO_4 \rightarrow Al_2(SO_4)_3 + 6H_2O$$

It is most commonly encountered in the form of *potash alum*, one of an important group of salts called *the alums*.

THE ALUMS

These are double salts of general formula

$$X_2SO_4 . Y_2(SO_4)_3 . 24H_2O$$

where X is Na, K or NH_4
and Y is Fe(ic), Al or Cr.*

(Note that X is a *mono*valent and Y a *tri*valent metal.)

The alums crystallise well from water. They all have similar crystalline shape, consequently crystalline layers of different alums may be deposited on one another to produce large, composite crystals with layers of varying colours.

The two commonest alums are:

Potash alum $K_2SO_4 . Al_2(SO_4)_3 . 24H_2O$ (colourless)
Ferric alum $(NH_4)_2SO_4 . Fe_2(SO_4)_3 . 24H_2O$ (purple)

Preparation of Potash Alum (commonly called simply "alum"). Potassium sulphate and aluminium sulphate are weighed out approximately in the proportions of their molecular weights.

$$K_2SO_4 : Al_2(SO_4)_3 . 18H_2O$$
174 gm.   666 gm.

Use, say, one-twentieth of these figures, i.e. 8.7 gm. and 33 gm. These amounts are dissolved, with heat, in as little water as possible. In the case of the aluminium salt, the water should be slightly acidified with dilute sulphuric acid. The hot solutions are then mixed and stirred. On cooling, colourless alum crystals separate out and are filtered, washed with cold distilled water and dried.

---

* Alums are also formed from some less common metals, for example caesium and rubidium.

Other alums can be prepared in a corresponding way.

Aluminium Nitrate, $Al(NO_3)_3 . 9H_2O$. This is an unimportant salt. It can be prepared by dissolving freshly prepared aluminium hydroxide in dilute nitric acid and crystallising in the usual way.

$$Al(OH)_3 + 3HNO_3 \rightarrow Al(NO_3)_3 + 3H_2O$$

It shows the usual behaviour of the nitrate of a heavy metal when heated.

$$4Al(NO_3)_3 \rightarrow 2Al_2O_3 + 12NO_2 + 3O_2$$

QUESTIONS

1. Name the most important ore of aluminium and outline the extraction of the metal from it. (The ore may be assumed pure.) How, and in what conditions does aluminium react with (a) hydrochloric acid, (b) sulphuric acid, (c) caustic soda?

2. What do you understand by the expression "an alum"?
Being provided with aluminium foil, concentrated sulphuric acid, iron filings, caustic potash and ammonia, how would you proceed to produce reasonably pure samples of (a) ordinary alum, (b) iron alum (ferric ammonium alum)? Water may be assumed to be available.

3. State briefly, giving essential experimental conditions, how anhydrous aluminium chloride may be prepared in the laboratory. What would be the effect of adding caustic potash solution slowly, with shaking, to a solution of this salt until the alkali was in excess?

4. Starting from aluminium metal and the usual laboratory reagents, how would you prepare reasonably pure samples of (a) aluminium hydroxide, (b) aluminium oxide, (c) aluminium sulphate?

CHAPTER XXXVII

REVISION NOTES

Mode of Revision. No two students will revise in quite the same way. For proper revision concentration is essential, and the following method is suggested, because it does ensure concentration.

(a) *Self-Expression.* Suppose you are revising a topic such as "Chlorine and Chlorides". It does not matter what the subject is, the procedure is the same. *Begin with a pencil and a large sheet of paper.* Write down in note form as many important ways of making chlorine as you can. Write down briefly its properties, under headings if such classification is possible. Make a list of all the metallic chlorides you know, show how to prepare them, and state their principal properties. For the preparation of many substances a well-labelled diagram, apart from the equation, will be all that is required for this purpose. Draw the diagram freehand, or use a stencil, for all that is required of a diagram is to show clearly the apparatus you would use. This need not be an "art" as well as a chemistry exercise.

Write down all you can, and do not give in too quickly, for there is a very great difference between a hasty revision and one in which you are determined to give in only when you have put down *all* the points you can possibly remember. Now turn to your book and you will find the correct answer to many points about which you were doubtful, and many points you did not know at all! The next time you revise that chapter, which should be some time after the first revision, you may content yourself with writing down only those points which you did not know before. The thing to remember is that **true revision must involve self-expression.** The following revision exercises are arranged with that point in mind.

(b) *Approach the Subject from a Different Angle.* If you have followed the text of this book, you will have met most of the matter about the various salts classified according to the acid radical contained in them. Thus all metallic carbonates are discussed under "carbonates", because they are similar in many ways, and all metal oxides are discussed under "oxides" and so on.

Now attempt to revise in a different way by picking out one metal, for example copper, and writing down the preparation and properties of its various compounds. Because this may waste a lot of time over unimportant compounds and because a little help often goes a long way, the table opposite has been drawn up to give you the starting point for a revision of this type.

To use this table for any particular metal, for example, copper:— Write down on a sheet of paper the formula for copper oxide, copper hydroxide, copper chloride, sulphate, nitrate, carbonate, sulphide.

Give a few words to indicate their preparation and properties, including such actions as those of heat, water, acids, alkalis, concentrated sulphuric acid, etc. By omitting certain numbers you can make the revision just as superficial or thorough as you please.

> By revising in this way you approach the matter from an entirely different angle and you test your capacity to extract any required knowledge from its context.

(c) *Read Widely.* You will find many excellent text-books and "popular" books on Chemistry either at your school or in your public library. Every one of these will give you new ideas, presenting old material in a different form. Chemistry is a "live" subject and of increasing importance to you in the civilised life you lead. Read about some of the applications and you will spend many interesting hours and widen and deepen your knowledge.

General Statements. The following list of statements of a general type is given purposely without the common exceptions to them. **Some are perfectly general and others less so, but all are of wide application.** Learn them and attempt to write down (the symbols or formulæ only will be quite sufficient to test yourself) any substances which are exceptions to the general statement. The exceptions are given later on p. 409.

1. Acids contain hydrogen which can be replaced by a metal.
2. Sodium, potassium and ammonium salts are soluble in water.
3. Nitrates are soluble in water.
4. An ammonium salt heated with any alkali and water yields ammonia gas.
5. Heavy metal carbonates yield the oxide and carbon dioxide when heated.
6. Heavy metal nitrates decompose under the action of heat to yield the oxide, nitrogen peroxide and oxygen.
7. Metals are attacked by nitric acid.
8. The action of an acid on a carbonate is to yield carbon dioxide.

Particular Statements. The following list of questions summarises

	O''	OH'	Cl'	Br'	I'	NO₃'	SO₄''	CO₃''	S'	HSO₄'	HS'	HCO₃'	SO₃''	HSO₃'
K	1	3	3	2	2	3	2	2	1	1	1	1	2	1
Na	1	3	3	2	2	3	2	3	1	1	1	3	1	1
Ca	3	3	2	—	—	1	2	3	—	—	—	3	—	—
Mg	2	1	1	1	1	—	1	1	—	—	—	1	—	—
Zn	2	1	1	—	—	1	2	1	1	—	—	—	—	—
Fe	2	2	2	—	—	—	2	—	2	—	—	—	—	—
Pb	3	2	2	—	—	2	2	1	2	—	—	—	—	—
H	3	—	3	2	2	3	3	3	3	—	—	—	3	—
Cu	3	2	1	—	—	1	3	1	1	—	—	—	—	—
Ag	—	—	3	2	2	3	—	—	1	—	—	—	—	—

3 = Very Important.
2 = Average Importance.
1 = Not very important.
‿ = Unimportant, or not known.

many of the unusual facts which are you likely to overlook. Do not turn to the answers (p. 410) until you have tried them all.

1. What is the ONLY common alkaline gas?
2. What is the ONLY gas which turns brown on exposure to air?
3. What is the ONLY common substance almost insoluble in cold water but quite soluble in hot water?
4. What common substance increases its solubility in water very little for a large increase in temperature?
5. What substances are LESS soluble in hot water than in cold?
6. Which salts cannot be prepared, in solution, by the following method?

$$\left.\begin{array}{c}\text{base}\\\text{or alkali}\end{array}\right\} + \text{acid} \rightarrow \text{SALT} + \text{water}$$

7. What are the 2 common insoluble chlorides?
8. What are the common insoluble sulphates?
9. What are the 3 common soluble carbonates?
10. What are the 4 common soluble metallic hydroxides?
11. What are the common amphoteric oxides?

(Answers on p. 410.)

COMMON GASES

There are about a dozen common gases.

Consider the following types of apparatus (Fig. 142). Look at

Diagram A.

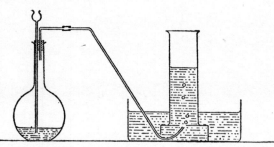

Example:—

Gas	Materials under equation	Test
H_2	$Zn + H_2SO_4 \rightarrow ZnSO_4 + H_2$ zinc dilute zinc hydrogen sulphuric sulphate acid	Explodes with air when flame applied.

FIG. 142A.

Diagram B.

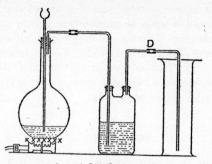

If you would use a second wash bottle, state in third column the liquid you would put into it.

Gas	Materials under equation	Test

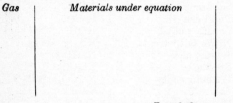

FIG. 142B.

Diagram C.

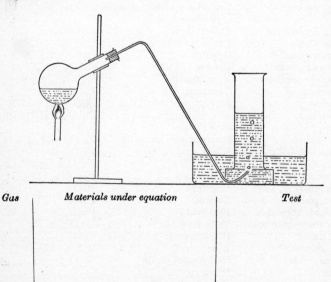

Gas	Materials under equation	Test

FIG. 142c.

them for a few minutes and then close your book. Make a fair copy of each one on a separate page of your exercise book. Under each diagram make a table of gases which can be prepared using this type of apparatus. (Some gases may come under two headings, according to state of purity required.) Fill in under the columns the details required. The answers are given on p. 408.

For any cases for which these diagrams do not apply draw a well-labelled sketch of the whole apparatus.

Common Names

Hydrochloric acid	Spirits of salt	HCl
Nitric acid.	Aqua fortis	HNO_3
Sulphuric acid	Oil of vitriol	H_2SO_4
Ammonium chloride	Sal-ammoniac	NH_4Cl
Potassium carbonate	Pearl-ash	K_2CO_3
Potassium hydroxide	Caustic potash	KOH
Potassium nitrate	Nitre, saltpetre	KNO_3
Sodium bicarbonate	Baking soda	$NaHCO_3$
Sodium carbonate	Soda-ash	Na_2CO_3
Sodium carbonate*	Washing soda	$Na_2CO_3 . 10H_2O$
Sodium chloride	Salt	$NaCl$
Sodium hydroxide	Caustic soda	$NaOH$
Sodium nitrate	Chile saltpetre	$NaNO_3$
Sodium sulphate*	Glauber's salt	$Na_2SO_4 . 10H_2O$
Calcium carbonate	Limestone, chalk, marble, calcite.	$CaCO_3$
Calcium hydroxide	Slaked lime.	$Ca(OH)_2$
Calcium oxide	Lime, quicklime	CaO
Calcium sulphate*	Gypsum	$CaSO_4 . 2H_2O$
Calcium sulphate*	Plaster of Paris	$CaSO_4 . \frac{1}{2}H_2O$
Magnesium sulphate*	Epsom salt	$MgSO_4 . 7H_2O$
Zinc carbonate	Calamine	$ZnCO_3$
Zinc oxide	Zinc white	ZnO
Zinc sulphate*	White vitriol	$ZnSO_4 . 7H_2O$
Zinc sulphide	Zinc blende	ZnS
Ferric oxide*	Rust; as ore, hæmatite	$Fe_2O_3 . nH_2O$
Triferric tetroxide	Black oxide of iron	Fe_3O_4
Ferrous sulphate*	Green vitriol	$FeSO_4 . 7H_2O$
Lead carbonate (basic).	White lead	$Pb(OH)_2 . 2PbCO_3$
Lead monoxide	Litharge	PbO
Lead sulphide	Galena	PbS
Triplumbic tetroxide	Red lead	Pb_3O_4
Copper carbonate (basic)	Malachite	$Cu(OH)_2 . CuCO_3$
Cupric oxide	Black copper oxide	CuO
Cupric sulphate*	Blue vitriol	$CuSO_4 . 5H_2O$
Cuprous oxide	Red copper oxide	Cu_2O
Carbon	Black lead	C
Sulphur	Brimstone	S

* Hydrated.

TESTS FOR ACID RADICALS IN SOLUTION

1. Sulphate Radical. To the solution of the suspected sulphate in water add dilute hydrochloric acid and then barium chloride solution. A white precipitate of barium sulphate indicates the presence of a sulphate in the original solution. For example,

$$BaCl_2 + Na_2SO_4 \rightarrow BaSO_4\downarrow + 2NaCl$$

barium sodium barium sodium
chloride sulphate sulphate chloride
(INSOLUBLE)

ionically: $Ba^{++} + SO_4^{--} \rightarrow BaSO_4\downarrow$

2. (a) Chloride Radical. To the solution of the suspected chloride in water add dilute nitric acid, followed by silver nitrate solution. A white curdy precipitate of silver chloride (soluble in ammonia) indicates the presence of the chloride radical in the original solution. For example,

$$AgNO_3 + KCl \rightarrow AgCl\downarrow + KNO_3$$

silver potassium silver potassium
nitrate chloride chloride nitrate
(INSOLUBLE)

ionically: $Ag^+ + Cl^- \rightarrow AgCl\downarrow$

(b) Bromide Radical. Repeat as 2 (a). A pale yellow precipitate of silver bromide, sparingly soluble in ammonia, indicates the presence of a bromide. For example,

$$AgNO_3 + NaBr \rightarrow AgBr\downarrow + NaNO_3$$

sodium silver
bromide bromide
(INSOLUBLE)

ionically: $Ag^+ + Br^- \rightarrow AgBr\downarrow$

(c) Iodide Radical. Repeat as 2 (a). A yellow precipitate of silver iodide, insoluble in ammonia, indicates the presence of an iodide.

$$AgNO_3 + KI \rightarrow AgI\downarrow + KNO_3$$

potassium silver
iodide iodide

ionically: $Ag^+ + I^- \rightarrow AgI\downarrow$

3. Nitrate Radical. (Brown ring test, see p. 343.) To the cold solution of the nitrate in a boiling-tube add ferrous sulphate solution and (with care!) pour concentrated sulphuric acid steadily down the side of the tube. A brown ring at the junction of the concentrated sulphuric acid layer and aqueous layer proves the presence of a nitrate.

4. Carbonate Radical. Add dilute nitric acid to the substance in a test-tube (or to its solution in water) Effervescence is observed and carbon dioxide is evolved which, if passed into lime-water, gives a white precipitate of chalk. For example,

$$CuCO_3 + 2HNO_3 \rightarrow Cu(NO_3)_2 + H_2O + CO_2 \uparrow$$
copper carbonate ... carbon dioxide

ionically: $CuCO_3 + 2H^+ \rightarrow Cu^{++} + H_2O + CO_2 \uparrow$

TESTS FOR BASIC RADICALS

The following are some simple tests for the basic radicals present in single salts (not mixtures). The metallic radicals are in combination, not free as elements. Thus the test for potassium will be given by any salt or compound of potassium.

Flame Colouration (see p. 287).

Potassium. Lilac. Visible through blue glass.

Sodium. Persistent golden yellow.

Calcium. Brick red.

Copper. Green or bluish green.

Action of caustic soda solution on solution of soluble salt of metal.

Zinc Salt. White precipitate of zinc hydroxide. Soluble in excess of alkali. Precipitate ignited in crucible forms zinc oxide (yellow hot, white cold).

For example:

$$ZnSO_4 + 2NaOH \rightarrow Na_2SO_4 + Zn(OH)_2$$
zinc hydroxide

ionically: $Zn^{++} + 2OH^- \rightarrow Zn(OH)_2 \downarrow$

$$Zn(OH)_2 \rightarrow ZnO + H_2O$$
zinc oxide

Iron. *Ferrous Salts*. Green gelatinous precipitate of ferrous hydroxide.

Ferric Salts. Reddish-brown gelatinous precipitate of ferric hydroxide.

For example:

$$FeSO_4 + 2NaOH \rightarrow Fe(OH)_2 + Na_2SO_4$$
ferrous hydroxide

ionically: $Fe^{++} + 2OH^- \rightarrow Fe(OH)_2 \downarrow$

$$FeCl_3 + 3NaOH \rightarrow Fe(OH)_3 + 3NaCl$$
ferric hydroxide

ionically: $Fe^{+++} + 3OH^- \rightarrow Fe(OH)_3 \downarrow$

Lead Salts. White precipitate of lead hydroxide soluble in excess of alkali. Precipitate ignited in crucible forms lead oxide, a yellow powder.

For example:

$$Pb(NO_3)_2 + 2NaOH \rightarrow 2NaNO_3 + Pb(OH)_2$$
lead
hydroxide

ionically: $Pb^{++} + 2OH^- \rightarrow Pb(OH)_2 \downarrow$

$$Pb(OH)_2 \rightarrow PbO + H_2O$$
lead
oxide

Ammonium Group, NH_4. *Boil* with caustic soda solution Ammonia gas (turns red litmus blue) evolved.

For example:

$$NH_4Cl + NaOH \rightarrow NH_3 + H_2O + NaCl$$
ammonia
gas

ionically: $NH_4^+ + OH^- \rightarrow NH_3 \uparrow + H_2O$

$$(NH_4)_2SO_4 + 2NaOH \rightarrow 2NH_3 + 2H_2O + Na_2SO_4$$

It will be seen that the common metallic radicals (if present singly) can be detected either by

(*a*) Flame colouration or

(*b*) Action of caustic soda solution.

Answer the following questions, using the above methods:—

1. How would you show that potassium chloride contained (*a*) potassium, (*b*) the chloride group?
2. How would you distinguish between zinc sulphate and sodium sulphate?
3. A weak solution contains either ferrous sulphate or ferric sulphate. How would you decide?
4. How would you distinguish between sodium nitrate and sodium chloride?
5. A given black powder is either black copper oxide or ferrous sulphide. Explain how you would decide which of the two it is.
6. A white powder is either potassium sulphate or potassium carbonate. How would you ascertain which it is?

ACTIONS OF HEAT ON COMMON SUBSTANCES

Basic oxides of metals.

No action except

(*a*) $2HgO \rightarrow 2Hg + O_2$ (Silver similarly)
mercuric   mercury   oxygen
oxide

Peroxides and dioxides of metals.

All decompose giving off oxygen (except sodium peroxide).

o

For example:

$$2H_2O_2 \rightarrow 2H_2O + O_2$$
hydrogen   water   oxygen
peroxide

$$2PbO_2 \rightarrow 2PbO + O_2$$
lead   litharge   oxygen
dioxide

Hydroxides decompose under action of heat (except sodium hydroxide and potassium hydroxide) to give the oxide.

$$Cu(OH)_2 \rightarrow CuO + H_2O$$
copper   copper   water
hydroxide   oxide

Chlorides. No action except on ammonium chloride, which sublimes.

$$NH_4Cl \rightarrow NH_3 + HCl$$

Nitrates

(a) Sodium and potassium nitrates.

$$2KNO_3 \rightarrow 2KNO_2 + O_2$$
potassium   oxygen
nitrite

(b) Heavy metal nitrates, e.g.,

$$2Pb(NO_3)_2 \rightarrow 2PbO + 4NO_2 + O_2$$ (nitrates of silver
lead   nitrogen   oxygen   and mercury
monoxide   peroxide   decompose to
metal)

(c) Ammonium nitrate.

$$NH_4NO_3 \rightarrow N_2O + 2H_2O$$
nitrous   water
oxide

Sulphates. Unimportant except

$$2FeSO_4 \rightarrow Fe_2O_3 + SO_2 + SO_3$$
ferrous   ferric   sulphur   sulphur
sulphate   oxide   dioxide   trioxide

$$Fe_2(SO_4)_3 \rightarrow Fe_2O_3 + 3SO_3$$
ferric sulphate

Carbonates. All decompose except sodium and potassium carbonate, e.g.,

$$CuCO_3 \rightarrow CuO + CO_2$$
copper   copper   carbon
carbonate   oxide   dioxide

Bicarbonates decompose to give carbonate, water and carbon dioxide, e.g.,

$$2NaHCO_3 \rightarrow Na_2CO_3 + H_2O + CO_2$$
sodium   sodium   carbon
bicarbonate   carbonate   dioxide

Ammonium salts always decompose; sometimes sublime, *e.g.*, ammonium chloride.

$$NH_4Cl \rightarrow NH_3 + HCl$$
ammonium
chloride

Ammonium nitrate. See Nitrates.

Metals. All metals oxidise if heated in air, except silver and gold, to form **BASIC OXIDES**, *e.g.*,

$$2Ca + O_2 \rightarrow 2CaO$$
calcium   calcium
oxide

$$2Mg + O_2 \rightarrow 2MgO$$
magnesium   magnesium
oxide

Non-metals. Carbon, phosphorus and sulphur combine with the oxygen of the air to form **ACIDIC OXIDES**. For example:

$$S + O_2 \rightarrow SO_2$$
sulphur   sulphur
dioxide

Miscellaneous.

Hydrates (that is, salts possessing water of crystallisation) give off water-vapour. For example:

$$Na_2CO_3.10H_2O \rightarrow Na_2CO_3 + 10H_2O$$
sodium carbonate   anhydrous   water
crystals   sodium
carbonate

Potassium Chlorate.

$$2KClO_3 \rightarrow 2KCl + 3O_2$$
potassium   potassium   oxygen
chlorate   chloride

Red Lead.

$$2Pb_3O_4 \rightarrow 6PbO + O_2$$
red lead   litharge   oxygen

GAS PREPARATIONS: ANSWERS

The following remarks should be considered together with the diagrams on p. 400–1.

GENERAL NOTES ON PREPARATIONS OF GASES

1. Do not collect gases of approximately the same density as air by displacement of air. If the gases are required dry they must be dried by a suitable substance and collected over mercury. This refers to oxygen, nitrous oxide, nitric oxide, nitrogen.

The following gases may be dried with concentrated sulphuric acid (symbol or formula only given):

$$O_2 \quad H_2 \quad N_2 \quad N_2O \quad HCl \quad CO_2 \quad SO_2 \quad Cl_2 \quad CO$$

For the following, use special drying agents.

Ammonia—quicklime.

Hydrogen sulphide—calcium chloride (quite satisfactory in practice.)

2. **NEVER DRY A GAS AND THEN COLLECT IT OVER WATER.**

3. Draw your diagrams with the following points in mind.

(a) The apparatus stands on the bench. Do not draw, for example, a wash-bottle in mid-air.

(b) Show a clear way through for the gas to pass. A diagram should be a section and not a pictorial illustration. Do not waste time on non-essentials.

(c) Label the diagram clearly. It makes a description much briefer and leaves no room for doubt.

(d) Indicate simply how the apparatus is supported, for example, tripod and gauze, clamps, etc.

4. If a steady supply of a dry gas is wanted (for example, hydrogen, or carbon monoxide for reduction of oxides) a calcium chloride tube is to be preferred as the drying apparatus, to a Woulff's bottle containing concentrated sulphuric acid. The latter gives a jerky supply of the gas, the former a steady supply.

5. Give the equation for the reaction concerned on or near the diagram. It is then clear to which action the equation refers, and you have then completed **two of the important steps in the description of any chemical process.**

Diagram A.   Flask, thistle funnel—no heat—collect over water.

Gas	Materials under Equation	Test
H_2	$Zn + H_2SO_4 \rightarrow ZnSO_4 + H_2$ zinc dilute zinc hydrogen sulphuric acid sulphate	Explodes with air when flame applied.
H_2S	$FeS + 2HCl \rightarrow FeCl_2 + H_2S$ ferrous fairly conc. ferrous hydrogen sulphide hydrochloric chloride sulphide acid	Blackens lead acetate paper. (Collect over HOT water.)
CO_2	$CaCo_3 + 2HCl \rightarrow CaCl_2 + H_2O + CO_2$ marble dilute calcium carbon hydrochloric chloride dioxide acid	Turns lime-water milky.
NO	$3Cu + 8HNO_3 \rightarrow 3Cu(NO_3)_2 +$ copper fairly conc. copper nitric acid nitrate $4H_2O + 2NO$ nitric oxide	Forms brown fumes on exposure to air.
Cl_2	$2KMnO_4 + 16HCl \rightarrow 2KCl +$ potassium concentrated potassium permanganate hydrochloric chloride acid $2MnCl_2 + 8H_2O + 5Cl_2$ manganese chlorine chloride	Bleaches damp litmus (greenish-yellow gas). (Collect over brine.)

Diagram B. Flask heated, wash-bottles, collect by displacement of air.

Gas	Materials under Equation	Test
HCl	$NaCl + H_2SO_4 \rightarrow NaHSO_4 + HCl$ sodium concentrated sodium hydrogen chloride sulphuric hydrogen chloride acid sulphate (Heat not essential).	Gives white precipitate of AgCl with silver nitrate in nitric acid solution. (Concentrated sulphuric acid in wash-bottle.)
SO$_2$	$Cu + 2H_2SO_4 \rightarrow CuSO_4 + 2H_2O + SO_2$ copper hot strong sulphur sulphuric dioxide acid	Decolourises potassium permanganate without precipitate of sulphur. (Concentrated sulphuric acid in wash-bottle.)
Cl$_2$	$MnO_2 + 4HCl \rightarrow MnCl_2 + 2H_2O + Cl_2$ man- concen- manganese chloride ganese trated chloride dioxide hydro- chloric acid (or common salt and concentrated sulphuric acid)	Bleaches damp litmus. (Water in first bottle and concentrated sulphuric acid in second.) Chlorine attacks mercury.
CO	$H_2C_2O_4 - H_2O \rightarrow CO + CO_2$ oxalic acid and carbon carbon concentrated monoxide dioxide sulphuric acid to remove the elements of water	Burns with blue flame to carbon dioxide (pass through **two** bottles of caustic potash solution and collect over water).

Diagram C. Hard glass tube or small flask. Collect over water.

O$_2$	$2KClO_3 \xrightarrow{MnO_2} 2KCl + 3O_2$ potassium potassium oxygen chlorate chloride	Rekindles glowing splint—not soluble in water.
N$_2$	$NH_4NO_2 \rightarrow N_2 + 2H_2O$ ammonium nitrogen steam nitrite solution	Inert gas. Gives negative test with splint and lime-water.
N$_2$O	$NH_4NO_3 \rightarrow N_2O + 2H_2O$ ammonium nitrous steam nitrate oxide (Do not heat flask to dryness)	Rekindles glowing splint—soluble in cold water. (Collect over hot water.)

Special diagrams for ammonia and carbon monoxide. (See pp. 335, 246.)

Answers to General Statements. (*N.B.* Common exceptions only given.) (See p. 398.)

1–5. No exceptions.

6. Silver nitrate yields the metal. Mercuric nitrate similar.

$$2AgNO_3 \rightarrow 2Ag + 2NO_2 + O_2$$

7. With concentrated nitric acid iron becomes "passive" (see p. 387).

8. Certain salts, being insoluble, form a protective layer round the carbonate, preventing the action of the acid. For example: calcium carbonate and dilute sulphuric acid, barium carbonate and dilute sulphuric acid.

Answers to Particular Statements. (*N.B.* Common exceptions only given.)

1. Ammonia.
2. Nitric oxide.
3. Lead chloride.
4. Common salt.
5. Calcium hydroxide. Sodium sulphate (over a certain temperature range).
6. Lead chloride, lead, calcium and barium sulphates. (Carbonates are not usually prepared by this method.)
7. Silver chloride, lead chloride.
8. Lead sulphate, barium sulphate.
9. Sodium, potassium and ammonium carbonates.
10. Sodium, potassium, ammonium and calcium hydroxides. (Calcium hydroxide is only slightly soluble.)
11. Zinc oxide, lead oxide.

ALLOTROPY

If an element can exist (without changing its state) in two or more different forms, the element is said to exhibit allotropy.

The forms of the element are known as allotropes of it. They always exhibit different physical properties and may have different chemical properties also.

The following tables give the different properties of some of the allotropes of the common elements.

Carbon.

GRAPHITE (stable allotrope).	DIAMOND (unstable allotrope).
Density 2·3 gm. per c.c.	Density 3·5 gm. per c.c.
Opaque.	Is colourless, transparent and has very high refractive index.
Very soft, marks paper.	Hardest known substance.
Attacked by potassium chlorate and nitric acid (together).	Unattacked by potassium chlorate and nitric acid.

Other forms of carbon, for example animal and wood charcoal, soot, gas carbon, sugar carbon and coke are now believed to be of the same crystalline structure as graphite.

Oxygen exists in two allotropic modifications—oxygen and ozone. Here the differences are due to the fact that oxygen contains two atoms per molecule and ozone contains three atoms per molecule.

OXYGEN (Stable allotrope).	OZONE (unstable allotrope).
Gas.	Gas.
Density 16 (H = 1).	Density 24 (H = 1).
Insoluble in turpentine.	Reacts with turpentine.
Heat has no action.	Heat decomposes ozone into oxygen. $2O_3 \rightarrow 3O_2$.
No effect on mercury.	Makes mercury "wet" glass ("tailing").
No effect on rubber.	Attacks rubber.
Has no effect on potassium iodide solution.	Liberates iodine from potassium iodide solution. $$2KI + O_3 + H_2O \rightarrow 2KOH + I_2 + O_2$$
Oxidising agent.	Vigorous oxidising agent.

Phosphorus.

RED (stable allotrope).	YELLOW (unstable allotrope).
Opaque red solid.	Colourless translucent solid (turns yellow).
Density 2·2 gm. per c.c.	Density 1·8 gm. per c.c.
Non-poisonous.	Very poisonous.
Melting-point 600° C.	Melting-point 43° C.
Insoluble in carbon disulphide.	Soluble in carbon disulphide.
Ignites in air at 260° C.	Ignites in air at 34° C.
No action with hot caustic soda solution.	Forms phosphine with hot caustic soda solution.
Unoxidised at ordinary temperatures.	Rapidly oxidised at ordinary temperatures.

Sulphur.

RHOMBIC (stable) (octahedral).	MONOCLINIC (unstable) (prismatic).
Yellow translucent crystals.	Transparent amber crystals.
Density 2·06 gm./c.c.	Density 1·98 gm./c.c.
Melting-point 114° C.	Melting-point 120° C.
Stable at temperatures below 96° C.	Unstable at temperatures below 96° C., reverting to rhombic variety.

To show that the Allotropes consist of the same Element.

(a) CARBON. Graphite is heated in oxygen and it can be shown that carbon dioxide is formed and nothing else. With a diamond, exactly the same product is obtained.

Further, if 1 gm. of graphite is heated in a stream of oxygen and the carbon dioxide thus formed absorbed by caustic potash, the weight of carbon dioxide formed is 2·73 gm.

In a similar manner, 1 gm. of diamond could be shown to produce exactly 2·73 gm. of carbon dioxide.

(b) OXYGEN AND OZONE. Ozone is made by the passing of a silent electrical discharge through oxygen (p. 234). Also, if ozone is heated in a closed tube to a temperature in excess of 300° C., oxygen is formed and nothing else.

(c) PHOSPHORUS. If 1 gm. of *yellow* phosphorus is heated in an enclosed space, out of contact with air, to a temperature of 250° C., exactly one gram of *red* phosphorus is obtained and nothing else.

(d) SULPHUR. If 1 gm. of prismatic sulphur is allowed to remain at ordinary temperatures for a few days, exactly 1 gm. of rhombic sulphur is obtained and nothing else.

Further, in any of the above cases, if fixed weights of the allotropes of the same element are separately converted into one definite compound of the element, the same weight of that compound is formed from the fixed weight of each of the allotropes.

APPENDIX

SIMPLE IDEAS OF ATOMIC STRUCTURE

It seems fairly certain that for most of the nineteenth century, atoms were regarded as very small spherical particles like a very minute lead shot. It was believed that no smaller particle could exist, and that atoms were solid and homogeneous. This state of affairs has been very greatly changed in recent years, mainly by the pioneer work of Lord Rutherford.

It is now known that atoms are themselves built up from three smaller particles—the proton, the electron and the neutron. The **proton** is a positively charged particle of mass about equal to that of a hydrogen atom. The **electron** is negatively charged, its charge being equal but opposite to the charge on a proton. It has a very small mass, about 1/1850 of the mass of the proton. The **neutron** has no charge, and its mass is about equal to the mass of a proton. It may be roughly regarded as the fusion of a proton and an electron.

	Charge	Mass
proton	+	1
electron	–	1/1850
neutron	nil	1

The protons and neutrons are concentrated in a very small nucleus in the centre of the atom (Rutherford's nuclear theory) while the electrons are all outside the nucleus. They are arranged in orbits or shells, at increasing distances from the nucleus, and revolve in them, controlled by the nucleus. The number of electrons is equal to the number of protons so that the atom, as a whole, is electrically neutral. The whole bulk of the atom, as defined by the outermost electron shell, is very great compared with the size of the nucleus (in Rutherford's analogy, about the same proportion as the dome of St. Paul's to a man's clenched fist).

o*

A diagrammatic representation of a typical atom would be:—

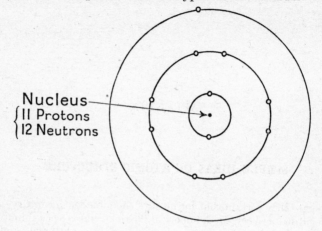

Nucleus
{ 11 Protons
{ 12 Neutrons

electrons revolving in orbits
2.8.1

Fig. 1.   Sodium Atom (diagrammatic)

The simplest atom is that of hydrogen. It consists of a single proton with one electron rotating round it. In order of complexity, the simpler atoms are made up as in the following table, neutrons being omitted for reasons explained later:—

		ELECTRONS		
ELEMENT	PROTONS	IN EACH SHELL		
hydrogen	1	1		
helium	2	2		
lithium	3	2	1	
beryllium	4	2	2	
boron	5	2	3	
carbon	6	2	4	
nitrogen	7	2	5	
oxygen	8	2	6	
fluorine	9	2	7	
neon	10	2	8	
sodium	11	2	8	1
magnesium	12	2	8	2
aluminium	13	2	8	3
silicon	14	2	8	4
phosphorus	15	2	8	5
sulphur	16	2	8	6
chlorine	17	2	8	7
argon	18	2	8	8
potassium	19	2	8	8	1

The number of protons on the nucleus (which equals the number of electrons in the shells) is called the **Atomic Number** of the element.

TYPES OF CHEMICAL COMBINATION

From the above table, it will be seen that neon and argon have *eight* electrons in their outermost electron layer, i.e. an *octet* of electrons. This structure is very stable and extremely difficult to disturb. In consequence, these two gases are chemically inert and form no compounds with other elements. They are self-satisfied. In the simpler rare-gas, helium, the duplet of electrons is equally stable and functions like the octet.

The tendency of all other elements is to try to attain this rare-gas structure of a stable outer octet (or duplet) of electrons and their chemical behaviour is a reflection of this tendency. On this general principle, elements combine in two main forms of combination, known as the **electro-valent** (or polar-valent) and **covalent types**.

ELECTRO-VALENT COMBINATION

(Also known as polar-valent.) In this type, a metallic element or group loses, from its outermost electron shell, a number of electrons equal to its valency. These electrons pass over to the outer electron shells of non-metallic atoms with which the metal is combining. By this means, an electron octet is *left behind* in the metal and *created* in the non-metal. Both elements now have the outer electron structure of a rare-gas, but the metallic particles have a positive charge from the excess proton(s) left on the nucleus, while the non-metallic particles are negatively charged from the added electron(s). The particles are then known as **ions**.

Thus:—	Sodium atom		Chlorine atom	
	Protons	*Electrons*	*Protons*	*Electrons*
Before combination	11	2.8.1	17	2.8.7
After combination	11	2.8	17	2.8.8
	Sodium ion +		Chlorine ion −	

Both ions now possess stable outer electron octets, like a rare-gas.

No molecules of sodium chloride are formed. Because of the attraction of the oppositely charged Na^+ and Cl^- ions for one another, the ions arrange themselves into a rigid, solid shape called a crystal, but they remain quite separate. No molecules of sodium chloride form. There is no "bond" between them and the combination can only be expressed in ionic form as $Na^+ Cl^-$, meaning an association of sodium and chlorine ions in equal numbers.

Characteristic Properties of Electro (or Polar) Valent Compounds.

(1) Polar compounds do not contain molecules. They consist of aggregates of oppositely charged ions. In consequence, if they are melted, or dissolved in water, to make the ions mobile, they conduct electricity and are, therefore, electrolytes (Chap. XII).

(2) They are solids and do not vaporise easily.

(3) They will not usually dissolve in organic solvents such as toluene, ether, benzene, etc.

Salts, alkalis and bases are electro-valent and acids, when in solution in water, also show electro-valency.

The following cases are given in further illustration of electro-valency.

Calcium Chloride

	Calcium atom		Two chlorine atoms	
	Protons	*Electrons*	*Protons*	*Electrons*
Before combination	20	2.8.8.2	17	2.8.7
			17	2.8.7

These valency electrons pass to the chlorine atoms.

	Calcium ion + +		Two chlorine ions −	
	Protons	*Electrons*	*Protons*	*Electrons*
After combination	20	2.8.8	17	2.8.8
			17	2.8.8

In the calcium ion, the two excess nuclear protons produce a double positive charge; in each chlorine ion, the excess electron produces a single negative charge, i.e. $Ca^{++} . 2Cl^{-}$.

Calcium Oxide

	Calcium atom		Oxygen atom	
	Protons	*Electrons*	*Protons*	*Electrons*
Before combination	20	2.8.8.2	8	2.6

These valency electrons pass to the oxygen atom

	Calcium ion + +		Oxygen ion − −	
	Protons	*Electrons*	*Protons*	*Electrons*
After combination	20	2.8.8	8	2.8

As stated above, the calcium ion acquires a double positive charge; the two excess electrons produce a double negative charge on the oxygen ion, i.e., $Ca^{++} . O^{--}$.

Note the presence of the outer *octet* of electrons in all the above ions.

COVALENT COMBINATION

In this type of valency, electrons are not actually gained or lost by the atoms concerned. They pass into a "shared" state.

Consider two chlorine atoms. Each has the electron structure 2.8.7. In covalency, the atoms contribute *one electron each* to a "shared-pair". In this way, both obtain an approximation to the external octet by making fourteen electrons do the work of sixteen.

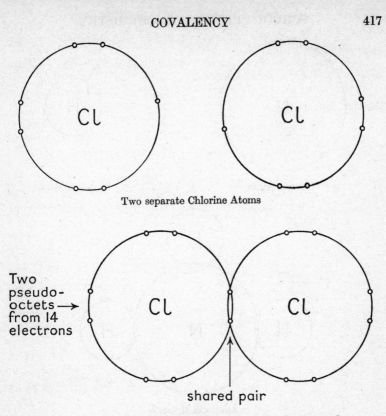

Two separate Chlorine Atoms

Two pseudo-octets → from 14 electrons

shared pair

FIG. 2. A Chlorine Molecule (diagrammatic; outer electrons only are shown)

Here, actual molecules are produced, not ions. Each "shared-pair" electron passes from an orbit controlled by the nucleus of *one* chlorine atom into an orbit controlled by the nuclei of *both* chlorine atoms. This joint control of the orbits constitutes the valency bond.

Characteristic Properties of Covalent Compounds

(1) Covalent compounds consist of molecules. They contain no ions, are unable to conduct electric current and are, therefore, non-electrolytes. (Chap. XII.)

(2) The simpler covalent compounds are gases or liquids of low boiling-point, i.e. covalent compounds are volatile.

(3) Covalent compounds are usually soluble in organic solvents.

The Ammonia Molecule

This is another illustration of covalency. It is formed from one nitrogen atom and three hydrogen atoms.

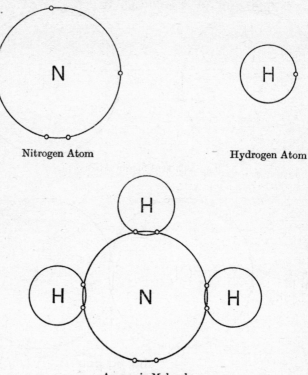

Nitrogen Atom   Hydrogen Atom

Ammonia Molecule
(*External electrons only are shown*)
FIG. 3.   Ammonia Molecule (diagrammatic)

By the creation of three shared-pairs of electrons, the nitrogen atom acquires the closest attainable approximation to an outer octet. Each hydrogen atom acquires a similar approximation to the stable helium duplet. Ammonia, a gas and a non-electrolyte if completely dry, is a typical covalent compound. Covalency is very common. It occurs in a multitude of organic compounds such as ether, chloroform, alcohol, methane, and in many compounds of non-metals, such as hydrogen chloride gas, ammonia, carbon dioxide, carbon monoxide and nitric oxide. The covalent bond is conventionally indicated by the sign –. Thus the ammonia molecule may be written:—

$$H - N - H$$
with an H above N

Addition of water alters the above electronic arrangement. For an explanation of this fact, the reader is referred to more advanced textbooks.

FUNCTION OF NEUTRONS IN THE ATOM

The above discussion of valency and chemical combination contains no mention of neutrons. They appear to have little influence on the chemical properties of the atom. Their chief function is to help to determine the weight of the atom. For example, the sodium atom, with 11 protons and 12 neutrons, has a total weight of 23 units. The 11 electrons are relatively negligible in weight.

Many cases occur, however, in which two atoms contain the same number of protons but differing numbers of neutrons. Having equal numbers of protons, these atoms must also have equal numbers of electrons. These are arranged in the same way and give the atoms identical chemical properties. But the differing numbers of neutrons cause the atoms to have different weights. An element showing these characteristic properties—that is, possessing atoms of similar chemical properties but different weights—is said to show *isotopy* and the varieties of the atom are called **isotopes** of the element.

A well-known example of isotopy occurs in chlorine.

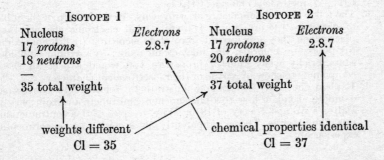

Dalton believed that all atoms of the same element were exactly alike. Isotopy has proved him wrong. But, except in one or two very exceptional cases, elements contain isotopes **in constant proportions** and so appear to act as if all their atoms are equal in weight. Chlorine, for example, is found to have its isotopes mixed in such proportions that its average chemical atomic weight appears constant. The lighter isotope predominates, giving a value of 35.46.

It may also be mentioned that, in spite of recent, very prominent activities in splitting the atom, it can still be regarded as an indivisible unit in **chemical** actions. Atom-splitting breaks up the atomic nucleus and is a **physical** process, not a chemical one. Apart from modifications in the electron shells, an atom is conveyed as a whole unit in chemical actions.

Uranium has two principal isotopes. Both possess 92 protons and 92 electrons. One isotope has 146 neutrons, giving U = 238; the other has 143 neutrons, giving U = 235. The lighter isotope constitutes about 7% of natural uranium. If the atom U = 235 acquires one extra neutron on the nucleus, it becomes unstable and divides into two approximately equal parts. This "fission" is accompanied by very great evolution of heat energy. At the same time, neutrons are emitted. If the mass of U = 235 is great enough, other atoms absorb these neutrons so that a chain-reaction is set up, causing an atomic explosion.

QUESTIONS

1. What are the three particles which make up ordinary matter? Tabulate their relative charges and masses. State briefly how they are arranged in a typical form of elementary matter and illustrate your statement by a diagrammatic representation of one atom of it.

2. The compounds named below are all covalent compounds. With the help of the table of electron-structures on p. 414, give a diagram for a molecule of each of these compounds, showing the outermost electron shells only: (i) carbon tetrachloride, CCl_4; (ii) phosphorus trichloride, PCl_3; (iii) silicomethane, SiH_4; (iv) chloroform, $CHCl_3$; (v) phosphine, PH_3; (vi) methylene chloride, CH_2Cl_2.

3. The following compounds are electrovalent. With the help of the table of electron-structures on p. 414, state what electronic changes take place when they are formed from their elements: (i) lithium oxide; (ii) potassium chloride; (iii) magnesium oxide; (iv) sodium sulphide. State briefly what kind of properties you would expect all these compounds to show by virtue of their electrovalent character.

4. Explain the term *isotopy* and illustrate by reference to one actual example. Explain how this phenomenon contradicts a certain part of Dalton's Atomic Theory of 1810. Why, in spite of this contradiction, was the Atomic Theory apparently in accord with experimental experience?

DEFINITIONS

An Acid is a substance which will turn blue litmus red and contains hydrogen, which can be replaced directly or indirectly by a metal.

Alkali is a base which is soluble in water.

Allotropy. If the same element can exist, without changing its state, in two or more different forms, the element is said to exhibit allotropy. These various forms are termed allotropes.

An amphoteric oxide (hydroxide) is one which exhibits both basic and acidic properties.

Analysis is the splitting up of a chemical compound into its elementary or simpler substances.

Anhydride is an acidic oxide of a non-metal.

Atom is the smallest indivisible particle of an element which can take part in a chemical change.

Atomic weight of an element is the number of times one atom of the element is heavier than one atom of hydrogen.

$$\text{Atomic weight of an element} = \frac{\text{Weight of 1 atom of the element}}{\text{Weight of 1 atom of Hydrogen}}$$

Avogadro's Hypothesis states that "equal volumes of all gases under the same conditions of temperature and pressure contain the same number of MOLECULES".

Base. If a metallic oxide or hydroxide will react with an acid to form a salt and water only, it is a base.

Basicity of an acid is the number of hydrogen atoms per molecule of it which can be replaced by a metal.

Boyle's Law states that the volume of a given mass of gas is inversely proportional to its pressure, temperature remaining constant.

Catalyst is a substance which, although present in small proportion, alters the speed of chemical reaction but remains *chemically unchanged at the end of* the reaction.

Charles' Law. For a given mass of gas the volume is proportional to the absolute temperature (pressure constant).

Deliquescence is the absorbing of moisture from the atmosphere by a solid to form a solution.

Diffusion is the process by which a gas fills the whole of a vessel into which it is placed.

421

Double Decomposition is an action of the type

$$AX + BY \rightarrow AY + BX$$

where A, B represent metals or metallic radicals and X, Y non-metallic or acidic radicals.

Dulong and Petit's Law states that

Atomic Weight of a solid element $\times$ Specific Heat of the element
$$= 6{\cdot}4 \text{ (approx.)}$$

Efflorescence is the giving up of water of crystallisation by a crystal to the atmosphere.

Electrolysis is the decomposition of a substance by the passing of an electric current.

Equivalent Weight of an element is the number of grams of the element which will combine with or displace 1 gm. of hydrogen, 8 gm. of oxygen, $35\frac{1}{2}$ gm. of chlorine, etc.

("Parts by weight" can be substituted for the word "grams" to make this definition complete.)

Gay-Lussac's Law. Gay-Lussac's law of combining volumes states: When gases react, they do so in volumes which bear a simple ratio to one another, and to the volume of the product if gaseous, temperature and pressure remaining constant.

G.M.V. The Gram-Molecular Volume of any gas is the volume occupied at N.T.P. by its gram-molecular weight, and is $22{\cdot}4$ litres.

Hydrolysis is a double decomposition between a salt and water, the hydroxyl group of the latter remaining intact.

$$AB + HOH \rightarrow HB + AOH$$

Law of Constant Composition. All pure samples of the same chemical compound contain the same elements combined in the same proportions by weight.

Law of Multiple Proportions states, if two elements A and B combine together to form more than one compound, then the several weights of A which separately combine with a fixed weight of B are in a simple ratio.

Law of Indestructibility of Matter (Conservation of mass). Matter is neither created nor destroyed in the course of chemical action.

Molecule of an element or compound is the smallest particle of it which can normally exist separately.

Molecular Weight of a substance is the number of times one molecule of the substance is heavier than 1 atom of hydrogen or

Molecular Weight of a substance $=$

$$\frac{\text{Weight of 1 molecule of substance}}{\text{Weight of 1 ATOM of hydrogen}}$$

Neutralisation is a reaction between an acid and a base producing a salt and water only.

A Normal Solution is one which contains the equivalent weight of a substance in grams in 1 litre of solution.

Oxidation is a reaction during which the proportion of the electronegative constituent in a substance is increased.

Reduction is a reaction during which the proportion of the electronegative constituent in a substance is decreased.

Salt. A salt is a substance obtained by replacing the hydrogen of an acid by a metal or metallic group.

If all the hydrogen of the acid is replaced, the salt is called a normal salt; if only part of the hydrogen is replaced, the salt is called an acid salt.

S.T.P. or N.T.P. "Standard" or "Normal" temperature and pressure, that is, 0° C. and 760 mm. of mercury.

Saturated solution of a solute at a particular temperature is one which contains as much of the solute as it can dissolve at that temperature, in the presence of solid particles of the solute.

Solubility of a solute in a solvent at a particular temperature is the number of grams of solute necessary to saturate 100 gm. of the solvent at that temperature.

Supersaturated solution. A solution is said to be supersaturated when it contains in solution more of the solute than it can hold at that temperature in the presence of the crystals of the solute.

Synthesis is the building up of a compound from elementary or simpler substances.

Thermal Dissociation is the decomposition of a compound by the action of heat. If the products are allowed to cool they will reform the original substance.

Valency of an element is the number of hydrogen atoms which will combine with or displace ONE ATOM of the element.

Water of crystallisation is that definite amount of water with which some substances are associated on crystallising out from an aqueous solution

GENERAL QUESTIONS

1. Answer SIX of the following questions:
   (a) Why is sodium kept under paraffin oil? and what is the nature of the crust usually observed on pieces of the metal?
   (b) Why are frames of bicycles enamelled or painted?
   (c) Why does metallic copper turn green when exposed to the air for a few weeks?
   (d) Why is it that crude common salt becomes moist and that washing soda crystals become powdery when exposed to the air for some time?
   (e) If the acid from an accumulator is spilt on the carpet, what common substance, usually kept in a house, can be used to neutralise it?
   (f) Why does a bunsen burner sometimes "light at the bottom"?
   (g) Why are the fumes from a motor-car exhaust pipe poisonous?
   Give brief explanations, using formulæ and equations where these add to the clearness of the answer, but do not spend more than five minutes on any one section. (B.)

2. Describe the preparation from metallic copper of pure dry specimens of (a) copper sulphate, (b) copper oxide.
   What is the action of (a) a solution of sodium hydroxide, (b) iron, (c) a solution of ammonia, on an aqueous solution of copper sulphate? (C.)

3. You are given iron filings, copper turnings, and the ordinary chemical reagents.
   How would you prepare fairly pure specimens of (a) ferric oxide, (b) ferrous sulphate, (c) cupric oxide, (d) cupric sulphate? (D.)

4. A sample of impure chalk is examined and it is found that 5 gm. of it when dissolved in excess of dilute hydrochloric acid give 588 c.c. of carbon dioxide at 780 mm. pressure and 21° C. Sketch an apparatus which could be used in this experiment. Calculate the percentage weight of calcium carbonate in the chalk. (Ca = 40, C = 12, O = 16, H = 1, Cl = 35·5.) (The gram-molecular weight of a gas occupies 22·4 litres at N.T.P.) (N.U.J.B.)

5. Name the materials and describe briefly the process used in the manufacture of glass.
   Describe the properties of glass, emphasising those which you have found particularly useful in the laboratory.
   How would you distinguish a rod of silica from one of glass? (D.)

6. Describe briefly how you would obtain a specimen of:
   (a) *Iron* from a mixture of powdered rock sulphur and iron dust.
   (b) *Water* from a solution of salt.
   (c) *Glass* from a mixture of powdered glass and lead carbonate, and
   (d) *Charcoal* from a mixture of powdered charcoal and powdered glass.
   In each case indicate the principle upon which your method of separation depends. (N.U.J.B.)

7. How would you distinguish experimentally between (a) hydrogen and marsh-gas, (b) producer-gas and water-gas, (c) starch and sugar?

Calculate the volume of carbon dioxide measured at 12° C. and 750 mm. pressure, which can be obtained by the complete combustion of 1 gm. of carbon.

Atomic weights: C = 12, O = 16.

A gram-molecular weight of a gas occupies 22·4 litres at 0° C. and 760 mm. pressure. (D.)

8. Describe in detail how you would prepare and isolate specimens of (a) lead nitrate starting from lead, (b) zinc oxide starting from zinc sulphate, and (c) anhydrous ferric chloride starting from iron. (N.U.J.B.)

9. Describe clearly the appearance of a crystal of copper sulphate. What happens to it when it is gently heated?

Give a detailed account of how you would prepare, from copper sulphate, reasonably pure specimens of (a) copper, (b) copper oxide. (O.)

10. Suppose that you were given a substance and told that it was either lead nitrate, lead carbonate, sodium nitrate, or sodium carbonate. Describe fully how you would find out which of these four substances it was. (L.)

11. You are given three powders which are respectively (a) sodium chloride or calcium oxide, (b) zinc oxide or magnesium carbonate, (c) potassium nitrate or ammonium nitrate.

Describe SIX experiments (TWO for each powder) by means of which the identities of the powders could be established. (N.U.J.B.)

12. You are given a graduated tube containing a mixture of carbon dioxide, carbon monoxide and nitrogen collected over mercury. Describe exactly what you would do to find out the volume that each gas would occupy at 0° C. and 760 mm. pressure. (D.)

13. How would you prepare and isolate from a dilute solution of copper sulphate (a) water, (b) crystals of copper sulphate ($CuSO_4 . 5H_2O$), (c) copper, (d) a dilute solution of sulphuric acid? (N.U.J.B.)

14. (a) Name in each case the principal mineral from which are produced (i) iron, (ii) zinc, (iii) lead.

(b) Describe how you would prepare (i) anhydrous ferric chloride from iron, (ii) zinc sulphide from zinc, and (iii) lead sulphate from lead. (N.U.J.B.)

15. Name four substances which can be employed for drying gases. Explain why each substance is used for this purpose, and state which are suitable and which are unsuitable for drying (a) ammonia, (b) hydrogen chloride, (c) carbon dioxide, and (d) hydrogen sulphide, giving the reason in each case. (L.)

16. (a) Name FIVE substances which produce respectively on heating (i) oxygen, (ii) nitrous oxide, (iii) carbon dioxide, (iv) sulphur trioxide, (v) nitrogen peroxide.

(b) Give labelled sketches to show the apparatus and materials you would use to prepare (i) ammonia, (ii) hydrogen chloride. What are the densities of the two last-named gases compared with hydrogen? (No equations need be given in the answers to Question 16.) (N.U.J.B.)

17. What experiments would you perform to show that (a) chalk contains carbon, (b) iron rust contains iron, (c) potassium chlorate contains chlorine? (O. and C.)

18. Describe simple tests by which you could distinguish the following substances from one another, giving *one* test for each substance.
    (a) Magnesium and iron.
    (b) Sodium nitrate and potassium chlorate.
    (c) Ammonium nitrate and ammonium sulphate.
    (d) Sodium phosphate and calcium chloride. (L.)

19. What chemical reactions can be brought about between zinc and (a) aqueous copper sulphate, (b) dilute sulphuric acid?
    Give equations, and explain how you would demonstrate by experiment the truth of *one* of them. (O. and C.)

20. How would you obtain specimens of reasonably pure
    (a) Potassium chlorate from a mixture of this substance with potassium chloride.
    (b) Sodium chloride from a mixture of this substance with ammonium chloride.
    (c) Sulphur from iron pyrites.
    (d) Copper from brass? (O.)

21. When a dilute solution of potassium chloride is partly frozen, ice separates, free from potassium chloride, and the concentration of salt in the solution is increased.
    How would you test the truth of this statement experimentally? (O. and C.)

22. Describe carefully how you would obtain each constituent from the following mixtures: (a) sodium chloride and sand; (b) oxygen and carbon dioxide; (c) water and potassium nitrate. (C.W.B.)

23. Choosing *four* of the following, explain why:—(a) Chalk dissolves in natural water but not in distilled water, (b) limestone is added to the charge in a blast furnace, (c) the yellow and the red varieties of phosphorus are regarded as different forms of the same element, (d) sulphuric acid yields two different crystalline products with caustic soda, (e) air is said to be a mixture of oxygen and nitrogen, (f) silica is considered to be an acidic oxide. (L.)

24. You are provided with concentrated sulphuric acid, slaked lime, ammonium chloride, potassium nitrate, water, a source of heat and any apparatus needed, but no other chemicals. Explain briefly how you could prepare (a) nitric acid, (b) ammonia solution, (c) quick-lime, (d) pure dry calcium sulphate. (N.U.J.B.)

25. Explain fully any *four* of the following:—(a) The precautions to be taken when mixing concentrated sulphuric acid and water, and the reasons for such care, (b) the change in the appearance of washing soda crystals when exposed to the air, (c) the production of water gas, (d) a laboratory method of obtaining a jar of oxygen from the air, (e) the bleaching action of chlorine. (L.)

ANSWERS TO NUMERICAL EXAMPLES

(Using the Approximate Atomic Weight table on p. 428.)

CHAPTER II, p. 26.   8. X_2O_3.

CHAPTER III, p. 33.

1. 2 : 3.   5. 1 : 2.   11. 4 : 3 : 2.   13. 1 : 2 : 3.
2. 4 : 2 : 1.   6. 1 : 2.   12. 28·00.   14. 1 : 4.
3. 1 : 2.   8. 25·5. 12·8.   18·67.
4. 1 : 2.   1 : 2.   1 : 2.

CHAPTER VI, p. 52.

(a) 253·3 c.c.   (e) 570 c.c.   (i) 51·2 c.c.
(b) 1,638 c.c.   (f) 637 c.c.   (j) 626 c.c.
(c) 1,110 c.c.   (g) 641·5 c.c.   (k) 76·1 c.c.
(d) 450 c.c.   (h) 133·5 c.c.   (l) 118·2 c.c.
                                             (m) 518·4 c.c.

CHAPTER VII, p. 62.

3. 104.   10. 59·53.   17. 9·0; 27;
4. 13·4 gm.   8·93. $X(NO_3)_3$; X_2O_3;
   7·9 gm.   11·91. $X_2(SO_4)_3$.
5. 317 c.c.   12. 31·75.   18. 8·908.
   0·0285 gm.   63·5.   79·93%.
   28·0.   13. 69·33.   20. 207.
6. 9·0.   208.   63·42.
   3·0.   208.   23·00.
   27·0.   14. 0·5306 gm.   21. 55·925.
7. 11·15 tons.   15. 99·5.   22. X_2O_3; XCl_3
8. 51·75.   16. 4·67. YO; YCl_2.
9. 108.   14.

CHAPTER VIII, p. 70.

1. 15·875 tons.   (d) 29·11%,   10. 3·286 oz.
2. 1·55 gm.   40·51%.   11. 73 gm.
3. $ZnCl_2$.   30·38%.   12. 3·036.
   NaCl.   5. 63 gm.   13. $CaCl_2\cdot2NH_3$.
   $CuSO_4$.   6. 2·67 gm.   2·24 litres.
   PbN_2O_6.   7. 20·04 gm.   14. 97·5%.
4. (a) 27·38%, 1·19%.   40·08 gm.   15. 80·85 c.c.
       14·29%. 57·14%. 8. 3·085 gm.   0·1601 gm.
   (b) 36·04%, 63·96%. 9. 15·89 gm.   90·91%.
   (c) 21·21%, 6·06%.   slaked lime.
       24·24%, 48·48%.   by 5·42 gm.

CHAPTER IX, p. 87.

1. 17 gm.   34 gm.   4. 1·083 litres.   8. 7·167 gm.
   28 gm.   71 gm.   5. 71.   8·336 gm.
   44 gm.   6. 1·551 litres.   10. 4 atoms.
2. 32, 64, 30.   7. 100 c.c.   11. 124.
3. 33·6 litres.   60%.   13. 1·63 gm.
                                                36·2.

Chapter X, p. 99.   6. 0·5152 gm.

Chapter XI, p. 107.

1. 0·667N.
2. 80·0%.
3. 12·0.

4. 20·83 c.c.
   0·833N.
5. 196·6 c.c.
6. 49·03.

7. 58·3%.
8. 63·0.
  90·0.
9. 12.

Chapter XVI, p. 195.   6. 7 mols.   8. 993·3 c.c.   496·7 c.c.

Chapter XIX, p. 222.   1. 9·82 gm. (using G.M.V.).
                     4. 68·5% of original mixture. 57·4% N_2, 42·6% H_2

Chapter XX, p. 229.   6. 14·4.

Chapter XXI, p. 235.   4. (b) 8·4 litres.   5. 20 c.c. 90 c.c.   0·2268 gm

Chapter XXIII, p. 263.   3. 37·12%.   10. 10·5 vols.

Chapter XXVII, p. 298.   9. 50·0 c.c.   11. 6·234 litres.

Chapter XXX, p. 329.   5. 6·604%.

Chapter XXXIII, p. 359.   6. 1·4 litres N_2O.
                       1·6 litres NO.

General Questions, p. 424.

4. 50·0%.   7. 1·975 litres.

LIST OF APPROXIMATE ATOMIC WEIGHTS

Aluminium	27	Magnesium	24
Barium	137	Manganese	55
Bromine	80	Mercury	200
Calcium	40	Nitrogen	14
Carbon	12	Oxygen	16
Chlorine	35·5	Phosphorus	31
Chromium	52	Platinum	195
Copper	63·5	Potassium	39
Hydrogen	1	Silver	108
Iodine	127	Sodium	23
Iron	56	Sulphur	32
Lead	207	Zinc	65

ATOMIC WEIGHTS, 1949

Taken by kind permission from the *Journal of the Chemical Society*.

Atomic weights in brackets denote the mass number of the most stable known isotope.

Atomic number	Name	Symbol	Atomic weight	Atomic number	Name	Symbol	Atomic weight
1	Hydrogen .	H	1·0080	49	Indium . .	In	114·76
2	Helium . .	He	4·003	50	Tin . .	Sn	118·70
3	Lithium. .	Li	6·940	51	Antimony .	Sb	121·76
4	Beryllium .	Be	9·013	52	Tellurium .	Te	127·61
5	Boron . .	B	10·82	53	Iodine . .	I	126·92
6	Carbon .	C	12·010	54	Xenon . .	Xe	131·3
7	Nitrogen .	N	14·008	55	Cæsium .	Cs	132·91
8	Oxygen . .	O	16·0000	56	Barium . .	Ba	137·36
9	Fluorine .	F	19·00	57	Lanthanum .	La	138·92
10	Neon . .	Ne	20·183	58	Cerium .	Ce	140·13
11	Sodium . .	Na	22·997	59	Praseodymium	Pr	140·92
12	Magnesium .	Mg	24·32	60	Neodymium .	Nd	144·27
13	Aluminium .	Al	26·97	61	Promethium .	Pm	[147]
14	Silicon . .	Si	28·06	62	Samarium .	Sm	150·43
15	Phosphorus .	P	30·98	63	Europium .	Eu	152·0
16	Sulphur .	S	32·066	64	Gadolinium .	Gd	156·91
17	Chlorine .	Cl	35·457	65	Terbium .	Tb	159·2
18	Argon . .	A	39·944	66	Dysprosium .	Dy	162·46
19	Potassium .	K	39·096	67	Holmium .	Ho	164·94
20	Calcium. .	Ca	40·08	68	Erbium .	Er	167·2
21	Scandium .	Sc	45·10	69	Thulium .	Tm	169·4
22	Titanium .	Ti	47·90	70	Ytterbium . .	Yb	173·04
23	Vanadium .	V	50·95	71	Lutecium .	Lu	174·99
24	Chromium .	Cr	52·01	72	Hafnium .	Hf	178·6
25	Manganese .	Mn	54·93	73	Tantalum .	Ta	180·881
26	Iron . .	Fe	55·85	74	Tungsten .	W	183·92
27	Cobalt . .	Co	58.94	75	Rhenium .	Re	186·31
28	Nickel . .	Ni	58·69	76	Osmium .	Os	190·2
29	Copper . .	Cu	63·54	77	Iridium .	Ir	193·1
30	Zinc . .	Zn	65·38	78	Platinum .	Pt	195·23
31	Gallium .	Ga	69·72	79	Gold . .	Au	197·2*
32	Germanium .	Ge	72·60	80	Mercury .	Hg	200·61
33	Arsenic . .	As	74·91	81	Thallium .	Tl	204·39
34	Selenium .	Se	78·96	82	Lead . .	Pb	207·21
35	Bromine .	Br	79·916	83	Bismuth. .	Bi	209·00
36	Krypton .	Kr	83·7	84	Polonium .	Po	210
37	Rubidium .	Rb	85·48	85	Astatine .	At	[210]
38	Strontium .	Sr	87·63	86	Radon .	Rn	222
39	Yttrium .	Y	88·92	87	Francium .	Fr	[223]
40	Zirconium .	Zr	91·22	88	Radium .	Ra	226·05
41	Niobium .	Nb	92·91	89	Actinium .	Ac	—
	(Columbium) .	(Cb)		90	Thorium .	Th	232·12
42	Molybdenum .	Mo	95·95	91	Protoactinium	Pa	231
43	Technetium .	Tc	[99]	92	Uranium .	U	238·07
44	Ruthenium .	Ru	101·7	93	Neptunium .	Np	[237]
45	Rhodium .	Rh	102·91	94	Plutonium .	Pv	[239]
46	Palladium .	Pd	106·7	95	Americium .	Am	[241]
47	Silver .	Ag	107·880	96	Curium .	Cm	[242]
48	Cadmium .	Cd	112·41				

LOGARITHMS OF NUMBERS

	0	1	2	3	4	5	6	7	8	9	1	2	3	4	5	6	7	8	9
10	0000	0043	0086	0128	0170	0212	0253	0294	0334	0374	4	8	12	16	20	24	28	32	36
											4	8	13	17	21	25	30	34	38
11	0414	0453	0492	0531	0569	0607	0645	0682	0719	0755	4	7	11	15	18	22	26	30	33
											4	8	12	15	19	23	27	31	35
12	0792	0828	0864	0899	0934	0969	1004	1038	1072	1106	3	7	10	14	17	20	24	27	31
											4	7	11	14	18	21	25	28	32
13	1139	1173	1206	1239	1271	1303	1335	1367	1399	1430	3	6	9	13	16	19	22	25	28
											3	7	10	13	16	20	23	26	30
14	1461	1492	1523	1553	1584	1614	1644	1673	1703	1732	3	6	9	12	15	18	21	24	27
											3	6	9	12	15	18	21	24	27
15	1761	1790	1818	1847	1875	1903	1931	1959	1987	2014	3	6	8	11	14	17	19	22	25
											3	6	9	11	14	17	20	23	26
16	2041	2068	2095	2122	2148	2175	2201	2227	2253	2279	3	5	8	10	13	16	18	21	23
											3	5	8	11	13	16	19	21	24
17	2304	2330	2355	2380	2405	2430	2455	2480	2504	2529	2	5	7	10	12	15	17	20	22
											3	5	8	10	13	15	18	20	23
18	2553	2577	2601	2625	2648	2672	2695	2718	2742	2765	2	5	7	9	12	14	16	19	21
											2	5	7	10	12	14	17	19	21
19	2788	2810	2833	2856	2878	2900	2923	2945	2967	2989	2	4	7	9	11	13	15	18	20
											2	5	7	9	11	14	16	18	20
20	3010	3032	3054	3075	3096	3118	3139	3160	3181	3201	2	4	6	8	11	13	15	17	19
21	3222	3243	3263	3284	3304	3324	3345	3365	3385	3404	2	4	6	8	10	12	14	16	18
22	3424	3444	3464	3483	3502	3522	3541	3560	3579	3598	2	4	6	8	10	12	14	15	17
23	3617	3636	3655	3674	3692	3711	3729	3747	3766	3784	2	4	6	7	9	11	13	15	17
24	3802	3820	3838	3856	3874	3892	3909	3927	3945	3962	2	4	5	7	9	11	12	14	16
25	3979	3997	4014	4031	4048	4065	4082	4099	4116	4133	2	3	5	7	9	10	12	14	15
26	4150	4166	4183	4200	4216	4232	4249	4265	4281	4298	2	3	5	7	8	10	11	13	15
27	4314	4330	4346	4362	4378	4393	4409	4425	4440	4456	2	3	5	6	8	9	11	13	14
28	4472	4487	4502	4518	4533	4548	4564	4579	4594	4609	2	3	5	6	8	9	11	12	14
29	4624	4639	4654	4669	4683	4698	4713	4728	4742	4757	1	3	4	6	7	9	10	12	13
30	4771	4786	4800	4814	4829	4843	4857	4871	4886	4900	1	3	4	6	7	9	10	11	13
31	4914	4928	4942	4955	4969	4983	4997	5011	5024	5038	1	3	4	6	7	8	10	11	12
32	5051	5065	5079	5092	5105	5119	5132	5145	5159	5172	1	3	4	5	7	8	9	11	12
33	5185	5198	5211	5224	5237	5250	5263	5276	5289	5302	1	3	4	5	6	8	9	10	12
34	5315	5328	5340	5353	5366	5378	5391	5403	5416	5428	1	3	4	5	6	8	9	10	11
35	5441	5453	5465	5478	5490	5502	5514	5527	5539	5551	1	2	4	5	6	7	9	10	11
36	5563	5575	5587	5599	5611	5623	5635	5647	5658	5670	1	2	4	5	6	7	8	10	11
37	5682	5694	5705	5717	5729	5740	5752	5763	5775	5786	1	2	3	5	6	7	8	9	10
38	5798	5809	5821	5832	5843	5855	5866	5877	5888	5899	1	2	3	5	6	7	8	9	10
39	5911	5922	5933	5944	5955	5966	5977	5988	5999	6010	1	2	3	4	5	7	8	9	10
40	6021	6031	6042	6053	6064	6075	6085	6096	6107	6117	1	2	3	4	5	6	8	9	10
41	6128	6138	6149	6160	6170	6180	6191	6201	6212	6222	1	2	3	4	5	6	7	8	9
42	6232	6243	6253	6263	6274	6284	6294	6304	6314	6325	1	2	3	4	5	6	7	8	9
43	6335	6345	6355	6365	6375	6385	6395	6405	6415	6425	1	2	3	4	5	6	7	8	9
44	6435	6444	6454	6464	6474	6484	6493	6503	6513	6522	1	2	3	4	5	6	7	8	9
45	6532	6542	6551	6561	6571	6580	6590	6599	6609	6618	1	2	3	4	5	6	7	8	9
46	6628	6637	6646	6656	6665	6675	6684	6693	6702	6712	1	2	3	4	5	6	7	7	8
47	6721	6730	6739	6749	6758	6767	6776	6785	6794	6803	1	2	3	4	5	5	6	7	8
48	6812	6821	6830	6839	6848	6857	6866	6875	6884	6893	1	2	3	4	4	5	6	7	8
49	6902	6911	6920	6928	6937	6946	6955	6964	6972	6981	1	2	3	4	4	5	6	7	8
50	6990	6998	7007	7016	7024	7033	7042	7050	7059	7067	1	2	3	3	4	5	6	7	8

From Gibbs & Richards' Mathematical Tables by permission of Messrs. Christophers.

LOGARITHMS OF NUMBERS

	0	1	2	3	4	5	6	7	8	9	1	2	3	4	5	6	7	8	9
51	7076	7084	7093	7101	7110	7118	7126	7135	7143	7152	1	2	3	3	4	5	6	7	8
52	7160	7168	7177	7185	7193	7202	7210	7218	7226	7235	1	2	2	3	4	5	6	6	7
53	7243	7251	7259	7267	7275	7284	7292	7300	7308	7316	1	2	2	3	4	5	6	6	7
54	7324	7332	7340	7348	7356	7364	7372	7380	7388	7396	1	2	2	3	4	5	6	6	7
55	7404	7412	7419	7427	7435	7443	7451	7459	7466	7474	1	2	2	3	4	5	5	6	7
56	7482	7490	7497	7505	7513	7520	7528	7536	7543	7551	1	2	2	3	4	5	5	6	7
57	7559	7566	7574	7582	7589	7597	7604	7612	7619	7627	1	2	2	3	4	5	5	6	7
58	7634	7642	7649	7657	7664	7672	7679	7686	7694	7701	1	1	2	3	4	4	5	6	7
59	7709	7716	7723	7731	7738	7745	7752	7760	7767	7774	1	1	2	3	4	4	5	6	7
60	7782	7789	7796	7803	7810	7818	7825	7832	7839	7846	1	1	2	3	4	4	5	6	6
61	7853	7860	7868	7875	7882	7889	7896	7903	7910	7917	1	1	2	3	4	4	5	6	6
62	7924	7931	7938	7945	7952	7959	7966	7973	7980	7987	1	1	2	3	3	4	5	6	6
63	7993	8000	8007	8014	8021	8028	8035	8041	8048	8055	1	1	2	3	3	4	5	5	6
64	8062	8069	8075	8082	8089	8096	8102	8109	8116	8122	1	1	2	3	3	4	5	5	6
65	8129	8136	8142	8149	8156	8162	8169	8176	8182	8189	1	1	2	3	3	4	5	5	6
66	8195	8202	8209	8215	8222	8228	8235	8241	8248	8254	1	1	2	3	3	4	5	5	6
67	8261	8267	8274	8280	8287	8293	8299	8306	8312	8319	1	1	2	3	3	4	5	5	6
68	8325	8331	8338	8344	8351	8357	8363	8370	8376	8382	1	1	2	3	3	4	4	5	6
69	8388	8395	8401	8407	8414	8420	8426	8432	8439	8445	1	1	2	2	3	4	4	5	6
70	8451	8457	8463	8470	8476	8482	8488	8494	8500	8506	1	1	2	2	3	4	4	5	6
71	8513	8519	8525	8531	8537	8543	8549	8555	8561	8567	1	1	2	2	3	4	4	5	5
72	8573	8579	8585	8591	8597	8603	8609	8615	8621	8627	1	1	2	2	3	4	4	5	5
73	8633	8639	8645	8651	8657	8663	8669	8675	8681	8686	1	1	2	2	3	4	4	5	5
74	8692	8698	8704	8710	8716	8722	8727	8733	8739	8745	1	1	2	2	3	4	4	5	5
75	8751	8756	8762	8768	8774	8779	8785	8791	8797	8802	1	1	2	2	3	3	4	5	5
76	8808	8814	8820	8825	8831	8837	8842	8848	8854	8859	1	1	2	2	3	3	4	5	5
77	8865	8871	8876	8882	8887	8893	8899	8904	8910	8915	1	1	2	2	3	3	4	4	5
78	8921	8927	8932	8938	8943	8949	8954	8960	8965	8971	1	1	2	2	3	3	4	4	5
79	8976	8982	8987	8993	8998	9004	9009	9015	9020	9025	1	1	2	2	3	3	4	4	5
80	9031	9036	9042	9047	9053	9058	9063	9069	9074	9079	1	1	2	2	3	3	4	4	5
81	9085	9090	9096	9101	9106	9112	9117	9122	9128	9133	1	1	2	2	3	3	4	4	5
82	9138	9143	9149	9154	9159	9165	9170	9175	9180	9186	1	1	2	2	3	3	4	4	5
83	9191	9196	9201	9206	9212	9217	9222	9227	9232	9238	1	1	2	2	3	3	4	4	5
84	9243	9248	9253	9258	9263	9269	9274	9279	9284	9289	1	1	2	2	3	3	4	4	5
85	9294	9299	9304	9309	9315	9320	9325	9330	9335	9340	1	1	2	2	3	3	4	4	5
86	9345	9350	9355	9360	9365	9370	9375	9380	9385	9390	1	1	2	2	3	3	4	4	4
87	9395	9400	9405	9410	9415	9420	9425	9430	9435	9440	0	1	1	2	2	3	3	4	4
88	9445	9450	9455	9460	9465	9469	9474	9479	9484	9489	0	1	1	2	2	3	3	4	4
89	9494	9499	9504	9509	9513	9518	9523	9528	9533	9538	0	1	1	2	2	3	3	4	4
90	9542	9547	9552	9557	9562	9566	9571	9576	9581	9586	0	1	1	2	2	3	3	4	4
91	9590	9595	9600	9605	9609	9614	9619	9624	9628	9633	0	1	1	2	2	3	3	4	4
92	9638	9643	9647	9652	9657	9661	9666	9671	9675	9680	0	1	1	2	2	3	3	4	4
93	9685	9689	9694	9699	9703	9708	9713	9717	9722	9727	0	1	1	2	2	3	3	4	4
94	9731	9736	9741	9745	9750	9754	9759	9763	9768	9773	0	1	1	2	2	3	3	4	4
95	9777	9782	9786	9791	9795	9800	9805	9809	9814	9818	0	1	1	2	2	3	3	4	4
96	9823	9827	9832	9836	9841	9845	9850	9854	9859	9863	0	1	1	2	2	3	3	4	4
97	9868	9872	9877	9881	9886	9890	9894	9899	9903	9908	0	1	1	2	2	3	3	4	4
98	9912	9917	9921	9926	9930	9934	9939	9943	9948	9952	0	1	1	2	2	3	3	4	4
99	9956	9961	9965	9969	9974	9978	9983	9987	9991	9996	0	1	1	2	2	3	3	3	4

INDEX

Where there are two or more references, the important one is in heavy type.
Reference should also be made to the pages following a main reference.